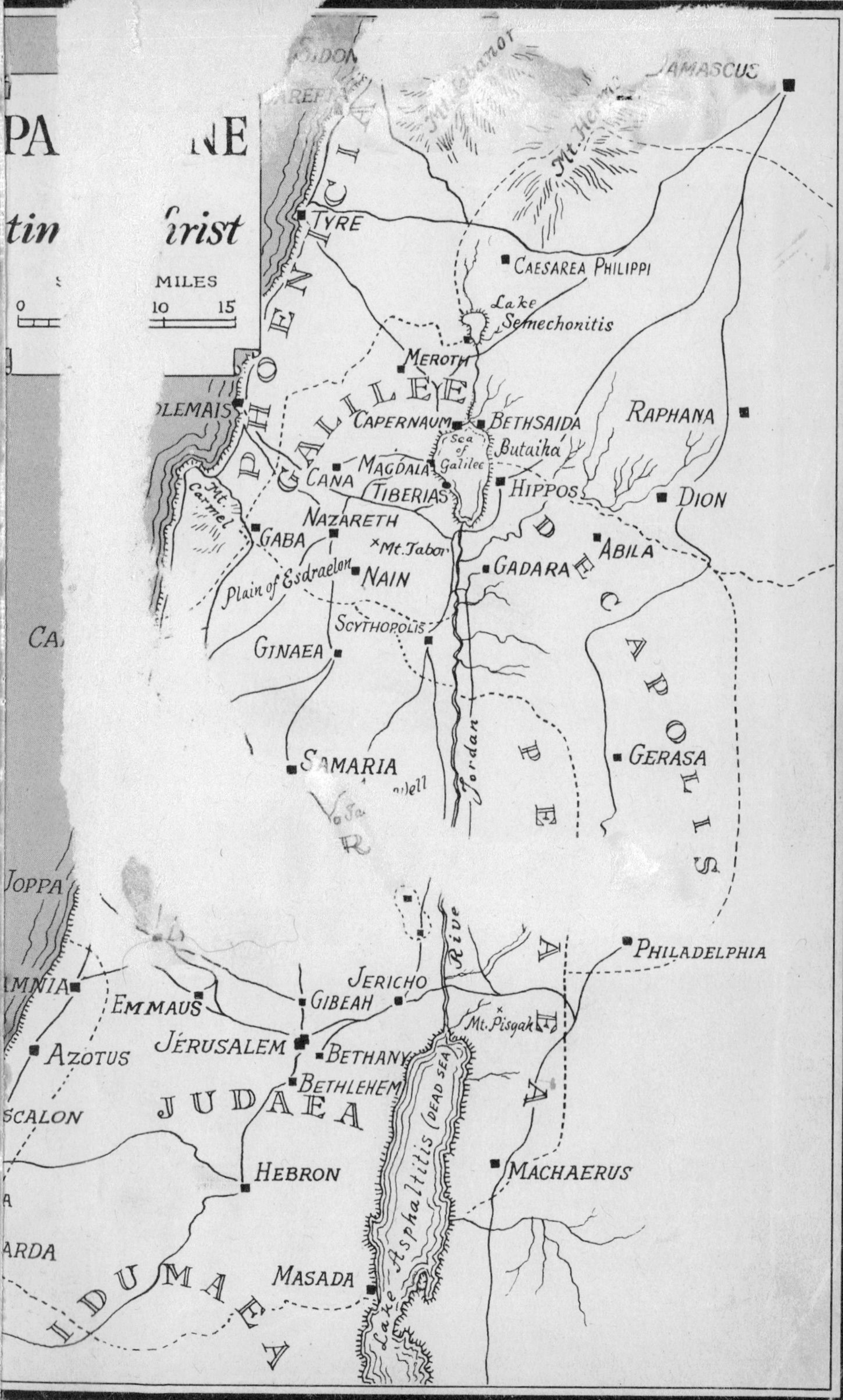

PA NE
tin rist
MILES
0
10
15
TYRE
CAESAREA PHILIPPI
Lake Semechonitis
MEROTH
PHOENICIA
GALILEE
CAPERNAUM
BETHSAIDA
Sea of Galilee
Butaiha
RAPHANA
MAGDALA
CANA
TIBERIAS
HIPPOS
DION
Mt. Carmel
NAZARETH
GABA
Mt. Tabor
ABILA
GADARA
Plain of Esdraelon
NAIN
SCYTHOPOLIS
GINAEA
DECAPOLIS
Jordan
PERAEA
GERASA
SAMARIA
JOPPA
River
PHILADELPHIA
JERICHO
EMMAUS
GIBEAH
Mt. Pisgah
JERUSALEM
AZOTUS
BETHANY
BETHLEHEM
JUDAEA
SCALON
Lake Asphaltitis (DEAD SEA)
HEBRON
MACHAERUS
ARDA
MASADA
IDUMAEA

"WHAT THINK YE OF CHRIST?"..."WE WOULD SEE JESUS." From generation to generation the age-old question and the age-old plea are new. In faith, learning, love and courage, Christians, decade by decade, year by year, give their answers greatly in a Life of Christ.

No two answers can be the same. Yet each presentation glorified by scholarship and inspired by the spirit of worship, each fresh attempt to revivify the earthly life of Jesus and to illuminate the strangest and most moving story in the world, is surely a service to mankind.

Greville Cooke's *The Light of the World* is a new and wonderful Life, an inspired personal portrait of the Master. It is his own reconstruction and interpretation, keeping as close to the Gospels as he found possible, yet pre-eminently a volume to be thought of as a work of art and of the imagination.

The Vicar of Cransley, an ancient and quiet England Midlands town, was engaged for seven years in writing this book, and nothing is more evident than that it was a labor of love. He read the multitudinous books on the Life of Jesus, on everything He said and did, studied the setting, absorbed each detail with all his heart and with all his mind, until he was ready to present, without resort to discussion or justification or the trappings of scholarship, a straightforward, unified story directed to the hearts of men. All is here that he thinks actually happened, all that he has seen, heard, comprehended, as in imagination he followed his Lord's life on earth.

Vividly in memory, striking, provocative, compelling, is exalted his Character of Christ; a Christ Who came to found a spiritual religion, Who used his powers always at the dictate of love, a Suffering Servant beset by the irony of being hated by His enemies because they understood Him, and misunderstood by His friends.

Greville Cooke's description of the scenic background and his relation of it to the thought and teaching of Christ, his profoundly interesting conception of the influence of the Prophets on His ideas and action, send the reader back to the Gospel with new eyes and new comprehension.

In form and style as well as substance *The Light of the World* is designed to reach the interest of a multitude. It arranges the Life of Christ as a drama in a prologue and five acts—the greatest drama ever staged, colossal and sublime. It is told in the manner of a novel, with a novelist's glowing presentation of character, setting, atmosphere, conflict. It avoids dogma because the author believes that Christ Himself hated dogma and all empty ceremonialism, to insist on Love; but on occasion it shows subtle skill in dialectic. The style reveals the musician's instinct for the cadence of words, and the whole work discloses the heart and sensitivity of a poet.

Humbled before a Hero Whose life transcends all art and literature, he was emboldened in his great attempt by love. "I love Him," writes Greville Cooke, "and He will forgive the wrong lines in my portrait."

No ordinary standards of criticism can apply to a personal book like this, yet unmistakably it has the power, provocation and conviction to shake even the modern defeatist, for it is the work of a religious genius stirred to the very depth of his being. In England press and pulpit testify to its strong appeal. In America advance readers, not always agreeing in detail, agree on its powerful impact. Christians, feeling the need of renewed faith and confirmed vows, see here the object of their devotion with clearer eyes and lifted hearts.

THE LIGHT
OF THE WORLD

A Reconstruction and Interpretation of
the Life of Christ

BY

GREVILLE COOKE

We would see Jesus...

THE BOBBS-MERRILL COMPANY, INC.
PUBLISHERS
INDIANAPOLIS • NEW YORK

To
MY DEAR MOTHER
who first taught me
to love Jesus

ACKNOWLEDGMENT

THE author acknowledges his indebtedness to the text of the Moffatt Translation of the Bible, and for permission from the publishers, Harper & Brothers, to use and adapt that text to the purposes of this book.

Contents

PROLOGUE

God said: "Let there be Light."

In the beginning was the Word,
and the Word was with God,
and the Word was God.
All things came into being through Him,
and apart from Him there is no existence.
In Him is life,
and that life is the Light of men.
That Light once shone in the darkness,
but the darkness prevailed not against It.

In the beginning, when the earth was made,
*   before the borders of the world stood,*
*   or ever the winds blew;*
*   before it thundered or lightened,*
*   or ever the foundations of Paradise were laid;*
*   ere the fair flowers were seen,*
*   ere ever the innumerable multitude of Angels were gathered to-*
*   gether,*
*   or ever the heights of the air were lifted up,*
*   or the measures of the firmament were named,*
*   or the volcanoes of earth were hot;*
*   ere the present years were sought out—*
*   or the inventions of them that sin were found,*
*   and before they were sealed that have gathered faith for a treasure;*
then did I consider these things:
they were made through Me alone,
and through none other.
By Me also shall they be ended,
and by none other.

The Lord possessed Me in the beginning of His way,
before His works of old.
I was set up from everlasting, even from the beginning;
when there were no depths, then was I brought forth.
When there were no fountains abounding with water;
ere He sank the bases of the great hills;
ere the heights existed, I was begotten;
while as yet He had not made the earth, nor the fields,
nor the very first clods of the world.
When He set the heavens up I was there.
When He drew the vaults o'er the abyss,
when He established the clouds o'erhead,
when He fixed the fountains of the deep,
when He set bounds to the sea,
when He laid the foundations of the earth,
    then was I beside Him—His master workman.
    I was daily His delight,
    playing continually in His presence,
    and finding My own delight most chiefly in human kind.

Where wast thou, O man, when I laid the foundations of the earth?
Who was it Who laid the cornerstone thereof—
    when the morning stars sang together,
    and all the sons of God shouted for joy?

Wisdom sought a dwelling place, where she might remain.
She came down to the children of men,
but found no dwelling place.
Then wisdom returned to her own place
and took her seat among the Angels.

The Word entered the world—
the world that existed alone through Him—
yet the world recognized Him not.
He came unto His own,
but His own did not welcome Him.
    But on those who did welcome Him—

that is, on those who believed on His name—
He has conferred the grace of being . . .
the sons of God.
And this sonship they owe, not to human descent,
                              nor to natural desire,
           but solely to God's good pleasure.
So it was that the Word became flesh,
and tarried awhile among us;
and we saw His glory . . .
              glory such as belongs solely to the only begotten
                              Son of the Father,
              full of grace and truth.
For it is from His own fulness that we have all received
grace for grace.
For grace and truth came through Jesus Christ.
No one has ever seen God.
Nevertheless, He has been revealed through the only begotten Son,
Who lies in the Father's bosom.

He is the Image of the invisible God,
the first-born, prior to all creation.
For by Him were all things created,
    both in Heaven and earth:
    the seen and the unseen,
    all the throned monarchs, the Angelic Captains,
    the celestial Powers and Rulers.
All were created by Him, and for Him.
He is prior to all,
and all coheres in Him.
In all things He has the pre-eminence;
for it pleased the Father that in Him should all fulness dwell.

PRELUDE

I

Nazareth

JESUS could never remember any home but the one in Nazareth. There were times when He pressed His father and mother to tell Him more about His early childhood; but often they would turn away and change the subject, so that He never came to know exactly the circumstances of His birth. Some of the Nazarenes looked askance at Him and Mary whenever He spoke of His birthday, as though they could have told Him a good deal if they would—or if they dared, for Joseph was both a strong man and a highly respected one, with whom it was always dangerous to trifle, though a gentle man at heart.

But at night, when Jesus was asleep with the rest of the children, Joseph and Mary would sometimes sit and recall those strange far-off days and their still stranger hints and omens. Zechariah's story, for instance. He had been Mary's kinsman, having married her cousin Elizabeth. One morning, having just heard the triple blast upon the silver trumpets blown from the pinnacle of the Temple in Jerusalem, as the first rays of the early morning sun struck over the far rim of the mountains of the Wilderness, he, the officiating Priest for that day, had seen in the Sanctuary a vision of an Archangel, who had promised him the birth of a son. He had doubted the Angel's word, owing to the advanced age of his wife and himself; whereupon he had been struck dumb and emerging from the Sanctuary had been forced to describe by gestures his experience in the Temple. But Gabriel's prophecy had come true in due course, and John had been born to them.

Mary would recall, too, the visit to her cousin Elizabeth, following that ineffably strange experience she had undergone, here in Nazareth, six months after Zechariah's vision. But she could never be persuaded to talk about that; nor could Joseph. It was something sacred shared by them together, and only to be mentioned in the privacy of an evening talk, when the children were safely in bed, and the neighbours had shut-to their doors.

At such times Joseph would recall, with a shudder, that terrible journey to Bethlehem; and especially their passing of the tomb of Rachel, a monument to the tragic death of his ancestress, who died in childbirth there by the roadside, before Jacob could reach haven with her in Bethlehem. And things had hardly been improved by the failure to find accommodation in the khan, and Mary's consequent childbearing in a stable. They often looked back wistfully to that night, seeing again the ass tethered close by, and the patient kine standing about moodily, their wet breath frostily visible in the dull lamplight. When the rough shepherds came with their strange tale of Angels singing and of the prophecy of the coming, that very night, of God's Messiah, it had seemed as though the cave had become suddenly the centre of the whole universe.

They would remember together, too, the visit to the Temple for the purification rites after childbirth, and the strange words of Simeon and Anna, both so old and so queerly inspired. It had seemed almost as though that visit were an ending and a beginning of vast epochs: as if prophecy had seen its final consummation in the song the old man had quaveringly sung—the swan song of a dispensation, and the opening of a new. Mary remembered the ominous words about the "sword that should pierce her heart," and how frightened she had been for Jesus, as she wrapped her arms closely about Him and hurried with Joseph out of the Temple. And that night, in a strange lodging, her eyes had filled with brimming tears, while Joseph listened helplessly to her weeping as the moonlight streamed slantingly through the shuttered lattice onto the sleeping Babe at her breast. Joseph often felt a great pity for Mary. She would muse and ponder deeply on those matters, and especially on the sayings uttered about her little Son. "Set for the falling and rising up of many. . . . A Sign that shall be spoken against." What could that have meant—or still mean—for her Son?

As for Jesus, He was beginning to take an interest in His father's carpentering business. He would hang about the workshop till Joseph gave Him some little job to do. He showed plenty of aptitude for the work, too. Joseph noted how carefully He would use the tools, how

smoothly He was learning to plane, what an eye He was developing
for the most suitable types of wood for different purposes. James, the
next boy, was of another mould altogether, a brooding type, with
deep-sunk eyes and a serious cast of mind. There were three other
sons as well, and some daughters—and Jesus was only about twelve
years old as yet. It was no easy task, feeding this large family; and
often Jesus would be sent down to the market place to buy the cheap-
est food obtainable. "Don't forget, you can get two sparrows for a
farthing, or five for a halfpenny"—and the Boy would go off by Himself, clutching His tiny coins. Often, too, Mary would be hard put to
it to know how to patch and darn the clothes the children were forever
growing out of. There came a time when it was no longer practicable
to patch a rent with new cloth. It only made the tear worse in the end.
As she would sigh and put the torn garment wearily aside, she would
see her Son's eyes upon her. He seemed to understand.

He would come and take her hand, too, when the cares and lets of
life overwhelmed her, with their reiterated questions: what they were
all to eat, what to drink, what to wear, and especially if a guest arrived
unexpectedly and the larder was empty and Joseph was forced to borrow a loaf or two from a neighbour.

Jesus regularly attended the Synagogue services on the Sabbath. He
had learned to love the Scriptures, especially the Psalms and the Prophets, and His favourite book of Moses, Deuteronomy. He loved, too,
to hear Joseph tell the children clustered round him of the stirring
deeds of Israel's heroes, of Samson and Barak and Gideon and David,
and the stories of the Patriarchs, Abraham and Isaac and Jacob, and
especially that of Joseph. Jesus liked nothing better than to curl up
at His father's knee and to hear, enraptured, how God had looked after
Israel and given her guidance and comfort in her sorrows.

Whenever Jesus thought of Jehovah, somehow the image of Joseph
came into His mind. He hoped that God was not too unlike Joseph.
It had been His invariable custom to speak of God as His "Father."
Indeed, He spoke of Him always as His "Abba"—the very first word
He had learned to lisp at Mary's knee. His parents were deeply shocked
and distressed, and tried hard to break Him of the habit, but in vain.
The Rabbi in Nazareth got to hear of it and spoke seriously to Joseph

of the necessity for reverence where the great Jehovah was concerned. But Mary thought it rather sweet . . . and a wonderful tribute—and a deserved one—to Joseph.

Whenever possible Jesus would slip away, especially in the cool of the evening, up through the sloping, winding streets, till the white-roofed houses were at last left behind; climbing still higher up the springy brown turf till the town sank down into the shadows far below and, with one last long stride, He would reach the very topmost level and could lie flat on the summit to rest and gaze and dream.

Almost all of Israel's long history was recalled to Him, spread out as on a relief map. To the southwest loomed the mighty shoulder of Mount Carmel, whence Elijah had thundered defiance to all the gods of the heathen and called down fire from Heaven. A little farther to the south rose Gilboa, rounded and strong, where Saul and Jonathan fought and fell. Closer at hand, arising out of the Plain, was the circular mound of Tabor, where Barak encamped before battling with Sisera. Down there, somewhere in the fields, Deborah the Prophetess had sung her wild and terrible song; where, all but hidden from view in its deep trench, ran the torrent Kishon, which, overflowing its banks suddenly, had swept away such of Israel's enemies as were not bogged in the surrounding marshes. In yonder vale Gideon and his three hundred had upheld Israel's honour in an epic victory.

Beyond the huge bluff of Carmel lay the dark blue line of the Mediterranean, clearly visible from this hilltop. Away to the east rose the mountain range in the lap of which nestled the Lake of Galilee; while beyond, the arid heights of the Hauran hills marked the bastions of Arabia's vast desert. To the north rose the wooded brows of Lebanon, magnificent in splendid serenity, well watered, thickly afforested, remote and strange with uncharted uplands and wild beasts and great birds. Royally the ridges lifted their great shoulders into the sky, towering up towards the stars, crowned by the snowbound summit of Hermon, nine thousand feet high, colossal, exalted, halfway to Heaven. Was it not called "God's Throne" by the Prophets? A type, indeed, of God Himself—*The government shall be upon His shoulder*. This north country always deeply attracted Jesus, calling to Him, beckoning upward. . . .

But was not Jerusalem the true Throne of Jehovah? Swinging round on the warm, sweet-scented grass, He would gaze long and intently at the far mountains of Samaria, beyond which lay the Holy City, the centre of the whole earth, the Shrine of the Shekinah, the Holy Place of the Most High. There, streaking away to the swooning south, ran the caravan road along which, one day soon, He Himself would be taken by His parents (they went up every year)—and then He would see God's Temple and become a "Son of the Law" and worship His Heavenly Father in His own House. . . .

Though, to be sure, God seemed very near to Him up here on the hills. Jesus felt a peace stealing through Him whenever He lay here; almost as if God were enfolding Him in His arms, as a shepherd would a lamb. Just over there, as He now lay outstretched on the sun-warm grass, Jesus could see a shepherd leading in his sheep to their fold. He loved to watch and company with the shepherds, many of whom were His close friends. They were a simple kindly fellowship, devoted to their charges, going out in all weathers and in the face of any danger to seek a lost sheep or lamb; even at times lying themselves across the entrance to the sheepfold—literally the door of the sheep—rather than risk any harm happening to them. Jesus could see how one sheep farmer often possessed more than one sheepfold—there they were in front of Him, far down below—but they all belonged to one flock. Sometimes hired men were called in to give a hand at lambing time or when shepherds fell sick; and Jesus noted how the sheep would not follow them, coax they ever so hard; but when the real shepherds returned the sheep would run to them one by one as their names were called out.

Not long before, news had reached Jesus that a shepherd friend of His was missing. He had never come home after a night on the hills; search was made for him, and his dead body had been found in a ravine, mangled and torn by wild beasts—a kind, good shepherd whom Jesus had loved, giving his life for the sheep.

The shepherds also taught Him weather lore; how a red dawn,— *terrible as an army with banners*—over the far Arabian hills (their summits stark and black against the glowing sky) betokened a wild, stormy day, with, perhaps, one of those sudden tempests that, blowing down through the gaunt rock ravines, whipped up the waves of Gennesaret to a frenzy of foaming billows. Or, even worse, a blistering, searing sirocco from the Hauran, withering up the leaves before their time. But the gentle southwest wind, blowing from over distant Carmel, heralded the merciful rain, falling on fields and roads, on vines and olive groves alike, as did the sunshine when the showers were over.

And now the sun was fast sinking behind the hills of Naphtali, and long shadows were streaking over the northern uplands. Somewhere there, only a few miles away, was Sepphoris, the fiery sky that flamed above it reminding Jesus of a dreadful night that had scared Him only a few months before. He could not even now think of it without a shudder. For Sepphoris had been the storm centre of an insurrection against Rome, caused by the Syrian Governor's order for the taking of a census—for further taxation, of course. Judas of Galilee, had raised the standard of revolt and had let loose the full flood of nationalistic passion, always strongly flowing in the north. Thither had swarmed all the young hotheads of the region. Along yonder highroad that wound round the foot of Nazareth's hill the eager groups of rebels had passed, till the gathering at Sepphoris had become a mighty army, fully ten thousand strong. Soon after, they all marched back again, singing the songs of Zion and watched by all the boys of Nazareth as they ran excitedly along the hilltops to keep the great army in sight as long as possible, till the dusty cloud was at length lost to view away to the far northwest. They were aiming for Tiberias, where Herod had reared his vast new palace—and where he kept his armoury, just ripe for pillaging. The plan had succeeded. The rebels broke in, seized the swords and spears, and marched on, singing and shouting, in order to fight with Rome and drive her hated legions into the Mediterranean or over Lebanon—anywhere so long as it was out of God's Promised Land, which would then be free forever.

But all this while the eagle of Rome was watching through narrow-slitted eyes, stealthily sharpening her claws. Then, silently, she rose high in air, breasting the wind a moment, poised over her victim—and struck like a thunderbolt. From the encampments at Caesarea and Decapolis, Varus the Roman general had gathered his legions, and the rebellion was crushed like rubble beneath falling rock. Whosoever fell on that rock was broken; but on whomsoever it fell, it ground him to powder.

Then the legions marched against Sepphoris. Their grim ranks could be seen from the hilltop above Nazareth, the hems of their tunics swinging to their measured tread (no songs this time) : an even greater —and very different—army, winding in reverse direction around the base of the hill. That night, the darkness was suddenly lighted up with an ever-growing red glow as a whole city was fired; and the flames leaped up and flared high to heaven till Sepphoris sank to earth in charred and embered ruin. All the inhabitants were sold into slavery, save some two thousand, who were ordered to be crucified. Crouched behind a boulder, Jesus saw for the first time the dread sight of condemned criminals moving to a terrible death and carrying their own crosses. He had been face to face with the horror and cruelty of war. It made Him feel lonelier than before, needing more than ever the company of His Heavenly Father out there on the hills. He missed, too, the friendship of His Judaean cousin John, who used to come every year for a holiday in the north. His parents were now dead and he had passed into the care of a relative somewhere in the south. They had enjoyed such jolly games together, especially that of "Weddings and Funerals," with the other children in the market place. Jesus had generally been chosen as the bridegroom, and John was always the bridegroom's friend. Would He ever see him again?

The sun by now was hidden behind the northern hills, and the air had suddenly become fresh and cold. It was time to go home. From far away came the bark of a fox. The grass was quite wet with the dew. . . .

II

Jerusalem

THE greatest day of Jesus' childhood, its climax and culmination, had arrived at last; the day when He, together with other boys of a like age, went up to Jerusalem to become a "Son of the Law," that is, a full member of the community of Israel. The Rabbi at Nazareth had allowed Joseph to take Jesus up a year earlier than was customary, owing to His advanced intelligence and religious insight. A large caravan had assembled in the market place, soon to mingle with other similar companies for mutual protection on the long trek southwards. Over eighty miles, mostly hilly country, separated Nazareth from Jerusalem; no easy walk for a boy of twelve, or even for an adult. Wineskins were being busily filled at the town's one and only well. Camels and asses were having their saddles and traces adjusted, and there was much strapping and shouting as last-minute farewells were exchanged before the signal was finally given for the caravan to move off down the hillside toward the levels of the great Plain. The boys, as usual, were in the forefront, talking to the caravan leader, and getting a first and uninterrupted view of each new scene as the road turned or breasted a hilltop. Their way ran through rich and fertile cornlands, past sleepy olive orchards, over running streams, by comfortable farmsteads and barns. Flowers were everywhere, for this was blossom time in Israel.

As the huge hills of Samaria loomed ever nearer, and the level miles were gradually traversed, the day wore on through high noon to late afternoon, and when they had at last arrived under the lee of mighty Gilboa, a halt was called, and the caravan unleashed for rest and sleep as the sun dipped low beyond Carmel. With what dreams the boys lay down that night, under the star-strewn skies! For, only a few days more now, and they would see Jerusalem for themselves and have the right to enter at will into God's holy Temple. Was it not written: *I will dwell in the midst of Jerusalem, and the streets of the City shall be full of boys and girls playing in the streets thereof?*

24

A day or two after they could just discern the distant hills of Judaea beckoning them to the Rock of Abraham—the very spot, so tradition said, on which Isaac had been offered up and reprieved. As they walked they sang the Songs of Ascent.

It was with especial fervour that Jesus sang: *I was glad when they said unto me: "Let us go up to the House of the Lord!"* They prayed, too, for deliverance from Rome and from Herod: *Turn our captivity, O Lord, even as these streams in the south*—which were now once again filled with sparkling, rushing water, after the long drought.

At length arrived the thrilling moment when first the Holy City burst into view, and the caravan halted on the Mount of Olives, the final camping ground. Towers and domes flashed in the bright sunlight, above the dark line of the walls. Beyond the ravine of the Kedron rose the enormous new Temple of Herod—not yet (nor for another fifty years or so, to be) completed. It was built of shining white stone, quarried out of the hill beneath, and was roofed over in part with gold.

The next morning Jesus was awakened out of sleep, there on the open hillside, by the bright stridency of silver trumpets blown at the sun's uprising. As the echoes slowly died away along the ravine leading to the Wilderness, the Pilgrims were astir preparing for their first visit to the Temple. They descended the slopes of Olivet, wended their way through olive orchards and past innumerable fig trees, till, looming high before them, rose the gigantic walls of the city. Soon they were in the shadow of the gateway and passing within its massive portals. Their voices rose exultantly: *Our feet are standing within thy gates, O Jerusalem!* A detour had to be made right round the southern side of the Temple in order to enter it by the western gate, as was customary with the Pilgrims. They had thus to pass over the colossal viaduct spanning the Tyropoean Valley (its arches being over forty feet wide and its spring stones measuring more than eight yards across). This deep rift in the rock mountain separated Mount Zion from Mount Moriah, on which stood the Temple. The valley here was over two hundred feet below the bridge parapet. Near its farther end was the Temple gate, the goal of this long Pilgrimage.

As Jesus entered the Temple, His hand tensed in His father's. What He saw before Him was breath-taking in its size and grandeur. He found Himself in a vast colonnade of immense pillars, each one over one hundred feet high, the whole vast nave extending for over nine hundred feet in length. Its roof was of cedarwood, overlaid on the outside with gold. There were also side aisles with pillars (like the others, of marble) fifty feet high. The whole vista was unbroken and regular—the finest nave ever built.

Arriving at the end, they turned northward to emerge into the Court of the Gentiles: an enormous space thronged with innumerable Pilgrims. There it was that Jesus suffered a heart shock, the memory of which He carried with Him throughout His life. For there were strange noises arising above the hum and stir of the crowds, noises not human, of penned beasts lowing and bleating in continuous supplication. Then He saw them: cattle, sheep, goats, doves, pigeons—there they were, cruelly packed together alongside the attached slaughter houses; all striving to escape, vainly looking for some sign of pity, for some hope of release from this ghastly fear and bewilderment, and from the reeking stench of blood and offal that rose everywhere. But no sign came, and the slaughter went on uninterruptedly—and horribly performed, too. This was altogether different from the Synagogue worship to which Jesus had been accustomed; altogether hateful, too, in its cruelty and repulsiveness. Why should these animals—God's own creatures, all of them—be doomed to die? In any case, how could this slaughter take away men's sin? Was this God's will? Jesus felt suffocated and sick at heart. He must find out more about this, and as soon as possible.

Now they were at the farther side of this vast Court, alongside a terraced wall, on the steps of which sat several elderly Rabbis, with groups of young men—yes, and a few boys—around them. The teachers were evidently instructing them in the Faith. Would it be possible to join such a group some time before returning home?

Then it was that Jesus received a further shock. For a notice was set up for all to see, carved in large Greek capitals:

LET NO FOREIGNER ENTER WITHIN THE SCREEN
AND ENCLOSURE AROUND THE HOLY PLACE.
WHOSOEVER IS TAKEN SO DOING WILL HIMSELF
BE THE CAUSE THAT DEATH OVERTAKES HIM.

Was Isaiah wrong, then, in describing the Temple as a *House of Prayer for all nations?* Was Israel right in thus saying to the Gentiles, *Stand by thyself; come not near unto me: for I am holier than thou?* Another question for the Rabbis to answer.

Then there was the commerce and money trafficking going on all the time in the Temple Courts, owing to the prohibition of Roman money in the sacred precincts. The money-changers were to be seen on all sides, with their neat little piles of coins arranged on their tables. It was common gossip that the family of the High Priest, Annas and his sons and sons-in-law, made an annual income of several million dollars by this exchange. It looked as though things were no better than in Jeremiah's time, when he, in God's name, had stigmatized the Jews for turning His House into *a den of robbers.* Jesus felt angry and hurt. The thrill of the Pilgrimage was evaporating into exasperation and bitterness.

By now Joseph was making his way out of the Temple, having purchased his lamb and arranged for its slaughter. He was to call for it later in the day, when he would carry it out to the camping ground, where they would, as a family, be celebrating the Passover together. Jesus turned away, sick with nausea, when He saw the little lamb which Joseph had chosen—so soft and so white and so young.

That evening Jesus, as the youngest person present, was given the role of Questioner, having to ask the ritual query: "What mean you by this Service?" And Joseph answered: "It is the Sacrifice of the Lord's Passover, Who passed over the houses of the children of Israel, and delivered our houses." But this really explained nothing. Perhaps the morrow would provide an opportunity for explanation.

The next morning the caravan was early astir, for the humble (though devout) Galileans could not afford a long stay in the Holy City. In the bustle of departure no one missed Jesus. Any who gave any thought to the matter imagined Him to be with others of the party. Nobody saw Him slip away in the dawn, run breathlessly down the slopes of Olivet, up the Kedron Valley, over the Tyropoean bridge and into the Temple. Arriving there, He had looked round to see if any Rabbis were abroad at this early hour, so that He might quickly question them and get back in time to Olivet for the caravan's departure. Even if it had started, He could soon catch up with it, the pace of the Pilgrims being leisurely and unhurried. The great Court was tenantless. It looked so huge and made Him feel even more lonely. But the poor animals were there still. There was no escape for them.

He waited awhile, in the hope of some Rabbis arriving. Soon the Court began to fill up, and Jesus found Himself torn between two conflicting loyalties. But this matter of the significance of His Father's House must be settled before He could return in peace of mind to Nazareth. At last He saw a blue-robed Rabbi coming down from the higher Court of the Women to seat himself on the stone-flighted terrace beyond which no Gentile might set his foot. He was followed by a few students, who disposed themselves about him to listen to his teaching. Soon Jesus, edging ever nearer, was in the midst of them, facing the Rabbi and his young friends. The subject of discussion was, inevitably, the Passover rite and its meaning. The Rabbi had no difficulty in defending the Sacrificial system from Scripture:

Offer your oblations of the cattle or sheep or goats for a burnt-offering and kill it on the side of the Altar northward before the Lord, and cut it in pieces. Or if it be of turtle-doves or of young pigeons, rend it by the wings thereof. The Priest must then take some of the blood and smear the knobs of the Altar of burnt-offering, doing it with his finger, afterwards pouring the rest of the blood away at the base of the Altar. All the fat he must remove, burning it on the Altar, as a soothing odour to God. So shall the Priest make expiation for the sin of the man.

Jesus found Himself alone in pitting His instinct, His mind and heart, against the ingrained tradition of centuries; against, too, the profitable traffic of a corrupt commercializing of religion. This was the opening round of the great battle to which He was to devote His life—yes, and His death; the battle for the Truth—that God was a forgiving Father: the very Spirit of Love. He was not yet sufficiently versed in the Scriptures fully to contend with the Rabbis and the others who soon joined them when they found that here was a young heretic, trying to argue about accepted traditions. Nevertheless, they could not but admire His astute and logical mind and the pertinency of the objections He put forward.

No wonder the hours slipped by so quickly; and when the Rabbis, politely and condescendingly evasive and dogmatic, said, as evening drew near, "Well, we'll talk about this again tomorrow, perhaps. Enough for tonight!" it was nothing to marvel at that Jesus could not tear Himself away from Jerusalem. In any case, it was now too late to rejoin the caravan that day. But He was desperately lonely during the night, out on the hillside among so many strangers. The meaning of life seemed very difficult to fathom. But of one thing He remained sure: that, in spite of all the Rabbis could say, God was still a Father, a God of Love. He made a solemn vow, there on the hill, under the starry sky: that nothing, all His life long, would ever make Him give up this, *His own* idea of God. *My God, I will praise Thee!*

Meanwhile, some six miles away, there was agony in the heart of a mother and father. Mary suddenly recalled the strange words of the aged seer; menacing words spoken when last Jesus was in the Temple, twelve long years before (though it seemed but yesterday). The sword was indeed piercing her heart as she and Joseph hurried along those uphill miles to search for their Son, One in a couple of million people. They had, of course, wondered where He was during the first day's journey, but they had naturally thought He was with their friends or relations—Mary's sister Salome and her husband Zebedee being of the party, having originally joined the Pilgrimage near Mount Gilboa, where the road from Bethsaida, where they lived, met that from Nazareth. Joseph and Mary searched everywhere but they never caught sight of Him, and there was no word of Him from anyone whom they knew that was still remaining in the city.

It was on the third day that they suddenly saw Him, there on the terrace steps, in the centre of a large group of Rabbis and students of the Law.

Mary rushed forward and clutched Him to her, saying, as the spectators looked on, astonished, "My Son, *why* have You behaved like this? Your father and I have been looking for You everywhere!"

He seemed taken aback—almost hurt. "How was it you didn't find Me? Couldn't you have guessed that I just *had* to be engaged on My Father's business?"

They hurried Him away and out of the Temple. The walk home to Nazareth had to be undertaken in company with another and strange caravan. It was a silent and oppressive journey, not lightened by His parents' brooding on His words in the Temple. *"Had* to be engaged."

"My Father's business. . . ." What did these expressions mean? All
the amazing events and utterances of His birth and infancy came rushing back to their memories. It was almost as though they had heard the
first far rumblings of a colossal storm. It awoke in them the sense of
an inescapable destiny awaiting their Son, something unique, dark, in-
decipherable, save—as Mary knew long afterward—in the lurid Light
shining from Calvary. In the long years that followed, His quiet
obedience seemed to conceal a tremendous resolution, held in check,
like a banked-up, shut-in fire, a volcano awaiting its hour.

But, oh, how lovable He was! There was a serenity, a radiance about
Him that brought peace and a deep joy into the hearts of those who
knew Him well.

Some words of the Book of Enoch often came into Joseph's mind:
*His eyes were beautiful; and when He opened His eyes He lit up the
whole house like a sun, and the whole house was ablaze with light. . . .*

Joseph winced a little as he remembered how the passage went on:
And His father was afraid of Him . . . and said:

*I have a strange Son. He is not like . . . men. . . but resembles what
the Children of the Angels in Heaven must be like; His nature is different. He is not like us. His eyes are as the rays of the sun, and His
countenance is glorious. His home is surely among the Angels. . . .*

III

The Carpenter

JOSEPH would watch his fast-growing Son with a sense of fear and foreboding, though with, at times, an almost overwhelming feeling of reverent pride and joy. Jesus was a unique blend of so many contrasting attributes: strength and gentleness, practical skill and mystic emotion, compassion and furious indignation. To a lovely power of poetic expression was allied an intensely effective faculty for using ironic humour as an aid to dialectic. He was growing up into a strong and vigorously healthy Boy, tall for His age; tradition says that He had auburn hair—an unusual thing in a Jew. As Mary, so long after, was to tell Luke, Jesus "waxed strong in wisdom and stature, and in favour with God and man." She could not express the beauty of His unfolding character better than by saying: "The grace of God was upon Him. . . ."

As for Jesus Himself, His life had once more settled down into the humdrum routine of everyday existence in Nazareth. As day succeeded day and no opportunity presented itself for fulfilling His vague longings to found a truly spiritual religion, He was forced to acquire a power of patience that often surprised even Himself, so great was the urgency, the need of religious reform and so long was the opportunity to begin it in coming. Little did He think that "being about His Father's business" meant, for Him, staying for a further eighteen years in Nazareth; helping His earthly father; becoming in time "the Carpenter" Himself; for Joseph died not many years after the Jerusalem visit, and the burden of caring for His widowed mother fell on Jesus.

Jesus learned to become a master workman at His trade. No one could vie with Him in the care with which He ensured that the yokes He made for the oxen really fitted. He would pass His strong hand gently over the smooth shoulders of each beast until He knew each muscle's track and each bone's moulding. "His yokes are easy," the

farmers would say, who learned to trust Him utterly. He had a wonderful way with all animals. They seemed unafraid of Him and He
could tame the wildest of them with a touch or a word. Especially
was He tender with the many grievously overburdened asses, oxen and
camels. He often longed to call them all to Him, that He might dis-
burden them of their heavy loads and give them the much needed rest
they craved. And He Himself learned from the patient, long-suffering
asses what strength and virtue lay in uncomplaining endurance. One
day, when a questioner asked Him "Who is there in the world that
can lead and draw us to the Kingdom—if that Kingdom be in Heav-
en?" He answered: "The birds of the air and all the creatures of earth
and sea—these are they that draw one." He used to stop if He saw a
little feathery corpse on the road, where some sparrow had fallen, or
been slain by a slingstone, and He would murmur: "God was here. . . .
He was here with it when it fell."

Though He longed passionately to be up and doing in the work for
which He believed God had sent Him—the work of founding a religion based on a gracious personal relationship between God and man
—yet He knew, especially after Joseph's death, that He would have
to delay action till Mary and His brothers and sisters were provided
for. And even then He would have to await the unmistakable call of
God. There could be no running away from His burdens. But He was
often almost unendurably lonely. No one seemed to understand.
They only wanted freedom from Rome, not freedom from fear and
poverty of soul. And yet He never lost His sense of the companionship of His Heavenly Father. He needed—and found—it increasingly
after Joseph died. He would look back to the days when He had
worked so happily beside His earthly father in the workshop; and
now that He was alone there, God seemed to speak to Him.

*Wherever there are two . . . they are never without God. And when
there is only One alone . . . I say I am with Him. Raise the stone—and
there you will find Me. Cleave the wood—and there am I.*

There was plenty of hard work to be done all the time—thank God.
Jesus learned the wisdom of building on secure foundations; and how
tiresome a tiny shaving of wood could be if it flew into the eye. He
learned, too, how to choose seasoned wood in place of sappy green
timber. Earning enough to feed and clothe a large family of growing

brothers and sisters taxed Jesus' strength to the utmost, though James helped Him as soon as he was old enough. Jesus was generally very tired when the long day's work was finished. But He never lost the chance of slipping away to the hills, to be alone for a while and to dream and plan.

There were times when, lying on His back on the grass, He would be overcome with a strange sense of remoteness from this world. The stars would seem the intimate playthings of some far-away childhood. Vague and nebulous thoughts—sensations, almost—swept through Him, filling His mind as with suddenly glimpsed memories of a former joyous existence: a life independent of time and space, free, omnipotent and beautiful beyond words. But a lamb's bleating or the far-off barking of a fox, maybe, would still the trepidancy in the air —as of the beating of innumerable Angels' wings—and the sound of singing, floating down as from an immense height, would suddenly die away into an imprisoning silence. Ordinary midnight above Nazareth was but a poor substitute for the almost blinding radiance that had seemed momently to shine about Him. At such times He would wonder how far His dreams had deluded Him, and why His imagination should play Him such tricks. And he would be silent and aloof for some days after, thinking of the Prophets of old and their visions of God. But now it was indeed *night in the world* and there *was no vision*. The sun was *gone down upon the Prophets and the day was dark over them*. Often He would cry in His heart: *How far has the night gone, watchman? How far has the night gone?*

And the watchman would seem to answer: *Morning comes. . . . Morning. . . .*

How long, O Lord, how long . . . ?

But no answer came.

ACT ONE

. . . .

The Christ of the Wilderness

I

The New Procurator

BUT His hour struck at last, and the door of the Carpenter's shop was to close behind Him for the last time. Not that there was anything sudden or dramatic in the timing of the moment of release. Rather was it the result of certain interrelated events, whose cumulative significance at length called for decisive action on the part of Jesus.

Pontius Pilate, a professional soldier of the patrician class, had just been appointed Procurator of Judaea. The Emperor Tiberius, far away in Rome, hoped he would stay there for a long time. He himself was in the habit of saying "An enriched governor, like a blood-sated fly, is better than a new and still rapacious one." Pontius would therefore need to mind his step. Entering upon a governorship was always a tricky business, and Judaea was one of the most difficult provinces to handle. Tiberius was especially interested in this particular appointment, for the new Procurator had married his, Tiberius', own step-daughter, Claudia Procula, who was a great-granddaughter of Caesar Augustus and a very great lady. Her husband was, perhaps, rather young for the position, but preferment was expected in such a case. Besides, it was just as well to keep descendants of Augustus at a safe distance.

As for Claudia herself, she found life at Caesarea Palestina a good deal less unpleasant than she had feared. From where she now sat, on the terrace of the headquarters in the city, she could see the gleaming marble of the many temples, the majestic curves of hippodrome and theatre, and, seaward, the grandeur of the immense mole that Herod the Great had constructed to protect the harbour from the ocean storms. From this high vantage point above the coast (for the Procurator's castle was set high on a vast rock in the centre of the bay) she and Pilate could watch the fleets of naval and commercial vessels that sailed in and out of the harbour. She glanced at her husband, standing there with his hands clasping the terrace balustrade, and searched his profile anew. There was the high, proud Roman brow, surmounted by the close-cropped hair of the professional soldier. His eyes were dark and lowering, there was a scowl about his mouth and heavy jaw. He was not in a good mood today—and no wonder. Those Jews had bested him after all.

Coming over with her on the voyage, he had boasted to her that he meant to stand no nonsense from these wretched fanatics. Their ridiculous superstitions must be treated as they deserved—with contempt. In especial, their refusal to allow the Roman standards within the precincts of their Temple—or even, so some said, in their capital city at all—was an implied disloyalty to Rome that maddened him. He would teach them a lesson that they would not soon forget. This time there was to be a Procurator in Judaea who would be master in his own Imperial province. Had he not the stupendous might of Rome behind him?

But he was to be speedily disillusioned. He had carried out his threat to defy the Jews. The Imperial standards had been duly borne in procession in Jerusalem, with the result that he had been besieged by enormous crowds here in Caesarea, clamouring for the recall of the standards. He had, of course, denied these demands, being zealous for Caesar's honour. But the crowds had not dispersed. Indeed, they had grown. After about six days of this, Pilate had commanded the Roman soldiers to lie in ambush within the hippodrome, whither he had called the Jews to a conference. Being seated on the Imperial dais, he once more told them of his inflexible determination to maintain Rome's honour; but being met with obdurate opposition he decided that the time for argument was past, and, giving a sign to an officer, he caused the soldiers to come out of their hiding places, and with drawn swords to stream over the arena where the Jews were massed. In the tense silence that followed this surprise move, he told them that unless they relinquished their suit and returned every one to his own house they would be put to death there and then. But, to his intense consternation, they, like one man, prostrated themselves on the sanded earth and bared their necks for the sword strokes, a spokesman telling him that they would all of them rather die than see their Law violated. Pilate was beaten, and he knew it. Caesar would not tolerate a massacre—not even for the honour of Rome. It was not long before the standards were transported back to Caesarea, and the new Governor found himself hated—and worse, laughed at. Round one had certainly gone against him. His pride had taken a nasty toss. But what could one do with such a people?

Claudia Procula, scanning Pilate's profile against the evening glow, felt a sinking of heart as she began to observe the fatal blend of obstinacy and weakness that augured so tragically for the future.

A centurion entered through the curtains, and saluted. He silently handed Pilate a despatch and withdrew. A moment later Pilate turned to Claudia.

"News from Judaea," he said. "Some crack-brained fanatic brawling in the Jordan Valley. Excitement among the Pilgrims. Danger of a possible riot. What's this? Baptizing, preaching, repentance? Do them good, anyway, if they did repent. Sounds harmless enough. In Herod's territory, in any case. Why can't these Jews be quiet for once?" And his brows were drawn down in anger . . . and frustration.

II

The Baptist

FAR away, in the torrid trench of the Jordan Valley, a wild, unkempt figure was standing on a little knoll and preaching in a dramatic, fiery way to an ever-growing crowd of Pilgrims. He was clad only in a rough garment of camel's hair, bound with a leather girdle that was wrapped about his loins: a gaunt, ascetic hermit, rugged and rectangular as the rocks and gullies of the Wilderness from which he had come. "A Prophet, indeed—at last!" the people said, reminding them inevitably of Elijah. It was rumoured that, like his prototype, he had dwelt for many years in the desert, eating, as did the Prophet, only such things as could be found there—locusts and wild honey. There was nothing else, anyway, in that arid region. Its original volcanic menace was mirrored in John, as if the pressure of internal fires had hourly grown till one day it had burst into furious eruption. There, in the dread Wilderness, conviction had come to him that he was, indeed—as had been foretold by an Angel of him, according to a family tradition—nothing less than the forerunner of the Messiah, *going before Him in the spirit and power of Elijah,* as had been prophesied in the Scriptures.

Behold, I will send you Elijah the Prophet, before the Coming of the great and terrible Day of the Lord; and he shall turn the hearts of the fathers to the children, and the hearts of the children to the fathers; lest I come and smite the earth with a curse.

He felt himself to be that *Voice in the Wilderness* which the Prophet had heard in his dreams, crying out that the crooked should be made straight and the rough places smooth, that all flesh might see the salvation of God. *And the Voice said, "Cry!" And he said, "What shall I cry?"* And back had come the answer: *Say unto the cities of Judah, "Behold your God!"*

John was convinced that if only Israel made herself ready—by repentance and purification—Messiah would come.

So the Pilgrims on the great caravan road that ran through the Jordan Valley saw a gaunt figure striding down those stupendous ravines toward the fords close to Jericho, where the caravans met as the roads converged and joined. There in the level plain he lifted up his voice and cried, "Repent!" And folk stayed to listen, and lingered, and spread the news of the advent of a Prophet in Israel. As the lean-sinewed, raw-boned Man of God roared aloud his thundering exhortations, hearts burned and nerves shivered; and children crouched against their mothers as his wild eyes scanned the listening groups hungrily, searching for the Coming One.

Jerusalem soon got wind of the strange news, and the blood of patriots and pietists alike tingled at the tidings, and all men counted John a true Prophet. The Jewish hierarchy, too, heard of it and wondered, uncomfortably. "A Prophet" indeed, after all these hundreds of years of settled, institutional religion! What would become of their conveniently profitable rule over Israel if everybody ran after this ranting fellow from the Wilderness? Of course the whole thing might well blow over. It might even be a release of pent-up expectations—especially beneficial if it ended in disappointment. But the matter obviously should be looked into. Indeed, the Pharisees joined together with their rivals the High Priestly Sadducees in demanding a thorough investigation. So certain selected members of their respective communities went together down the twenty-mile descent to Jericho and along the Jordan Valley road, to wherever the wretched fellow was posturing.

But John both saw them—and saw through them. He knew that such men had no use for Prophets—unless they were nicely dead and buried, their teaching copied out in scrolls, pigeonholed and quietly ignored. He could well imagine their respective thoughts. A disruptive type, Prophets, apt to query the authority of the Law once and for all delivered to the Chosen Race; apt even to query the peculiar status of the Chosen Race itself. There were many passages in the Scriptures that were best forgotten: never read in the Synagogues, at any rate. The Pharisees were the rightful custodians of the Law, together with their scholarly experts, the Scribes. As for the Sadducees, they were aristocratic cynics superior to crazy ideas about Angels and Resurrection; Persian importations, anyway. They had, on the whole, made very comfortable terms with Rome. Pilate was not such a bad fellow, really, when you came to know him. He, like themselves, had no use for the rabble.

So, there among the crowds by the waterside, John saw these Legalists and Latitudinarians allied together in unholy opposition to himself. You could hardly miss them, in any case, with their flaunting phylacteries and their obvious superiority complex. Someone who was picnicking near them had evidently failed to beat out quickly enough the leaping flames of a little blaze, where a spark from a cooking fire had set the dry, crackling brushwood alight. Suddenly the flames spread, and a brood of young adders, hidden in the undergrowth, swarmed out among the crowd and wriggled away before the burning grass. And the men of Jerusalem over there had been forced to beat a hasty retreat—indeed, a most undignified scurry—as the wind blew the flames in their direction.

Like a flash, John rapped out his scathing comment: "O brood of vipers—who's warned *you* to flee from before the wrath to come?"

The huge crowd roared their delight. But the hierarchy of Jerusalem never forgave John. For his words seared and shrivelled in more deadly fashion than any sudden-flaring bush fire, and they could not be stamped out either. Save by death, thought the furious Jews, as they took themselves back to the capital.

John followed up his thrust by quoting the Scriptures: "Listen to the words of Isaiah: *The Lord shall kindle a burning like the burning of a Fire, and the Light of Israel shall be Himself a Fire, and the Holy One a Flame. It shall burn and devour the thorns and briars in one day, and shall consume the glory of the forest and of the fruitful field, both soul and body—and the rest of the trees shall be so few that a child might count them. Behold, the Lord shall lop the boughs with terror, and the high ones in stature shall be hewn down, and the haughty shall be humbled. Yea, He shall cut down the thickets of His forest—with Iron!*

"I tell you," he went on, "even *now* is the axe laid to the root of the trees! Every tree, therefore, that fails to produce good fruit shall be hewn down—and cast into the fire!"

This was preaching indeed. From the little brushwood fire to the conflagration of the wrath to come: the joint vision of both Isaiah and John. The people listened spellbound.

The voice was thundering again: "It's not enough merely to repent. You've got to bring forth *fruits,* fruits *worthy* of that repentance. And it's not the slightest use your saying: 'As for us, we are Abraham's children, the Chosen Race, God's peculiar people': for I tell you that race counts for absolutely nothing in God's sight. It doesn't matter to Him whether you are Israelites—or one of these stones!" kicked away contemptuously with his foot as the gallant words were spoken. And the astounding thing was that John was not stoned himself. The people must have winced—but they stayed. There was, indeed, a fire within him that not only seared but purified.

His personal magnetism and terrific sincerity held them as in a spell. Suddenly a voice rang out: "Tell us what we must *do.*"

The fiery Prophet at once became the practical man at the words. "Share and share alike. Whoever has two coats should give one of them to someone who has none. And the same with food or anything else."

His words were answered by a rumble of wholehearted assent, and scathing glances were directed against some tax farmers on the outskirts of the crowd, specially hated because as the servants of Rome they paid the Emperor a sum down and were allowed to exact as much over as they could extort from the people.

One of them, to the intense surprise of the crowd, called out, "Master, what must *we* do?"

Every eye was turned toward him. He did not flinch, but gazed steadily at the Prophet. It seemed he really was sincere.

Back came the inevitable answer: "Exact no more than the lawful amount from each person."

This raised a great cheer. Someone then pointed to the soldiers, standing warily on the edge of the throng. "What about them?" asked a hoarse voice.

John's answer made no reference to Rome's tyranny. He was there to call to repentance, not to raise a rebellion. "Never intimidate anyone, or lay false charges; and be content with your pay."

Then he began to baptize his converts, leading each one down into the shallows of the Jordan ford, and receiving from them there an assurance of their sincerity before he dipped them one by one in the water and pronounced over them God's blessing.

When the last one to come forward had been baptized he turned to the crowds and said, "You see, *I* only baptize with water. But there is One, far mightier than I am, Who is surely coming soon! One Who is so much greater than I am that I am not fit even to stoop down and unloose His sandal straps."

The people were hushed and a tense excitement surged in their hearts. "*He* will baptize you with the Holy Spirit and with fire! Yes, I see Him in vision even now! His winnowing fan is in His hand. He is thoroughly cleaning out His threshing floor, gathering the wheat into His granary, but burning up the chaff with unquenchable fire!"

In John's mind shone a Figure, radiant, omnipotent. He took a last look at the crowds. No. Messiah was not among them . . . but within his heart a cry arose:

I see Him! . . . but not now. I behold Him! . . . but not nigh.

And in the hearts of the people rang an insistent query: *Is the Lord among us or not?*

Then the Prophet turned and left the Jordan, striking up in the bleak hills that loomed behind him. And all the people were in expectancy, musing in their hearts. When would Messiah come? And was He already here in the world? And, if so, Who was He? There were no answers to these questions. But the hills seemed charged with a glad triumph. The crowds lifted their eyes to their summits, and the words of the Psalmist rang in their ears:

Let the rivers clap their hands, and the mountains sing for joy together before the Lord. Let all the trees of the forest sing for joy. For He comes! He comes!—to rule the earth, and with righteousness to judge the world, and the people with His truth!

III

Baptism and Temptation

THE hilltop above Nazareth shone silver-pale beneath the sickle moon, sailing soundlessly toward the sleeping sea. The last few minutes of the long vigil were being gathered up into the arms of the past. Suddenly a dog barked far away. Something had roused him . . . perhaps the click of the latch as a door was opened and a Man stepped quietly into the moonlit street. His form could be seen ascending the hillpath toward the summit.

It is the Lord's Release! Jesus' decision had at last been taken and all preparations made. There was nothing now remaining to be done save to climb the beloved hill and say good-bye to all its scenes and associations. It was early spring. The sap was rising in His soul. The rains were over and gone and the flowers had appeared on the earth, and the time of the singing of birds was come. The far trumpet voice of the herald had echoed even among these Galilean hills. The dawn of a new day was at hand.

A New Day! Already its tremulous glimmerings made pallid the waning moonlight. His eyes scanned the familiar horizons as the first flush of dawn revealed the summits of the far Hauran mountains, like the serrated edge of some gargantuan saw. Suddenly the peaks of Hermon away to the north shone like roselit beacons and a message knocked at Jesus' soul:

And the Lord said: "Get Thee up from Thy kindred, and from Thy father's house, and Thou shalt be a Blessing; for in Thee shall all the families of the earth be blessed." So He departed even as the Lord had spoken unto Him.

But Mary sighed and muttered: "The Lord God, Who fed me all my life long—until this day—bless the Lad."

Afterward Jesus found it all but impossible to tell even His closest friends what had happened to Him in His baptism. For a long time

45

He was unsure Himself; not as to the actual experience—that was unmistakable, vivid, unique; but as to its exact objective nature. That was a mystery only to be solved through suffering.

After John had led Him down into the water (not recognizing Him, as Jesus could see)—just as He was rising up from the immersion, a blinding Light had shone about Him, and for a brief moment the Heavens were rent asunder and He saw through the bounds of space and time straight into the very heart of God; and Something— a Blessing, a Grace, a Divine Commission—had seemed to float down softly, almost like a dove descending and alighting; suffusing Him with light and an ineffable happiness and with a sense of power. There had rung in His ears a Voice, gentle, intimate: *Thou art My Son . . . the Beloved. In Thee is My delight!*

The echoes of that amazing Revelation were still ringing in His ears as He rose, blind and dazed, out of the water. He found Himself unable to stop walking, though He was exhausted with emotion. It was almost as if He were being driven forward, away from the crowds, away from all human contacts, to some desolate region where He could be alone to think out the implications of this stupendous experience, somewhere where He could pray without any chance of interruption. He found Himself moving up toward the Wilderness, as if some supernal huntsman were at His heels unmercifully lashing Him forward, though He was ready to drop with physical and psychical fatigue.

At length He arrived among the vast hills and ravines of the Wilderness. Gigantic cliffs reared a thousand feet over Him, and dread abysses a thousand feet deep dropped sheer away from Him on the other side. There was no vegetation; not even a blade of grass, much less a tree, grew in that waste. There was hardly any soil, nothing but naked rock and loose stones and shifting sand. Earth here foretasted her ultimate doom. It was to a dead star, as if to the very craters of the moon, that Jesus was driven; a world grotesque, repellent, Satanic indeed. Here was the crucible wherein earth had once burned herself out, and only a chaos of charred and embered cinders remained to bear witness to that primal conflagration. The repulsively contorted strata were piled up in wanton fury, as if God had suddenly immobilized earth's dying agonies, or some mid-ocean frenzy had been

abruptly struck into stark stone. Its surface was blistered and peeling.
The very ground beneath His feet sounded hollow, as though it were
only a step (on a crumbling crust of rock) through to the bottomless
pit. Waterless gullies led only to the Dead Sea, below which lay the
sepulchral ashes of Sodom and Gomorrah.

Jeremiah knew its terrors well enough:

I look over the earth . . . and, lo, all is chaos.
I look up at the heavens, and their light is extinguished.
I look at the hills . . . and they are trembling and swooning in the
haze.
I look around . . . and, lo, no man can be seen, and even the very
birds of heaven are fled.
I look forth . . . and see nothing but the Wilderness, and all the
former cities shattered by the rage of the Lord God.

Here it was that Jesus wandered, neath the blistering, pitiless sun.
His problem obsessed Him. He was oblivious of the needs of the
body. All day—and often at night—the question hammered at His
mind: Am I in very truth the Son of God? Or was it all a subtle delu-
sion, wrought of an emotional crisis in a super-sensitive brain? No
one else had seemed to hear the Voice or see the Vision. But would
not such a Revelation be rightly a personal experience?

A further question followed hard on this. If He really were the
son of God, the Messiah, then how best should He fulfil His great
Mission? His mind inevitably sought to recall all the Scriptural passages that dealt with the Person and Mission of the Messiah. Most of
all He sought in the Scriptures for some confirmation of His own
sense of commission. But for a time only the dire suffering—physical
and mental—of Job was revived in Him:

A Thing . . . was secretly brought to me, and mine ear received a
whisper of It. . . . In thoughts and trances of the night, wrapt I lay in
my visions. Terror and trembling seized me till all my bones shud-
dered. A Spirit glided before me till my hair was bristling. There It
stood—this Form before mine eyes . . . and in the hush I heard It
mumuring: "Can a man . . . be just, like God? Can a man . . . be pure
like his Maker? Why, even upon His Heavenly Servants He cannot
rely. His very Angels He convicts of error. What, then, of those in

habitations of clay, with foundations of dust, frail as a moth, crushed in a single day, perishing utterly, unnoticed?"

But one dread doubt occurred again and again to trouble Him: *Have I then seen that which I knew not, and heard that which I could not comprehend?* Or was My sense deceived—or My soul in a dream?

Isaiah's words confirmed His doubts: *Yea, thou heardest not. Yea, thou knewest not.* Was, then, His sense of commission but a wicked blasphemy against God? Had He committed the unforgivable sin?

Then had come the terrible hunger and the scorching thirst. In the intensity of His spiritual struggle, with its alternating ecstasies and nauseas, He was largely unconscious of the needs of the body. The memory of His experience in baptism had given Him meat to eat and water to drink of which we can have but little knowledge, and in the strength of which, like Elijah of old, He was able to sustain life over an incredibly long period. But the claims of the flesh became insistent with the passage of time. The stones of the desert were very like little loaves in appearance. *If He were the Son of God,* the power to turn such stones into bread was implicit in Him. Should, then, He test this power—and so His Sonship—with a view to easing His hunger?

In spite of the gnawing pangs that racked His body, this personal and fleshly temptation was set aside. Whatever powers were in Him, they were surely to be used solely for others, never for Himself. But if so, surely it would be meet and right that He should miraculously provide that plenty that was so sadly lacking among the poor and destitute? Indeed, had not His own mother taught Him that one day the Kingdom of God would be ruled by a Messiah Who would "fill the hungry with good things"? Such an aim was obviously right.

But the means? This was where doubt crept in. God would, assuredly, have all men, and especially the rich, kindlier and more generous; but to exert force, to work miracles in this cause might be to make void the whole aim. For such charity, to be permanent and universal, must come from men's hearts, or it profited nothing. True, God had said: *Keep My judgments, and the land shall yield her fruit, and you shall eat your fill and dwell in safety.* But the emphasis was on the condition: *Keep My judgments.* What was needed was not so much the plenty in itself, but the pity that made it available; and pity was spiritual, not material. Jesus saw clearly, the more He thought about it, that if only people would seek first God's Kingdom and His righteousness, all these other blessings would inevitably follow. Further, if privation brought by personal experience a sense of the needs of others, then that too could be blessed of God.

Jesus recalled Moses' great words: *God humbled Thee and suffered Thee to hunger—that He might make Thee know that man doth not live by bread alone, but by every word that proceedeth out of the mouth of God.*

For the Kingdom of God could never be a matter of eating or drinking; but of righteousness and joy and peace in the Holy Spirit. It became increasingly clear to Him that the exercise of His miraculous endowment was barred to Him as a means of implementing His Messiahship. He must trust to God instead, in all circumstances.

"Trust to God instead . . ." As the long hours slowly passed, an all-absorbing question occupied His mind: how might He trust God most fully, not only to feed and care for Himself, but for all men? If (as He now felt sure was God's will) He could not, even metaphorically, make bread of these stones, lest He should be presuming upon God's prerogative, was there any other way in which He could prove, not only to Israel but still more to Himself, that He was content to leave everything to God, to trust Him utterly and irrevocably? And not only that: to prove to God that He Himself did *not* doubt His own Sonship?

In His reaction away from presuming on His undoubted powers, He swung over to the opposite extreme. He would not only repudiate the use of miracle to satisfy His own or the world's hunger, but He would openly cast Himself, and the world with Him, on to God's providential care. He *was* God's Son. How could He ever have doubted this? Death by starvation could never happen to Him—with His Mission unfulfilled, too. It was a pity that all the world could not see how unreservedly He trusted in the Father's care; in the Father's love of His Son.

Then it was that, with the first rays of the rising sun, came what seemed a God-given Sign. For there, far away on the eastern horizon where lay the Holy City, suddenly flashed a reflection of the sun's light from the gold roofing on some high point of the Temple itself. Soon its topmost pinnacle could be clearly seen as the dawn rose over the hills. Jesus gazed upon it, spellbound.

Was it not written: *The Lord, Whom you seek, shall suddenly come to His Temple?* "*Suddenly* come." How? Evidently, in some dramatic way, to the amazement of all observers. Could this mean . . . from above? He saw in vision the teeming Passover crowds filling the Temple Courts and the valleys around its walls. He was by now sure that He was indeed God's Son. God, therefore, would assuredly attest His Son's authority—and, so, His demands upon Him—before all Israel. How better could this be done than if He, Jesus, were to stand upon yonder gleaming pinnacle, in full view of the densely packed throngs from every nation under heaven, and then to throw Himself down . . . and alight among the people, unhurt? God would not *suffer His foot to be moved* as He waited, poised on the pinnacle. He would be His *Keeper and His defence upon His right hand.*

Was it not written: *Death shall not come nigh Thee. There shall no evil befall Thee?*

As Jesus gazed on that flashing, Heaven-aspiring pinnacle, His faith in God soared and settled as on a focal point. A strange, mystic sense of immunity, miraculous and glorious, swept over Him and braced His soul. He would trust in the Spirit of God, Whose wings, strong as an eagle's, soft as a dove's, would carry Him to safety among those dumb-struck crowds, even if He were to leap off that far pinnacle. For underneath would always be the Everlasting Arms. Was not He Himself addressed in the Scriptures by God?

I will give Mine Angels charge over Thee, to keep Thee in all Thy ways. They shall bear Thee up in their hands, lest at any time Thou dash Thy foot against a stone.

Behold, there came with the clouds of Heaven One like unto a Son of Man; and there was given unto Him dominion and glory and a Kingdom; that all peoples, nations and languages should serve Him.

If Daniel thus rightly foresaw the future, then this paltry descent into the shadows of Kedron were but a step compared with that great cosmic flight from Heaven to earth, past the clustered stars, through the piled-up thunderclouds, toward the Throne of the world.

In refusing to satisfy His own needs by the exertion of miraculous powers, He had been forced back upon the providence of God, even as

Elijah of old had been dependent only upon the divine care. If He were to fling Himself from that pinnacle this dependence upon God would be proved for all to see. As for His own safety, *He* was willing thus to be put to the test by God.

Yet . . . *was* it He that would be put to the test? Would it not rather be He that would be putting *God* to the test?

In this connexion, Moses had a decisive word to say: *You shall* not *put God to the test.*

There suddenly swept over Him the reactions to His own previous reaction. He knew now that it would be dire presumption to challenge God to protect Him from the hazards attendant on foolhardiness; that He could no more presume upon God's care than upon His own miraculous powers. His Sonship must never be attested or exploited through mere wonder-working. As a man amongst men rather than as the Son of God must He win the world and conquer the hosts of evil.

Was there, then, any possible way of achieving dominion *without* the aid of miracle? Was there any path to the throne of the world that could be trodden by feet firmly planted upon earth?

Once again, He had recourse to His memory of the Scriptures. Had they any guidance to give Him?

I will lift up Mine eyes unto the hills . . .

As He mused on the great theme of His Mission and its fulfilment, this text knocked at His mind insistently, almost as though the path to world domination led upward in a literal sense. There was a vast mountain on the horizon that called to Him, its peak o'ertopping the wreckage of a lost world. Through long days of blistering heat, through long nights of shivering cold, He wandered inevitably toward that lonely peak. There were howls, bestial and Satanic, that echoed along the dark caverns and ravines and were lost in uneasy silence; eyes in the night that gleamed and flashed, or stared unmovingly as He passed, ever upward.

When at last He gained the summit as dawn rose over the far Hauran mountains, He found Himself looking down upon the Jordan Valley, lying misty and shadowed a thousand feet below, a green oasis in a waste of barren hills stretching out of sight. But to the east one

colossal peak rose over the horizon, mocking His present stance from
its own towering height. Suddenly He realized its identity—Pisgah,
the mountain peak wherefrom Moses had viewed the Promised Land.
There, before Israel's dying leader, had lain outspread, like a gigantic
relief map, the future dominion of Jehovah. But now, thought Jesus,
it was not Canaan only that remained to be won for God. He knew
that His Father was Overlord of the whole earth, and that His will
would never be fulfilled till every land and nation owned that Lordship. Jesus, in imagination, was Himself standing on that far peak,
bathed in the warm glow of the morning sunlight, a mightier Moses
surveying a mightier Canaan. The shadow was shortening every minute as, in His mind's eye, more and more of the prospect was lightened
and warmed by the sun; and as the vision intensified in vividness and
seeming reality, He felt Himself viewing the full extent of the territory *yet* to be won for God, not only as from Pisgah's height, but as
from a peak high enough in the heavens to survey all the kingdoms
of the world, the earth looking like some great star set in horrifying
propinquity. From this remote mid-stellar peak the eye of mystic
vision saw each kingdom—each city, even—as from an immense distance, yet with startling clarity. Ephesus, Corinth, Philippi, Athens,
Thessalonica, each revealed to that Watcher in the skies its special
glory, its teeming myriads, its beauty and its pride. And there, central and regnant, lay Rome itself, resplendent in all her proud dignity; mistress of the earth, inviolate, serene, secure . . . cruel, godless.
Hers was a majesty founded upon fear and relying only upon force.
Jesus saw that only the power of Jehovah could ever overthrow that
tyrannizing domination. He, in Whose sight the nations of the
world were but as the dust in the balance, alone through His Anointed
Messiah could vanquish Caesar and rule over a freed world. Jesus
felt Himself destined to fill the greatest role in all history.

As He stood there on that vast rock, the words of Isaiah came into
His mind: *He shall dwell on high. His place of defence shall be set
upon a rock. Bread shall be given Him. His waters shall be sure.
Thine eyes shall there behold the King in all His beauty. Yea, they
shall behold the land that is very far off. . . .*

Jesus remembered His mother's teaching; her insistence on the
inevitability with which God would eventually right all earth's in-

equalities and wrongs; how she used often to tell Him and James—and John when he was there—that God would one day show the full strength of His arm, scattering the proud with their scheming ways, dethroning princes, sending the rich away empty-handed while uplifting the lowly and satisfying the hungry.

Again Isaiah's words rang in His ears—from the selfsame passage as before: *It is only the impious that leave the hungry to starve and stint the thirsty of their drink. Yet one day from the heights of heaven—a Spirit shall be poured into us, till the Wilderness shall become an orchard, and the orchard become a forest; till justice fills the desert and honesty the fields, and peace shall be secure and My people dwell safely in quiet resting-places.*

His thoughts went back to His experience in baptism, and to the Psalm whose words were then echoed from Heaven.

He that sits in the Heavens shall laugh them to scorn. The Lord shall have them in derision. For I, God, have set My King upon My holy hill. Yea, the Lord has said unto Me: "Thou art My Son. This day have I begotten Thee. Ask of Me, and I will give Thee the heathen for Thine inheritance, and the uttermost parts of the earth for Thy possession." . . . Be wise, now, therefore, O you Kings; and all you rulers of the earth, take warning: Do homage to the Son . . . lest He be angry and you end in ruin . . . for His wrath is quickly kindled.

The more Jesus pondered over the commission given Him by God in His baptism, the more did this Scripture take on significance and the context of the message from Heaven, *quoted from this very Psalm,* become all-important in Jesus' eyes; for its use then *by God Himself* infallibly attested its original Divine inspiration and its present application. Thus it seemed predestined by Heaven itself that Jesus should fulfil its glorious promises; that He should become Master of the world, God's Regent, Dictator of all mankind.

This could only mean that Jesus would wage a Holy War against the hosts of evil, conquering all nations, overcoming all tyrants, in the name of Jehovah. And if this were to be accomplished without the use of miracle—and surely that was by now clear—then it must portend a military campaign carried to ultimate and overwhelming success through the personal genius, magnetism and courage of the Messiah Himself. He knew He could accomplish this; that powers were His, so far unused, that, scorning miraculous aid, would bring the whole world to His feet. Had not the Scriptures foretold of the Christ that He should be a Warrior King?

The Lord shall go forth as a mighty man. He shall stir up zeal like a man of war. He shall cry, yea, roar, and shall prevail against His enemies. I have long time held My peace. I have been still and refrained Myself. But now I will make darkness light before Thee, and crooked things straight. I will not forsake Thee.

Then it was that Jesus realized suddenly that Messiah was hailed as the *Prince of Peace,* and He recalled the sentence that preceded this: *For all the armour of the armed man in the tumult, and all the garments rolled in blood, shall be even for burning, and for fuel of fire.* Jesus saw, in place of the holocaust of slaughter, a funeral pyre whereon all the weapons of war should perish for ever. For what words followed? *Of the increase of His government,* and of peace, *there shall be no end* . . . And in the mind of Jesus rose an intense conviction that these warlike dreams were of the Devil; that to indulge them would be to sell His soul to Satan. What could it profit a man were He to gain the whole world—spread out there before Him—if, in doing so, He should lose His soul? This notion of the Warrior King was a concept of the false religions of ignorant men. What had Moses cried before he had lain down to die, there on the very height of Pisgah? *And it shall be that when the Lord your God shall have brought you into the land, that you shall beware lest you forget the Lord your God. You must not go after other gods—the gods of people round about; but you must worship the Lord your God, and Him only shall you serve.*

Yes, He must worship *His* God, the God He had learned to love and trust, Who was a God of love and of peace; never a God of war. To drive out force by force would be to leave force the victor.

So the mystic vision faded before Jesus' eyes . . . and He found Himself back again on the rock mountain in the Wilderness, looking down on the Jordan vale, with its green oases and its pastoral villages. The kingdoms of the world and their glory no longer attracted Him.

Not that He had abandoned His intention to conquer the world for God—as a practicable venture and without miracle; but that this from henceforward meant for Him the conquest of individual hearts, the peregrination of humble villages, the way of patient persuasion. Enough for Him that He could never surrender His "Abba," Father, for any unworthy (no matter how Scriptural) conception of God. The Scriptures acclaimed other gods and other ideals. Conscience and conviction alone counted for integrity and authority. *Let the counsel of Thine own heart stand. For there is no man more faithful unto Thee than it. For a man's mind is sometime wont to tell Him more than seven watchmen, that sit above in a high tower. And above all, pray to The Most High, that He will direct Thy way in truth.*

As He turned away from that dizzy height, from which He now recoiled in horror, a great peace flooded His soul. The defeat of these three temptations was a mightier victory than any dreamed of on that star-girt peak. He had won His battle. *"Not by power, not by might,"* saith the Lord of Hosts, *"but by My Spirit."*

"By My Spirit"—that Spirit which had lighted upon Him in His baptism; the will of God for Him and for the world: the power of God to implement that will. Here was His commission, clear at last. He knew His path—down there toward the valley of humble service. The Scriptures spoke to Him now with no uncertain voice: *Behold My Servant, Whom I uphold; Mine Elect, in Whom My soul delights; I have endowed Him with Spirit—to carry true religion to the nations. I, the Lord, have called Thee—in righteousness; and I will hold Thine hand and keep Thee.* None knew better than Jesus the tyranny and cruelty with which the world's government was sustained. But the tyranny of sin was crueler; the slavery of self harder to escape from. It would be His task to *open the blind eyes, to bring out the prisoners from the prison, and them that sit in darkness from the house of bondage.* From henceforth His Mission would be summed up in the great words of Isaiah:

The spirit of the Lord God is upon Me, because He has anointed Me—to preach good tidings to the meek, to bind up the broken hearts, to proclaim liberty to the captives and the opening of the prison to them that are bound; to comfort all that mourn; to give them the garment of praise for the spirit of heaviness. Yea, My soul shall be

joyful in My God . . . for He has clothed Me with a robe of righteous-
ness—even as a Bridegroom. For as the earth brings forth her buds,
and as the garden seeds spring up and grow—so shall the Lord God
cause righteousness and praise to spring up before all nations!

This authority was final and complete. From henceforth this remained the proof text of His Messianic Mission. It was an unspectacu-
lar role. It meant living as an ordinary man amongst men, eschewing
"signs," refusing to be acclaimed as Messiah save through the witness
of each man's conscience. He foresaw possible disappointment among
the people—though surely they would follow Him when they really
understood. The Priests would almost certainly be hostile to His plan,
since it included the abrogation of sacrifices and the setting up of a
new Temple not made with hands; nothing less than the sovereignty
of God in men's hearts. But He would be doing God's will, among
God's people. He was happy and radiant—*even as a Bridegroom.*

And somewhere down there, along the winding trench of the
Jordan Valley, was the Bridegroom's friend, awaiting His return. He
would not keep that loyal heart waiting any longer. He was ready
now to descend to the world of men again, to the early summer loveliness of the fields and streams. So, not on wings from a pinnacle of
the Temple, but on His own tired feet from the crags and gullies
of the Wilderness, the Son of Man came down from the heights of
cosmic contest to the level plains. In quietness and confidence was
His strength. He would wait upon the Lord. It were better to be
able to *run and not be weary* than to *mount up on wings as eagles.*
Best of all to *walk and not faint.*

IV

The First Disciples

. . . .

(I) PETER

JOHN had wondered wherever Jesus could have been all these weeks. He himself had moved up the banks of Jordan and was now at a ford not far from Bethshean, close to the border hills separating Samaria from Galilee. Greater throngs surrounded him than ever before. The authorities at Jerusalem were more perturbed than they would admit even among themselves. They had sent down another group of emissaries to spy on John in order to learn, if they could, what he was aiming at—and, above all, who he claimed to be. This time there were Priests and Levites in the group, whose mission it was to "place" John, if possible. They decided to come out into the open and question him concerning his person and teaching. They were faced with the necessity of undermining his authority in the eyes of the people. One thing was certain. He had no regular authority at all. He had rejected his birthright of following in his father's footsteps and becoming a Priest. There were ridiculous rumours going round that he might turn out to be the Messiah. So they came forward in a body and demanded of him: "Who are you?"

John knew well enough what was troubling them, and answered frankly—even bluntly, "I am *not* the Messiah." The Jews were fully satisfied with that. They had never dreamed he was the Messiah. It was well, however, for the crowds to hear his denial. That was, indeed, a point gained. But there was a consequence of that denial, and they would make John face it.

"What then is your role?" they asked: "Do you claim to be a reincarnation of Elijah?"

This was a hard one to answer, since John had expressly been brought up to believe that he was destined to carry out his mission as the forerunner of the Messiah *in the spirit and power of Elijah*. But John felt himself utterly unworthy to be compared, much less identified, with Elijah. (He was not to know that in Christ's judgment he outsoared even Elijah and all God's Prophets, and was indeed "that Elijah that was to come.") If, then, this question were any temptation to him, he overcame it.

"I am not," he answered.

They thought of the great Prophet foretold by Moses: *The Lord God will raise up for you a Prophet from among you, like unto myself; and to that Prophet you must listen. For the Lord said to me: "I will raise up a Prophet for them from amongst themselves, like unto yourself. I will put My words into his lips, and he shall speak to them all that I shall command him to. Anyone who does not listen to him, I Myself will make him answer for it!"*

"Are you that great Prophet whose coming was foretold by Moses?" they asked him.

"No!"

They were growing impatient of so many negatives. "If you are not the Messiah, nor Elijah, nor that other great Prophet, who are you? Come, tell us, so that we can give some sort of answer to those who sent us. What account can you give of yourself?"

Here was the challenge. He could but tell the truth, as he felt it burning within him. "I am . . . *the Voice of one crying in the Wilderness: 'Level a highway for our God,'* even as Isaiah foretold."

His mind inevitably mused upon the words that followed this Scripture: *The Voice said, "Cry!" "What shall I cry?" "Raise your voice aloud, O herald of happiness: lift it up, be not afraid; say unto the cities of Judah: 'Behold your God! Here is the Lord, coming in power, maintaining mightily His cause. Here He is bringing what He has won—what He has gained!'"*

Even as he mused upon this seal of his commission he caught sight of Jesus striding down from the hills; a conqueror indeed, mightily maintaining His cause, and bringing with Him His trophies of battle, won there in the heart of the desert. John did not know—yet— who Jesus was. He had failed—naturally, after so long a time—to recognize Him as his own cousin; nor did he know that Jesus had been the recipient of any strange experience in baptism. Much less did he realize that yonder Figure descending the hillside was the Messiah of God, of Whom he himself was the forerunner. But as Jesus was at length lost to sight amid the dense throngs lining the waterside, John felt within him a sudden quickening of spiritual awareness, a sense of impending crisis, of growing rapture. So that, when the Jews asked him why, if he were no recognizable reincarnation, he troubled to preach or to baptize, he at once answered (as on a former occasion, but with one startling difference):

"*I* can only baptize you with water . . . but I feel sure that even now there stands, *there somewhere in your very midst*, One Whom none of us has recognized as yet. He it is Who supersedes me. He is the One of Whom I formerly spoke, saying that I was not worthy even to stoop down and unfasten the latchet of His sandals."

This terrific pronouncement sent a thrill through his vast congregation. Each man scanned his neighbours around him and wondered to Whom the Baptist could be referring. In tense silence they listened for a further and more exact identification. But none came. The preaching was evidently over for today.

But when the crowds, excited and thrilled, had departed, and the sun had set behind the Samaritan hills, Jesus sought out His cousin and made Himself known to him. John was staggered to hear of Jesus' experience in baptism and His terrible struggle in the desert. "I never realized . . ." he kept on saying. It seemed to trouble him that he, the forerunner, should so have failed in his mission. When Jesus had left him, he could not leave the subject of his own remissness. But he tried to make up for it by pointing his disciples to his Successor.

The next day, standing with two of his disciples during a break in the spate of preaching, John caught sight of Jesus passing by and drew their attention to Him. One of the men was named Andrew, a fisherman from Bethsaida, a village at the head of the Lake of Galilee. The other was a young scholar from Jerusalem, an aristocrat who had been trained in the university of Alexandria under the well-known philosopher Philo. He was a dreamer, and a poet—a born mystic.

Hearing what John whispered to them, they immediately followed after Jesus, Who turned round and saw them, asking: "What can I do for you?"

Not knowing quite what to say, they stammered out, "Teacher . . . where do You live?"

Jesus replied, "Come along with Me, and you will see."

So they went with Him and saw where He was staying (it then being about ten o'clock in the morning), and stayed with Him for the rest of that day. Jesus told them of His intention to depart northward as soon as possible; so early the next morning Andrew sought out his brother, Simon, telling him eagerly: "We have found the Man the Baptist spoke about!"

Arrived at Jesus' lodging, Andrew brought forward his brother— a strong, rugged type of man, impulsive, warm-hearted, eminently lovable. Jesus gazed at him for so long a time that Simon was embarrassed. Then the tall, auburn-haired Stranger uttered words that Simon never forgot.

"What did you say your name was—'Simon, son of Jonah'? Well, I shall call you 'Peter,' for you are just like a 'rock'!"

Simon burned with pride and self-consciousness, but one could not easily discern his tendency to flush, so brown was he. He felt that the earnest gaze of Jesus had pierced through to the inmost depths of his soul. It made him feel terribly humble—almost sick at heart. The same steadfast gaze of Jesus was, he was soon to discover, a characteristic of the Master, and he often found himself watching Jesus and noting that unwavering, searching stare. It saw through to bedrock truth, to the good and bad in men and women. It saw through the limits of time and space to Heaven itself—and to Hell.

The day following, Jesus determined to leave for Galilee, and Andrew and "Peter" (for he liked to be called by his new nickname) found themselves faced with an urgent problem. Were they to remain with their former master, the Baptist, or could they join up with this new Friend? But He was not teaching as yet, though He had told them a little of His plans; albeit these seemed vague and nebulous to the two brothers, who could not be expected to see into Jesus' mind so soon. Nevertheless, they felt they could not let Jesus go northward without them; and they easily rationalized their wish: it was high time, anyway, for them to return home to their fishing. They had been away quite long enough. Jesus welcomed their company on the northward walk, but told them first to bid farewell to John. He Himself went with them and took leave of that lion-hearted friend and then departed up through the Gap of Jezreel.

John watched them go . . . his own work nearly done now, his disciples adhering to the new Leader, and leaving him lonely and humbled. But his soul could not but confess the essential rightness of it all: the overwhelming magnetism of Jesus and the inevitability of his own eclipse. And as he watched those four figures—Jesus, Andrew, Simon and young John—growing smaller and smaller till they were lost in the green shadows of the glen, he marvelled at the inscrutable ways of God. He himself had fulfilled his destiny—to herald the Messiah. It was strange that God's Anointed One should turn out to be his own cousin, Jesus, with Whom he had so often played when a boy. Stranger still that he—the herald—should not have recognized Him as Messiah when first he saw Him after the long interval of some twenty years. But he glowed to think that God had so greatly blessed and sealed that baptism—his own. Nevertheless, the departure of Jesus so soon after the revelation of His Messiahship to John was a problem almost impossible to solve. To be sure, Jesus had explained that His presence was required at a relative's wedding in Cana of Galilee; but that seemed a poor excuse for leaving, and in any case it did not explain why His Messiahship should not be publicly proclaimed to the crowds. *Why* had Jesus been so insistent on secrecy? Why could not he, John, tell it out to all the world that here was the Christ, the Son of the Living God? As it was, Jesus had gone north with but three young friends, none of whom yet knew His secret. John had felt sure that the sole reason for his own mission was that the Messiah might be openly proclaimed to Israel. But the crowds were still speculating as to the identity of the Successor. And now Jesus' absence might mean that the whole thing would be treated as another illusion, and his own baptism to repentance be frustrated. But he believed in Jesus' utter sincerity. God knew best how the Kingdom might be established upon earth.

Meanwhile, the Bridegroom had departed and the friend of the Bridegroom was left forlorn—and a little dismayed. How was he to know that in pointing a few friends to Jesus he had adopted Jesus' own method, Who Himself was relying, as it turned out, upon the same little handful of friends? Little could John realize that he had just laid the foundation of the Church of Christ; that around that tiny nucleus was to gather a mighty army before which even Rome would eventually surrender and Hell itself would crumble. John had built better than he knew.

(II) NATHANAEL

THESE new friends of Jesus were walking through the flower-sweet fields of Samaria as the full glory of early summer unfolded in that rivered vale. They passed by orchards of blossoming fruit trees, through wide fields of green, growing corn, under the lee of mighty hills—their heights bare and brown against the burning blue of the sky—across the Great Plain of Esdraelon, at last mounting up toward the high wind-swept uplands of their own beloved Galilee (for all of them, save young John, were from the northern province). In the far northeastern distance they here and there caught sight of a patch of startlingly deep blue—the Lake of Galilee! And all the while their friendship for Jesus, seemingly begun so casually, was ripening into a rapt and devoted discipleship. There was a telltale adoration, a radiant enthusiasm, in their eyes as they looked at their new Master— He was already very dear to them.

Somewhere on the road, they fell in with Philip—hailed by Andrew and Peter, who, like Philip, came from the same town of Bethsaida. He heard from them of their new Friend, and of the Baptist's opinion of Him. Together the brothers brought Philip to Jesus, and the five friends proceeded on their journey, a new gladness suffusing Philip's face. Indeed, so enthusiastic was he that when at length they reached Cana, whither they were bound, he at once sought out a special friend of his who lived there. "The very man to help You," he told Jesus.

Nathanael was intrigued—and just a little amused too, by Philip's enthusiasm and breathless message:

"We have come across a Man, an extraordinary Person; it's just possible, we think, that He might turn out to be the One of Whom Moses and the Prophets wrote about—you know, the Messiah!"

"Really? And who is it?"

"Jesus, the Son of Joseph, who was the carpenter at Nazareth!"

"*Nazareth?*" smiled Nathanael. "*Can* anything good come out of Nazareth?" It was a well-known gibe—among those who did not live there.

"Well, come along and meet Him, anyway."

Nathanael rose good-humouredly, but it was a tiresome business rushing round behind impatient young fanatics, excited by the latest Messianic "find." Besides, Philip had interrupted a deep reverie. Nathanael had been resting beneath the broad shade of a wide-spreading fig tree in his garden, musing upon the Rabbinic Meditation for the Passover month, which ended with the words: *Happy is he who has the God of Jacob for his help.* This had led him to dwell on the story of Jacob's vision at Bethel, where the Patriarch had lain down, weary, to sleep, and, pillowed upon a stone, had dreamed of a great stairway reaching up from earth to Heaven,—*and, behold, the Angels of God, ascending and descending upon it,* and at the viewless apex in the central height, *God . . .* hidden in excess of light.

Meditating on this chapter, Nathanael had recalled how Jacob, the guileful deceiver, became "Israel," in token of prevailing persever-ance with God. Allegorizing the story, as a good Rabbi, he realized that such reformation was the only way to attempt to rise from earth to Heaven. But the great gulf remained; that separating the Creator from the creature: Heaven from earth. Where was the symbolic lad-der that could bridge that gulf? Upon these solemn meditations had burst in Philip with his startling news and its laughable anticlimax about some carpenter fellow—from Nazareth, of all places.

Nathanael was all the more startled that Jesus, on seeing him, exclaimed, "Behold! A genuine '*Israel*'-ite, indeed—and one, this time, in whom there is *no* guile."

But this was astonishing, incredible. Nathanael could hardly gasp out his surprise. "How do *You* come to know anything about me?"

"Why," exclaimed Jesus, "before ever Philip burst in upon you, I saw you in vision, meditating under the fig tree in your garden, and I knew all your thoughts and longings."

This was surely a sign from Heaven. Nathanael remembered the Psalmist's words: *O Lord, Thou hast searched me out and known me. Thou knowest my down-sitting and mine uprising. Thou understandest my thoughts afar off.* The end of the Bethel story, too, found Jacob breathing out the astounding words: *Surely the Lord is in this place . . . and I knew it not.*

The strange relevancy of this with Philip's news so astonished Nathanael that, involuntarily, he fell on his knees at Jesus' feet, saying, "Rabbi, *You* are the King for all true Israelites!"

Jesus loved this spiritually minded thinker, and led him out along the cosmic radiances of His own imagination.

"Is it merely because I could read your thoughts that you believe in Me? You shall see more wonderful things than this."

His beautiful voice rang with poetry and passion. "For, truly I tell you, you shall yourself one day see Heaven wide open . . . and God's Angels ascending and descending—*upon the Son of Man!*"

He knew Himself to be the Way, as well as the Truth and the Life. No man could approach the Father but by Him. He would, in deepest truth, actually be the living ladder linking earth and Heaven; Himself the very stairway under men's feet, reaching down into the lowest depths of Hell, and rising up into the viewless heights of Heaven, where God shone in His blinding glory.

(III) THE CANA WEDDING

It was the day of the wedding. The bridegroom was a younger brother of Jesus, who had settled down in Cana, and Mary was helping to superintend the arrangements. It came as rather a shock at first to her to find Jesus a "Master" now, with—how many?—five disciples. Anyway, He was home again in His own beloved Galilee, and safe from those dangerous Romans. These extra mouths to feed were, however, a source of worry. Combined relief and tension, therefore, reacted in her to produce a mood of excitable impulsiveness.

It came as no surprise to her to hear that the wine was running short. Jesus and young John were with her in the kitchen when the hired servants brought the news, Jesus having left the guests a moment to help His mother. Force of long habit (for Joseph had been dead many years now) and a sense that Jesus Himself was to a large extent responsible for the deficiency by bringing so many friends with Him, made Mary turn to her elder Son in the emergency. "There! They've run short of wine! I thought they would!"

This was a grave and, indeed, a culpable defect in an Eastern banquet, wherein lavish hospitality was the first necessity of good manners. Jesus' immediate impulse was to help . . . somehow. Then He suddenly realized that by now the market would be closed, and to advertise one's family's neglect on such an occasion by borrowing from a neighbour was unthinkable. Their own good name depended on keeping the deficiency secret. But, in these circumstances, to help in a practical way would mean miraculous intervention, and against such a course was set the full significance of His victory in the desert. Besides, if He were to use His powers, this would be His first, His Inaugural Miracle. And what moral purpose would be served, in any case? Here were men who had already drunk deep and yet were asking for more.

He glanced at Mary critically. "Well . . . what of it?" And then, finding her eyes upon Him in surprise at His tone, He added, "In any case, My hour is not yet come."

But Mary, who was used to the slightest inflexion in His voice, sensed the hesitation in His mind, and turned to the servants, saying, "Whatever He tells you to do, do it!" in a hurried whisper, before busily engaging herself with other jobs.

Jesus, however, continued to feel acutely uncomfortable. It had been far easier, there in the Wilderness, to resist the blandishments of Satan than here to refuse a mother's appeal, issued, as He well knew, in the face of a present human need and the prospect of real unhappiness. But this, He thought, only served to make the temptation more insidious. Indeed, perhaps the most subtle note of all lay in the realization that it was itself a loving impulse that was jeopardizing His reliance upon love alone.

Then followed an overwhelming revulsion of thought. What if these very scruples should turn out to be the most subtle temptation He had so far encountered? Was it right, and according to God's will to prefer a principle to a loving impulse? If God were love, then to obey the heart were to obey God. And perhaps the very inadequacy of the occasion—and its comparative privacy—constituted a humbling element which would be in line with God's will for Him. After all, God performed His daily and continuous miracles in secret behind the Veil.

In a moment of swift decision He flung all further scruple to the winds and acted. Caution, prudence, pride, even principle, all were surrendered to loving impulse. A young couple were in a tight corner and needed help. What if His hour were not yet come? There could be no "hour" for the free exercise of love's impulses. Love knew no delimiting instant, recognized no excess, calculated no overplus, considered no proprieties. To what purpose was this waste? But love can never be wasted. God's follies were wiser than man's rectitudes.

"Fill up the waterpots with water!" He commanded the servants. And they hastened to obey Him, filling the six great jars till they nearly overflowed.

"Now pour some out, and take it in to the President of the feast!"

And it was duly borne in, while Mary and young John, who was with her, listened to hear, if they could, how it was received. There was a moment's silence; then a merry voice was heard crying out, "Why, it's usual to serve the good wine first, and then, when people have drunk freely, to offer them the inferior. But, dear me, you've reserved the *best* wine till now!"

And Mary and young John were awed and not a little frightened, as they glanced wonderingly at Jesus. But He turned away and strode out of the house and did not return till long after all the last guests had gone. Young John thought it glorious of Him to do so great a work just to help out a bridal couple. When, long after, he reflected on it, he saw it as the first sign or manifestation of that glory that was His always, could men have but seen: indeed a very lovely Inaugural Miracle.

(IV) AT AENON NEAR TO SALIM

AFTER this He and His mother and brothers went to visit their relations in Capernaum. Mary's sister Salome had married a Lakeside fisherman named Zebedee. He and his two sons, James and John, had prospered well and now had more than one boat and several hired men. They had recently formed a partnership with the two brothers, Andrew and Simon, who came from Bethsaida. It was always a joy to Jesus to be beside the Lake. Its waters were so blue and its shores so green. Besides, there was so much life to be seen there. The great Roman road, the *Via Maris,* ran alongside the Lake, near Capernaum and Herod's new city of Tiberias, where he had built his splendid palace. When it came to talk of fishing, the partners made it clear that they did not think much of the opinion of their landsmen cousins.

The Nazarene family did not usually stay long in Capernaum, and this visit was no exception to the rule. When it was time to leave Capernaum, Jesus proposed to His friends that if any of them, including James and John, cared to accompany Him, they might all go southward for a while to assist the Baptist in his great work. They agreed, eagerly; and so, with superb humility, Jesus reappeared not far from the fords of Jordan—this time near to Salim, at a place called Aenon, where John was then baptizing, there being plenty of water available from the seven springs that welled up from the ground near by. John was deeply touched by this supreme condescension on the part of Jesus, knowing that Jesus was thus trying to show him that he, John, was still a leader in Israel.

The summer months passed by and soon the autumnal tints were enriching the wooded hills and valleys of Samaria. Jesus and His few friends enjoyed the peace and quiet of the evening talks after the last convert had come up out of the water and the day's work was done. But there inevitably came a time when the natural magnetism of Jesus had its effect upon the crowds. They hung around Him, to hear Him talk or just to be near Him. Soon some of John's disciples complained to their master that Jesus was becoming too popular.

It had all started when a Jew questioned the wisdom of allowing two people to baptize, especially when men were asserting that the teaching of Jesus was different from that of John on the all-important subject of what this purification really meant. Jesus taught that the rite signified nothing apart from internal repentance. That was the supreme necessity. Besides, He often was extremely reluctant to perform the rite Himself, lest the crowds should imagine that He was setting Himself up as a rival to John. And now the very crisis He had done His best to avoid was upon them.

John's disciples came forward, saying, "Teacher, you remember the Man Who was with you when you were on the other side of Jordan—the One you told us about? Well, as you know, He is also baptizing, and everybody's crowding round *Him*."

John's answer was as ripely mellow as the mature and sombre beauty of the autumnal woods and hills around. The gaunt features of the forerunner glowed with a grave exaltation as he gazed along the valley toward where, not far away, Jesus was stealing his thunder and lightning and turning it, in His own magical way, into the glad sunlight of day. He could just make out His figure, seated on the bank of a stream, and that unforgettable voice could be heard echoing along the river valley, though no words could be distinguished. Jesus had everything—a young God. . . .

Then John turned to his disciples and said, "No man can receive anything, save as a gift from Heaven. You yourselves can bear me out that I openly said 'I am *not* the Messiah.' All that I ever claimed to be was the forerunner."

He saw the friends of Jesus as the "Bride" of Christ. *As the Bridegroom rejoices over the Bride, so shall thy God rejoice over thee*. "And the Bridegroom's friend, who stands aside—*and hears His voice from afar*—can but rejoice also at the glad sound of the Bridegroom's voice!"

He paused again to listen as the rise and fall of that golden voice came to him from the distance. "Such is my joy," he added, "and it is complete!"

John was never greater than at this moment. In his sublime humility he had reached the apex of his glory. Then, in inspired utterance, he spoke his own finest epitaph: "He must wax, but I must wane."

He now knew a peace that was proof against all desertion and all danger.

But danger there was, all the time; and it was growing as the months sped by and autumn merged into winter. For Aenon was not far from Tiberias, where Herod held his court. The superstitious King was watching John closely. Eventually he sent for him and found himself at last face to face with the stern and rugged Prophet. And John amazed all who were present by openly indicting the King and Herodias his Queen with committing adultery.

"It is not lawful," he told Herod, "for you to have your brother's wife!"

Everyone shrank in awe and fear as the dread words were uttered, for Herod had indeed divorced his own wife, the daughter of Aretas, the King of Nabataea, on the south of Peraea, and had married Herodias, the wife of his half-brother Philip.

But the threatened explosion never came; and, instead, the superstitious King gazed on John in mortal fear. But Herodias was furious, and allowed Herod no rest till her demand for John's arrest was fulfilled. And one day the fearless Prophet saw a posse of Herod's soldiers approaching; but he stood his ground, and presently they carried him away southward to the black dungeons of far-off Machaerus, set high, bleak and impregnable, upon the rock ranges overhanging the Dead Sea.

So the mighty voice was at last silenced, the eagle caged.

ACT TWO

. . . .

The Christ of Galilee

THE ACCEPTABLE YEAR OF THE LORD

I

The New Covenant

. . . .

(I) THE FIRST PASSOVER

THE news of John's arrest was decisive for Jesus. The time of waiting was over; the hour for action had come. He went south with
urgent haste, His spirit flaming like a refiner's fire. He was going to
purge and purify the sons of Levi—till He found men ready to offer
sacrifices of righteousness.

Ever since that far-off day when as a Boy of twelve He had first
entered the Temple, He had longed for this hour to strike. He
thought it had struck when He came south a year before, but His experience in baptism and His struggle in the Wilderness had altered
His plans. Then had followed the cramping suspense of trying not
to hurt John's feelings. The months had dragged wearily by, as winter gave way to spring. But now God's enemies had forced the pace.
The hour of crisis, of challenge, was at hand. The stored and accumulated passions of a lifetime were now to be released in burning fury.
Jesus went up to Jerusalem.

His young followers were a little scared at the grim set to His jaw
and the fiery glint in His eye. He knew the odds. He had calculated
the cost. He was but one Man, against the accumulated tradition of
centuries; against custom initiated (as men believed) by God's express
command, sanctified by long usage and guarded by armed authority.
The very Scriptures could be quoted against Him. The Law of Moses
was explicit in its commands. Animal sacrifices—which were supposed to take away a man's personal sin—were not only expressly ordered but were detailed in horrific regulations. The whole religious
system of Jewry depended upon the due observance of the Levitical
Law. The very Sanctuary stood solely for the enshrining of these

customs. God was supposed to dwell in the central focus of the sacrificial system. All Heaven seemed behind it.

And yet Jesus went forward, single-handed, to abolish it all. That was the measure of His heroism and of the certainty that His conception of God was the right one. In this, however, He was not alone, having the consensus of Prophetic opinion behind Him. This confirmed Him in His deep-rooted preference for the Prophetic, rather than for the Priestly, viewpoint. He knew how, nearly always, great spiritual movements originated in Prophetic fervour and moral insight and degenerated into Priestly ritual and formal custom. To obey a Priest was so much easier than to follow a Prophet. It heartened Him as He strode forward to know that Amos and Hosea and Micah and Isaiah and Jeremiah had each in turn thundered their hatred of the sacrificial system.

In particular, two aspects of the present Temple worship infuriated Him: namely, the appalling commercialism of the Temple traffic and the narrow exclusiveness of its racial attitude. *Is this My House?—this which is called by My name which has become nothing less than a den of robbers?*—the Sanctuary which, in Isaiah's vision, should have been, instead, *a House of Prayer for all nations.* The burning words of the most courageous of all God's Prophets rang in His ears: *"The Day is coming when I will make a New Covenant—not according to the former Covenant. For this is the Covenant that I will make," saith the Lord. "I will put My Law in their inward parts, and in their hearts will I write it; and I will be their God and they shall be My people. They shall no more have to teach every man his neighbour, saying 'Know the Lord'; for they shall all know Me."*

But the founding of this glorious New Covenant needed a Leader who could not only defy Israel's Priests but lead God's people out of thraldom into the liberty of love. Had not God cried of old: *Oh, that there were but* one *among you that would shut the doors, that you could no longer kindle fire on My altar in vain!* In the heart of Jesus rang the words: *Sacrifices and meat-offerings Thou dost not require; but Mine ears hast Thou opened! Then said I: "Lo, I come!"*

Thus it was that Jesus went forward to destroy the old mistaken Covenant, founded on fear and a wrong conception of God, and to build a Temple not made with hands, eternal in the Heavens. Now was the moment for Messiah to rise—and to strike. The greatest of all the Prophets lay fettered in a black dungeon. Therefore the Captain of God's Hosts would go into action against God's enemies. *God breaketh the battle!*

As Jesus led His frightened followers up to Jerusalem and into the Temple, His eyes were aflame with anger. Entering the Court of the Gentiles, He once again glanced with sick horror at the terrified animals and recoiled at the foul smell of slaughter.

Then, bracing Himself for the launching of His new revelation of the Father, He swept His gaze round the great Court, at the money-changers and traffickers, crying out in strident wrath, "Listen! I am come out to put an end to sacrifices; and unless you all cease from sacrificing, God's anger will not cease from you!"

There was an instant silence, as the crowds assembled for the Passover suddenly realized that something was afoot. They watched Him stoop down to pick up some of the loose strands of cord littering the market, and soon His strong hands were twisting them into a whip. Slowly and deliberately He tied it to a stout stick. He was ready. For what? The whole multitude waited, spellbound, as if struck into stone. Then again He shouted, "Clear out, all of you!"

A man, startled into activity, moved toward a crate of doves, and began to carry it across the courtyard.

"Put it down!" thundered Jesus. "Do you hear? No one is to touch anything."

And the man, dumbfounded, set down his burden and scurried off. Jesus strode over to the dove crate itself, and opened it. The birds flew away and up into the sky. Jesus turned to the other dove dealers there.

"Take these things away!" He cried, turning over with a sweep of His arm the stalls at which they traded. "I won't have My Father's House turned into a market!"

Then He ordered His friends, "Open up the dove cages!" and, a moment later, the air was trepidant with the beating of wings, heaven-free at last. The dealers staggered back, overawed. Then He moved toward the great pens where the cattle and sheep were tightly packed. He unlatched the iron gates, went boldly within, and, using His whip —though gently—He drove the scared animals out into the vast Court, where they stampeded all over the great spaces, while the crowds scattered precipitously. In a moment He was at the money-changers' tables. Out swung a strong arm, and soon all the neatly piled-up heaps of coins were clanging and rolling on the marble floor. A right hand here and a left there, and soon there was not a single table standing. Someone opened a pair of gates to let the animals out of the Temple, the people and the merchants meanwhile seeking refuge on the colonnades and terraces. Presently He was left, in the centre of the Court—in command, alone.

Then His voice rang out again: "It is written," He cried, pointing to a group of Jewish Elders huddled together on a terrace, *"My House shall be called a House of Prayer for all nations"* (pointing to that dread inscription, threatening death to intruding Gentiles) "but *you* have turned it into a *den of robbers!"*

Someone, more brave than the rest, raised a cheer at this, and there was a murmur of approval, which rose gradually to a deep-throated roar, as thousands of defrauded Pilgrims (especially the Galileans) recognized a champion of the poor and an enemy of the extortionate Sons of Annas. The Temple Guards entered the Court, but there followed a threatening surge forward of the crowd toward their champion, and the authorities were powerless to arrest Him. They feared the people. And even more, they feared Him.

(II) "AUTHORITY"

THE Temple was filled to capacity the next morning. The Pilgrims were not disappointed. Jesus was there at an early hour, calmly walking about as though nothing unusual had happened the day before. Everyone remarked on His courage. The Jews, meanwhile, had held an informal meeting at which they had decided to attack Him on what they regarded as His weakest side—that of His utter lack of authority. This, they felt, was the surest way to humiliate Him before the Passover crowds. It was, therefore, an impressive assemblage of the Jewish hierarchy that ranged itself before Him on learning of His presence in the Temple: the Chief Priests and the Scribes and Elders—the members, in fact, of the Sanhedrin, the High Council of Jewry. Annas was there, old and crafty and infinitely sinister; and Caiaphas, forbidding, hard and shrewd. Their numerous relations were gathered around them, hangers-on, all of them, in the Temple racket. They had come to laugh savagely over the impending discomfiture of this provincial upstart who had dared to challenge them (and, incidentally, to defy God) in his ridiculous condemnation of the sacrificial system. Besides, there was the little matter of their annual profits, now in real danger if this fanatic got the upper hand. The gorgeously vested Elders faced the tall Galilean. Drawn up in a menacing row before Him, they asked Him what they thought was an unanswerable question.

"Tell us, by what authority have You done . . . all this? And who, we should like to know, gave You this 'authority'?"

There was a tense pause, while the thoughts of Jesus flashed around the implications of their cunning. Then, like lightning, that superb brain struck, with deadly precision, at the basic weakness of all mere outward "authority"; its lack of self-authentication when compared with inward intrinsic authority. He seized on the most telling illustration possible in revealing this weakness.

Clearly His calm voice cut into the silence. "I also will ask you—just one question. If you can answer Me, I will answer you."

They braced themselves for the test. He continued: "Take the baptism of John. Was that 'by authority'? If so, whose? From whence did its validity come? From Heaven? Or only from men? Or perhaps you think it had no validity at all? Now what do you say?"

There followed a yet more strained silence, as men's hearts stirred in them at the mention of the Baptist, imprisoned in the dread fortress of Machaerus. For everyone knew him for the avowed enemy of these scheming, grasping Priests—as of all hypocrites. All eyes were turned upon the embarrassed dignitaries—and *they* were doing some swift thinking now. The crowd edged nearer and strained forward to watch; and as the tension grew, derisive smiles broke out on many eager faces.

The ecclesiastics were in a dilemma. This was indeed an unanswerable question—far harder to deal with than even their own question. For if they replied that the baptism of John was authorized by Heaven, Jesus would, in a flash, have pinned them down with the further question: "Then why didn't you yourselves accept John's baptism?" For everybody knew that the Elders had rejected it both for themselves and, by their counsel, for the people. On the other hand, if they held that John's baptism was something authorized by man only, there would have arisen a howl of anger and derision, since everyone unwaveringly held John to be indeed a Prophet—as great as Elijah or Isaiah or Jeremiah. So they could only mutter, shamefacedly, "We cannot tell. . . ."

There was a sigh of relief and satisfaction from the crowd. Jesus, with a wave of His arm, clinched the argument with a curt, conclusive: "Neither will I tell you by what authority I do . . . these things," with an easy gesture toward the empty pens.

The people were delighted, the Elders furious. For both Jesus and John had not a vestige of external authority, yet the people were obviously backing them all the way. Indeed, they were openly saying that Jesus did possess that true authority that so many of the official teachers lacked. But this attitude of the crowds supported an unorthodox idea of authority, since it disregarded any outward commission, and based itself solely on internal, intrinsic conviction of truth.

Jesus decided to ram home this lesson—so vital to the founding of the Temple not made with hands. So He clarified His implicit teaching by a self-evident parable.

"Tell Me what you make of this. A man had two sons. He went to the first and said, 'Son, go to work today in my vineyard.' 'I go, Sir,' he replied. *But he didn't go.* The man then went to the second son and said the same thing to him. *His* answer was: 'I will not go!' But, nevertheless, he afterward changed his mind *and went.* Now, tell Me, which of these two, do you think, carried out his father's will?"

Again the Priests could but answer sullenly, "The last. . . ."

Jesus was exultant. "The last, exactly! *Not* the one who accepted an outward commission only to dishonour it; but the one who refused such an outward authority—as John did—to honour it in his deeds."

He then swung round upon the discomfited ecclesiastics (it was a very bad day for them) and cried, "I tell you, the very taxgatherers—yes, and even the harlots—will go into God's Kingdom ahead of you! For John revealed to you the way of goodness, but you refused to believe him; whereas the taxgatherers and harlots believed him. And even though you saw this happening, you wouldn't change your attitude and believe."

The Priests, however, were not beaten yet. They were insistent, even desperate, to turn the tables if they could.

Elijah's authority, they recalled, was attested by signs wrought in God's name. And here they were on safer ground, since the Baptist had performed no such "signs." Nor (for all they knew) had Jesus, so far. So they once more challenged Him.

"Well, what *proof* of Your authority have You to show us, what sign or wonder, seeing You are doing . . . all this?"

This was terribly hard for Jesus. Not because He could not satisfy them on this point, but precisely because He could—but would not. There, at Cana, He had gone back on His resolution taken in the Wilderness, because it was a private occasion. Here, in the ideal circumstances—of a public challenge—for the performing of a public miracle, He felt it incumbent upon Him to refuse to give a "sign." A consistent line emerged from these reactions: that He would feel able to perform a miracle at the call of utter need and for others, but nothing would make Him perform any miracle merely as an attestation of His Messiahship, for that would not only be for Himself, but it would, at one stroke, vitiate the grand principle of that Messianic sovereignty—that it was a kingdom of hearts; and not only that: it was a kingdom of hearts freely won and never compulsively impressed. Love alone must rule all His actions. At Cana, love had its way by giving way. Here in Jerusalem it was love that refused to comply. Besides, miracle must never supersede love's self-authentication. There was only one authority in the world: that of love, since God was love.

Nevertheless, He had to give some answer to this challenge. There could, in the very nature of His Message and Mission, be only one true "sign" of His Messiahship; the building of the New Temple in the hearts of the people; the founding of the New Covenant of grace, of the New Religion of love, the manifestation of true authority based on spiritual worth. He looked around Him at the glorious Temple of Herod, still in process of building; but it was inevitably doomed to destruction.

So He cried to the Jews, "Go on as you are doing! Destroy this man-made Temple if you must! Never mind. As Hosea said, *tomorrow—or certainly by the day after tomorrow*—I will build another, but this time one *not* made with hands!"

The Jewish Leaders preferred to take His words literally. Not that they failed to grasp His true meaning. Indeed it was precisely because they did fully understand that He foresaw an eventual nonsacrificial worship of God that they were so furious with Him now. It sounded better, however, to make Him out both an impostor and a lunatic.

"What? Rebuild it in a day or two, would You? *Very* interesting! Do You happen to know how long this Temple has so far taken in building? Over forty years already! And yet You'd build it again by— *the day after tomorrow!*"

And yet, in a sense, they did rightly in both taking Him literally as well as metaphorically. For they were in process of destroying their Temple not only spiritually but in actual fact. Another forty years would not have passed before it was in ruins, and its worship destroyed with it. The tragedy lay in the fact that the Priests, seeing both the literal and spiritual meanings of His words, decided that they could never allow any upstart fanatic to preach so spiritual a Gospel that it actually endangered their profitable ceremonies. Ideas were all very well, but institutional religion was what man needed. As for what *God* wanted—who could read His mind?

(III) NICODEMUS

BUT there was one Jew there whose conscience smote him in all this baiting of Jesus. Nicodemus felt himself attracted to this strangely compelling Teacher. To be sure, He had many newfangled ideas; but they were not so new either, when you came to reflect on them. The Prophets had said much the same things long ago. But people had come to reverence the Law above the Prophets. Uncomfortable fellows, Prophets. Disturbing. Was this Man, then, a Prophet? Was John one? He supposed both were, in God's sight. Besides, both of them—and this Jesus, in particular—had such enormous self-confidence. Not that they were conceited, or anything like that. Humble at heart, he shouldn't wonder. But they had such natural authority. Yes, that was their great asset. How else could John have got the crowds on his side against the Jerusalem delegation, there on the banks of Jordan? How, too, could this other Man have managed to clear the Temple Courts, and not only evade arrest, but arouse such enthusiasm among the Pilgrims? How, indeed? Surely God must have been with Him. And deep down in his heart, Nicodemus knew that Jesus had right on His side. The Temple traffic was a scandal. But, to return to this all-important question of authority, if Jesus were right, then authority, in its institutional sense, had no eternal significance. It was, at the best, only a temporary expedient. But this would cut at the heart of all organized religion as man had so far known it. A few dreamers and seers had, to be sure, preached a purer religion. But that, in the very nature of things, could never satisfy the ordinary man. One had to have authority. And yet . . .

Nicodemus felt that he had to trace out this matter to its source. It was all so dreadfully revolutionary. But he must see Jesus, if possible. Not openly, of course. As a member of the Sanhedrin, he himself was a marked man. It would never do for him to be seen trailing after heretics. At night, perhaps. . . . Where was Jesus staying? With young John, who was well known to many of the Priests. A deeply spiritual youth, with the mind of a poet and the soul of a saint. But that would make everything quite easy. A messenger was sent with a sealed letter for John. After a time he returned. It was all fixed up, and for tonight!

With growing excitement Nicodemus watched the sun go down and the stars come out. The night winds were stirring for a possible storm. After a time he stole out, his mantle wrapped about him, and furtively made his way in the shadowy moonlight to the house of his young friend. It was a large house, with an outer stairway to the guest chamber on the roof. Fitful gusts of wind played with his mantle as he nervously climbed the stone steps. John ushered him in, and in a moment he was face to face with Jesus. But this time there was a marked changed in their relations. They met now as friends. Nicodemus bowed low to the Prophet. He had come to learn, and moved straight to the point at issue.

"Teacher," he began, "believe me, some of us do realize that Your authority to teach and act must come from God; for no one else could have single-handed cleared the Temple Courts unless God's power had been with him."

Jesus remembered what John had said when told about His own

popularity: "A man can receive *nothing* . . . unless it has been given him from Heaven."

It was necessary to make Nicodemus see that not only authority, but everything that was of value must come from above—a gift from God and so of intrinsic, rather than extrinsic, worth. Worth-ship was the real meaning of worship. Indeed, it was *worth that determined authority: not authority that determined worth.* To see reality clearly and steadily was tantamount to a new birth, to a new life. Especially was this true of someone—like Nicodemus—who was steeped in a religion of outward authority, propitiatory sacrifice and codified conduct.

Jesus looked long at the elderly Jewish Ruler. Could he, even at this advanced stage of life, escape into a new world of freedom and reality? He must, at any rate, be given the chance. So Jesus said to him: "In most solemn truth I tell you that unless a man is *born*—re-born—from above, that is, anew—he just cannot *experience* the Kingdom of God!"

Nicodemus tried to understand, but he also knew his own age—and so his prejudices, ingrained traditions and habits of thought. He replied, therefore (maintaining Jesus' own metaphor): "But . . . how is it possible for a man to be thus 'reborn' when he is already old? Physical rebirth is an impossibility for even the most ardent wisher."

Jesus knew Nicodemus' difficulties. Nevertheless, unless he were so reborn he would never see the truth of things. The thought of John's baptism of Himself in Jordan recalled to Jesus the wonder of that experience of rebirth, of endowment from above. The Spirit of God had descended upon Him: the Spirit that would fain enter fully into every man, but *can* only go where it finds access.

He voiced His thoughts aloud: "Again, in most solemn truth I tell you, that unless a man is reborn as of living water and the wind of the Spirit, he cannot enter into the Kingdom of Heaven."

In the silence that followed, they heard the night wind soughing in the trees of John's garden. Jesus suddenly realized that in this He had the most perfect illustration of the truth He was trying so hard to impart. Besides, the very word He had just used to represent "Spirit" in the Aramaic tongue was also used for wind or breath (as in the Greek and Latin languages, too). "Listen . . . you hear the wind sighing? It is free to blow in any direction it wants to. But, as also with water, it can only, even then, go where the laws of nature allow it to. So is it in the case of anyone reborn of the Spirit; as with the movement and workings of the Spirit, always. Spirit cannot be canalized, any more than wind or water, if they are to remain fresh; for both become stale if you try to store them.

"Another point, and one with a direct bearing on this question of authority. You can't tell from what direction the wind is blowing nor where it is going to, merely from the sound. But you know, nevertheless, from that sound that the wind *is* at work, present in our midst. So it is, again, with the working of the Spirit. You can't predetermine its course—or its authority—by Levitical descent or by Rabbinical training, nor by initiation into the mysteries of the Priesthood. You only know the authority of the Spirit-filled man when you see its results. And only they who inbreathe the breath of the Spirit can truly be said to live. So don't be so surprised when I tell you that *all* men need this rebirth from above if they are to live. True authority is spiritual and self-authenticating; for just as matter can only derive from matter, so Spirit can only derive from Spirit."

Nicodemus sighed. "How do You ever expect to bring all this about?"

Jesus turned round in simulated answering surprise. "*You,* a Master in Israel, one of her accredited Teachers, so ignorant of these essentials? In most solemn truth I tell you that we who dare thus to speak are only telling you of what we know from personal experience to be true. But you Rulers have rejected our testimony—that of the Baptist and of Myself. Besides, if you refused to believe My prophecy about the destruction of the Temple in a literal sense, how can you be expected to accept it in a spiritual sense?"

When Nicodemus went home late that night he felt bewildered and dazed; almost as if blinded by excess of light, seen there in the darkness of the world's night, shining about the person of the Prophet of Nazareth. Who was He? Where did He come from? *From above?*

(IV) IN SAMARIA

WHILE in Jerusalem Jesus heard that the Pharisees had become aware of His growing popularity, not merely as an occasional champion of the people against the exactions of the Temple but, a far more serious matter, as a possible successor to John. Indeed, rumour said that this popularity was assuming greater proportions than any that had ever been accorded to the Baptist. John was now effectively silenced. It would be doubly exasperating if his work were continued, and by an even more popular successor, especially if that successor were an open opponent of the sacrificial system.

Jesus was thus in real danger of His life; His Mission not accomplished, His Church not yet in being. So He left Judaea—enemy country, rocky soil, indeed; and, to avoid the Jordan Valley, with its hordes of Pilgrims, who might so easily have caused a crisis by premature acclamation, He decided to return to Galilee by the central route which ran in a direct line northward through Samaria, which was, of course, outside the territory of Herod and boycotted by all orthodox Jews. Once in His own beloved Galilee, He would be comparatively safe; if He were surrounded by the eager patriots whom He knew so well, it would not be easy for any arrest to be made. Besides, the purely personal reasons which impelled Herodias to encompass John's death were inoperative in the case of Jesus.

The thoughts of Jesus on the trek northward were mixed in character. He had flung down the challenge in no uncertain terms, and it had been accepted. The visit of Nicodemus was a comforting incident to look back on. But the Elders were defiantly hostile. The people who had supported Him at the feast were for the most part drawn from Galilee—always ready for a fight with orthodox Jewry. For Judaea had compromised with Rome. That was its fatal error, which Galilee could never forgive.

Ahead of Him as He walked through the fields of Samaria was a land whose people would welcome the Good News of God He had come to bring. This Gospel was meat and drink to men. Just as the breath one drew maintained life on earth, so the inspiration of the Spirit was life to them who could receive It. Purification by Spirit: water and wind: the things that were free for all to receive. Neither could be stored without being staled. Both were free to go where they listed, where they could—and so *must*—most freely go. He saw the streams flowing among the hills, and felt the breezes fanning His cheek. Life and freedom, and obedience to Law—God's Law, not man's; conviction, not convention. He would trust the Divine Daemon within Him, against all the world.

He drew long and deep breaths, feeling the glow of health, the gladness of love's certainties, as they passed through the fertile valleys of Samaria and approached the pass that led between the twin mountains of Ebal and Gerizim. His mind inevitably recalled the causes of the age-old quarrel dividing the Jews from the Samaritans; how Shalmanezer, King of Assyria, having carried away his Israelitish captives to Babylon, replaced them with immigrants from his own country. Finding the land overrun by beasts of prey, a result of years of intervening depopulation, the Assyrians in Samaria sought to propitiate the local deity by the importation of an Israelitish Priest, to teach them *the manner of the God of the land.* This inevitably led to the practice of a hybrid pseudo-Judaism, by a race of foreign origin in the very centre of the Promised Land. Friction was unavoidable and the dispute flared up anew in the time of Ezra, when the Samaritans asked to be allowed to help in the rebuilding of the Temple.

But Zerubbabel and Joshua and the rest of the chiefs of the Fathers of Israel said unto them: "Ye have nothing to do with us. We ourselves will build it." In consequence, the Samaritans *weakened the hands of the people of Judah and troubled them in building.*

One could hardly blame them, thought Jesus; and they, for their part, never forgave the Jews for their gratuitous insult. Jesus recalled how the Samaritans thereupon determined to build a Sanctuary of their own, upon Mount Gerizim—which was just coming into sight as Jesus and His friends were slowly breasting an intervening hill. The offended Samaritans showed in this decision a very sound instinct for both historical significance and dramatic congruity. For in the glorious vale of Shechem, which could now be seen nestling between its twin mountains of Gerizim and Ebal, was once gathered by Joshua the most momentous assemblage Israel had ever seen; nothing less than the whole of the Twelve Tribes, with all their families. They had then split up, six Tribes gathering on Mount Gerizim and six on Mount Ebal. Joshua had thereupon, from the head of the valley, read aloud the Law of Moses, after which the Levites on Mount Ebal had shouted the Cursings, followed by the Blessings similarly shouted from Mount Gerizim. As each clause was concluded came a thundering Amen from that colossal congregation, echoing to and fro from hill to hill—a mighty affirmation from earth to Heaven endorsed by all Israel. As a result, Gerizim had come to be regarded as a sacred mountain, above all others in Samaria. Indeed, there were many who said it was there, and not in Jerusalem, that Abraham had offered up Isaac.

But, as Jesus gazed upon this sublime scene with its equally sublime history, He knew within Him that no place could ever be intrinsically, but only associatively, more sacred than any other, since all had been created by the same God. Ebal was no more—and no less—a place of cursing or blessing than was Gerizim; nor did it really matter where Abraham had offered up Isaac. God was everywhere, but especially in the repentant heart. . . . Jacob had found God at Bethel, and at Mahanaim and at Peniel, before erecting an altar to Him down there at Shechem, in the vale.

It had been a hot day, but now the sun was sinking below the hills, and their shadowed outlines could be seen sweeping over the vallied wheat fields, already white to harvest that mid-May evening. They were drawing near to the very well that Jacob had dug—there it was, on the shoulder of Mount Gerizim. Jesus was tired and decided to rest in the cool shade of the trees growing around the well. Young John, who had companied with them, stayed with Jesus, but the others went forward to the village of Sychar to buy provisions for their evening meal. They were soon lost to sight and hearing, and Jesus and His young follower were left to muse upon the long history of the well.

It had been dug seventeen hundred years before Jesus was born. Jacob had given the well to Joseph, whose tomb lay near by, and the God of Jacob and of Joseph was not a God of the dead, but of the living. Jesus thought of them as watching from Heaven at that very moment, wondering how the young Prince of Glory would fare in His great enterprise of founding the New Covenant and the New Temple, not made with hands, placeless, ubiquitous. This very well was a type of that Temple, a sustainer of life, flowing from the living water of the Spirit. Food—the wheat fields. . . . Drink, here, at this well. Drink. . . . Yes, He was very thirsty. But there was no vessel to be seen; only a coil of rope around a wooden spindle. Not even the Lord of Heaven and earth, now that He had taken upon Himself the form and fashion of a man, could drink from those cool depths without a vessel.

Suddenly a light footstep was heard, and they saw a woman approaching. She was almost on them before she herself noticed the two Jews, seated there in the mottled shadows of the wellside. She bore a waterpot on her head, held lightly in one hand. She was startled on seeing the men, but held her ground and silently went about her business of drawing water—unwinding the long rope and fastening it to the jar. Men she did not mind. The women of Sychar, with their sneers and scornful head tossings, their whispers and their turned shoulders, had driven her away from the village well, so that she was forced to tramp to Jacob's well every evening to get water. She was about to let down the jar into the cool depths of the well (it was a hundred feet in depth) when Jesus spoke to her.

"Give Me a drink, please," He asked in a quiet friendly voice. She turned an appraising look upon Him. No. This Man didn't seem a philanderer . . . but it wasn't usual for any man to talk to a strange woman—especially a Jew (which was obvious from His dress) to a Samaritan. But she was no shy, shrinking girl; and as she handed the now filled waterjar to Jesus to drink from, she coolly faced this rather intriguing situation.

"Tell me," she asked, "how comes it that You, a Jew, ask a drink of me, a Samaritan?"

But Jesus was not going to be embroiled in mere tribal friction. The water of life was free to everybody, without respect of race or country. The great words of Isaiah came into His mind: *Ho!—every one that thirsteth, come to the well . . . and he that has no money, come. Buy and eat—without money and without price.* (He looked at the woman, raddled and tawdry, obviously a harlot, ekeing out a hard living by precarious accostings.) *Why do you spend money upon that which is not bread?—and your labour for that which can never satisfy? . . . Listen closely to Me, and you'll be eating that which is good, and your soul can then delight itself in abundance. Seek the Lord while He may still be found. Call upon Him, while He is yet near; for My thoughts are not your thoughts, neither are your ways My ways. For as the heavens are higher than the earth, so are My ways higher than your ways, and My thoughts than your thoughts. For as the rain or snow come down, and both from Heaven—and return not thither till they have watered the earth and made it to bring forth and bud, that they may give seed to the sower, and bread to the hungry—so shall My words, that go forth out of My mouth, never return to Me void, but shall instead accomplish what I will, even to the fulfilment of My purpose. . . . My teaching shall drop down even as a cloud of dew upon the heat of harvest. . . . But My people have committed two evils. They have forsaken Me, the fountain of living waters; and have hewed themselves out cisterns . . . even broken cisterns, that can hold no water.*

With these thoughts in mind, Jesus answered the woman. "If only you knew what God is even now freely offering you—and Who it is that is now asking you for a drink—you would have asked *Him*, and He would have given you living water!"

"I don't know what You're talking about," replied the woman, "but as You've nothing to draw water with—and the well is mighty deep—I'd like to know where You think You're going to get Your 'living water' from."

She eyed Him scornfully. Obviously a trifle queer, she thought, adding, ". . . unless, of course, You're a greater person than Jacob—*our* ancestor—who gave us this well, yes, and drank from it himself as did his sons and his cattle."

Her glance was defiantly patriotic, saying clearly, "You see, we've got a thing or two of historical and sacred interest even in despised Samaria."

But Jesus remained tranquil, and the evening light of calm reflection illuminated His thought.

"In spite of all that," He answered, "whoever drinks even of this well will thirst again; and you yourself will have to come here again tomorrow evening. But whoever drinks of the water that I shall give him will never thirst again. For the water that I shall give him will become in him a pure spring of water welling up within him unto Everlasting Life."

The woman's mind was shrewd, literal, worldly. There was a cool irony in her voice as she answered. "Ah, Sir, give me this water You speak of; for then not only will I never get thirsty, but I'll never any more have to come continually—all this way—to draw water."

"All this way . . ." And there was a copious spring in Sychar, strong enough even to drive a mill. The steady gaze of Jesus was upon her as she made this lame, but only too obvious complaint. For the truth was that both Jacob and this woman found it expedient to leave the other well alone because it was frequented by potential enemies. Jesus read her like a book.

"Go," He said, "bring your husband here."

It was not easy to lie to this Man. "I have no husband. . . ."

"I quite agree," said Jesus. "Since you have had five 'husbands,' he with whom you are now living is not your husband. Yes, you were certainly right there."

This was uncanny . . . and far too personal. It was high time the conversation was steered away from these quicksands. With remarkable adroitness, she fastened on this queer Man's pet foible, that He was a Prophet and a greater than Jacob. It did look, too, as though He might be one. Quickly she searched round for a controversial subject—and one which would be of interest to a would-be Prophet. She hit on one that was at hand, here on the slopes of Mount Gerizim. Her manner assumed an added brightness as she artfully used His very knowledge of her past as the point of departure from a distressing embarrassment.

"Oh, Sir, I can see that You evidently *are* a Prophet! Do tell me, now You are here, which do *You* think is the true Sanctuary of Jehovah—I mean, the really proper place for worship—here, at Gerizim, where *our* ancestors have always worshipped, or at Jerusalem, which you Jews hold is the only true Sanctuary?"

She eyed Him narrowly. That was a nasty corner turned, she thought. But Jesus was unconcerned with ancient feuds, based on false conceptions of God. He brushed the whole miserable controversy aside, and got down to the root of the matter.

"Believe Me," He cried, "the time is coming when no one will any longer trouble about 'correct' places of worship; when neither *this* mountain, nor yet Jerusalem, will be considered as 'special' Sanctuaries. In any case, you Samaritans, in thinking of God locally, are worshipping Him ignorantly. The Jews are in the same case. But *we—*" indicating young John and Himself with a gesture—"*we* worship a God Whom we know. And the time is coming—nay, it has already come for some of us—when the true worshippers will worship the one Father of all, in Spirit and so in truth. For the Father is longing for such worshippers, and for such worship. For God is not something material, to be localized. God is Spirit, Breath; like the very air about us, He is everywhere, and anyone who would worship God *must* worship Him with true, that is, spiritual worship."

But the woman was entirely literal in mind. Religion meant nothing to her, anyway. She shrugged her shoulders, and fell back upon a stereotyped observation as a refuge from these tiresome abstractions.

"Ah, well—" she sighed complacently—"when Messiah comes, doubtless He'll explain everything. . . ." And picking up her waterpot, she prepared to depart.

She hardly heard the rapt, exalted murmur of Jesus, His eyes still on the sunset skies: "I—Who am now talking to you—*I am* . . ."

For her quick ears had heard the sound of approaching voices, and soon the returning disciples had descended the stone steps and were gathered about their Master. They were immeasurably shocked to see Him talking to a Samaritan woman—and a free-and-easy one, too, by the look of her. But they kept their astonishment to themselves, and merely stared silently as the woman hurriedly climbed up to the level of the roadside and set off toward the village. John noticed that she left her waterpot behind after all. There followed a moment or two of silent diffidence as Peter and the others unstrapped their purchases and showed them to Jesus, spreading them out on the ground in readiness for their evening meal. The sun's last rays lighted to gold the harvest fields of the valley, and Jesus was staring at the lovely scene as if in a spell. They awaited the usual blessing of the coming meal by the Master, but in vain.

Peter was becoming a little impatient. They were hungry, and he and the others had gone a longish way to get the necessaries for the meal. "Master, do eat something!" he exclaimed.

But the thoughts of Jesus were far away, upon that day, surely not so very distant now, when all the peoples of the world should not only feel after, but find God; being, in very truth, inspired, filled with the Spirit, the breath that gives life.

"I have food to eat of which you know nothing."

The disciples gazed at Him as He murmured the strange words. He was certainly in a queer mood this evening. A whisper went round. Eyebrows were lifted interrogatively.

"Has anybody—" with a nod down the hill—"brought Him anything to eat?"

They looked inquiringly at young John. But he was too deeply moved to speak.

Jesus turned at last. "My food is to do the will of Him that sent Me and to complete His work!" He said this with yet another glance at the cornfields. There man's sowings were consummated in a rich harvest. He Himself was but just starting off toward Galilee, beginning God's sowing. But He saw it as if already accomplished, and in His ears His last triumphant "It is finished!" echoed from afar across the chasm of the years.

At that very moment there came into sight that which illustrated and gave dramatic point to His faith. For the woman, as she had hurried off down the hillside, was pleasantly bemused and not a little excited. She had gone straight to the market; that was where her friends, the men, were likely to be found. Excitedly she told them, "Come quickly—I've found such a queer Man. He's probably up there still, by the well. Do you know, He told me all my past history!" The men glanced amusedly at one another; that was no secret to them. The woman continued, "Do you think He might possibly be—the Messiah?"

They were intrigued. "I'll take you to Him if you like," she added, and they all moved off together. Jesus, seated in the shadows under the sunlit trees, saw the group coming along the road, the woman leading and the men following.

He turned to the disciples. "How does the saying go? 'Four months—then harvest'?" He pointed to the approaching group. "Look! I tell you the fields are already white for harvesting. Today *I* have sown seed and see! I am already getting My reward. Sower and Reaper am I, simultaneously—both rejoicing together! But you have yet another proverb: 'One sows. Another reaps.' I sent you just now to buy food made from a previous harvest, from other men's labours, and *we* reap the reward! So, you see, I the Sower and you the reapers can all rejoice together now, not only in this our common meal but still more in the harvest to be gathered from yonder crowd—the harvest of My sowing!"

By now the group on the road had come close and the villagers were gathering around Jesus, the woman somewhat awkwardly trying to explain their presence, and Jesus striving to make them feel welcome and to bridge the gulf between these foreigners and His disciples. The measure of His courtesy and tact was found in their request that both He and His disciples, all Jews, should "tarry with them." He promptly accepted their invitation, in the end breaking His northbound journey by a two days' sojourn in Sychar. During this time He did His best to teach them, and some of them were impressed. Indeed, they told the woman, "We no longer believe merely because of what *you* said. We have now heard Him for ourselves."

II

The Lakeside Ministry: The First Phase

. . . .

(I) THE NOBLEMAN'S SON

SAYING farewell to His new-found friend in Samaria, Jesus took the road once again toward Galilee, passing near Mount Gilboa and so out on to the level plain of Esdraelon, golden with its vistas of waving corn, beyond which the blue hills beckoned Him home again. Near Shunem, where the roads divided, Jesus parted company from His Lakeside disciples, Himself taking the northward road for Nazareth, together with Nathanael, who lived at Cana, a few miles beyond.

As He said good-bye to Peter and Andrew and Philip, He added, "Wait for Me. Go on with your ordinary work for the time being. But be ready, at a moment's notice, to lay it down and follow Me. For I am coming soon to claim you as My fellow workers when I start My great Galilean campaign. And tell James and John to be ready also."

Young John of Jerusalem decided to go on with Jesus and Nathanael. He could not yet tear himself away from Jesus. As for Peter and the others, though they were sorry to part company with Jesus, they knew it was only for a short time. When they surmounted the ridge near the Horns of Hattin, they caught a first glimpse of their beloved Lake, blue and shining in the sunlight. Standing a moment there, they drew in copious draughts of this, their native air; and when at length they arrived by the Lakeside, they took the first opportunity at eventide of going down to the beaches and fingering their nets and tackle, itching to be out once more on the level waters. In their hearts was a leaping joy; for Jesus had given His word. And one day soon His tall form would be seen coming ever closer along the strand, and that beloved voice would call "Peter! Andrew!" and the new life would have begun. Meanwhile, it was good to stand barefoot in the cool, lapping wavelets and to feel the shrinking shingle under one's feet. Peter took a special pride in telling the story of Jesus' clash with the Elders; and the cleansing of the Temple aroused great enthusiasm among the Galileans. The returned Passover Pilgrims corroborated all he said, and everywhere men's talk was of the new Prophet.

The day came when Peter found himself called upon to tell his story once again, and this time to a very great official of King Herod's court. It made him very proud. Farther along the southward shore of the Lake, not far from the King's splendid palace of gleaming white marble (it was only about ten years old) lived Lord Chuza, Herod's Steward of the Household. He was in terrible trouble, for his son had been struck down with a sudden attack of the fever that was the scourge of the low-lying Lakeside. The boy was dying. The father and mother were at their wits' end. Could nothing be done? The physicians shook their heads sadly and crept out of the sick room. It was hardly expected that the lad would outlast this day's sunlight, and it was already late afternoon.

Then someone came in and whispered. What was that? Something about Simon Bar-Jonah? Some Friend of his? A Prophet? One Who could work miracles? Well, where was the Man? Couldn't someone fetch Simon at once, and so get hold of his Friend? Others nodded. Yes, they too had heard of the Nazarene. The Pilgrims said He had stood up to the High Priests and slated them for their cheating ways.

Soon Simon came in, shyly and awkwardly. Yes, he knew Jesus. So far as he knew, He was in His home at Nazareth—or possibly at Cana, where He had some relations. As Cana was nearer the Lake than Nazareth, a visit there first would settle the matter. Why, once at Cana——

But the overwrought and desperate father did not wait to hear. He rushed out and was on his speediest horse galloping up the Nazareth road and out of sight, all in a few moments. Simon stayed behind to comfort the Lady Joanna and to talk of Jesus . . . and to wonder—would he see Him soon?—for, surely, He would accompany Chuza on his return.

Meanwhile, in Cana, in the same house where He had turned the water into wine, the Master was wondering when and how best to begin His Galilean Ministry: when to return to the Lakeside and call Peter and the others to be His full-time followers. But danger lay ahead, chiefly, here in the north, from Herod, whose palace at Tiberias was so near to the proposed headquarters of Jesus' Ministry at Capernaum. If only the Herodian danger could have been obviated or, at any rate, lessened! Was there no one high in Herod's confidence who might possibly be drawn to the ideal of His New Covenant? If so, it might be that one obstacle to the free and full consummation of His destiny would be removed.

The household with whom He and young John were staying—the bride and bridegroom of the wedding—was about to settle down to its evening meal. It was about seven o'clock. Suddenly there came a frantic knocking at the outer door, and presently there burst in a travel-stained man, obviously a courtier, as they could tell from his dress. His eyes searched the group reclining at the meal. Instinctively he addressed Jesus—no thought, now, of Eastern courtesies or of the difference in rank. Breathlessly he blurted out his desperate entreaty: "My son, there at the Lakeside, is dying. Come down and heal him!" Even as he spoke he was filled with a sinking premonition that the boy might be dead already. There was an agonizing appeal in his eyes as he stared at Jesus.

The Master rose in consternation. Here was yet another temptation, involving an instant decision. A golden chance was here presented: a high officer of Herod's court was begging Him to heal his son. This was a Heaven-sent opportunity surely not to be lost. Yet . . . He longed so desperately to be loved for Himself and His Message, not for His power to work miracles, no matter how right and proper it was to possess this power if He were—the Son of God. He turned aside with a despairing gesture, uttering His thoughts aloud. "Signs and wonders!" He sighed, "always signs and wonders!"

He felt Himself in the throes of a torturing dilemma. Love's impulse, as once before here in Cana, was to go down with this stricken father and to heal his son. But He had so longed that men should learn to believe in Him for love's sake alone and not out of mere gratitude for miracles. Was this fight—against performing them—to go on indefinitely? If so, why had God given these powers to Him? What was it the father had said? "My son is dying. . . ." Then the matter was desperately urgent. The boy might well be dead before they could reach Capernaum. If He were to trust love's impulse once again, He must heal this boy. But the healing must be done *here and now,* not at Capernaum, if the boy's life were to be saved. Could He heal at a distance? Was the sufferer's faith a prerequisite of any healing miracle? Yet, to doubt His power were to doubt God's equipment given to His Beloved Son. On the other hand if He were to fail, all further trust in Him by the people would be forfeited. His claim, whenever He should pronounce it, to be the Messiah, would be proved false. Again, was this but a repetition of that dread second temptation, to presume upon God's favour? It was also so suspiciously convenient for His plans—a high officer of Herod's needing His help like this, and just at this critical time. But even these scruples were overcome, in love's name. One last point remained to be considered. As the sufferer himself could not be present to yield an answering faith, was the father's faith a sufficient force to release the flow of power?

Again, He spoke His thoughts aloud. "I suppose that unless you people actually *see* these signs and wonders, you won't ever be able to believe?"

But the father had no time for these subtleties. "Sir," he pleaded, "come down with me—before my boy . . . is dead!" This pitiful pleading moved Jesus to His very depths. He could but trust love to the utmost.

He drew Himself up to His full height, and after a long silence of inward prayer, cried, "You may go home. Your boy lives!"

The father hesitated but a moment. Dare he trust this Man's word? To have come all this way, and then to go back without Him! What would his wife say when he returned without the Prophet? Whoever heard of any healing wrought at a distance? Yet . . . the eyes of the Prophet gazed into his own, challenging his faith, even as he himself was challenging that of Jesus. Then the words used by Jesus came back into mind. "Unless you actually *see* you won't believe." Suddenly he felt able to give Jesus His answer. He read it in His eyes. He would show the Prophet that he, for one, was able to believe, without any need for visual evidence. Without a word, he turned on his heel and hurried out. There was a clatter of horse hoofs and then silence. Jesus relaxed, and a smile of glowing happiness irradiated

His features. His own trust in God had been met by an answering trust in Himself. From now on, He would not hesitate to heal, always providing that He did His utmost to avoid gaining popularity, or even publicity, by this means. He felt a load off His mind. The decisions taken in the Wilderness were still right. But He was, nevertheless, free to relieve suffering.

As for the father, he did a very lovely thing. His horse was tired. To race home on another one, hired here in Cana, would be almost to mistrust Jesus. No. He would rest somewhere for the night, rise up early when his horse had been properly rested, and ride leisurely home. All would be well. So he went to the nearest khan, and put up for the night, giving his horse to a groom to feed and water.

But when he had lain down on his bed, he found it impossible to sleep. Complex, harassing thoughts raced through his mind, and the eyes of his boy haunted him. Long before dawn he was up and saddling his horse, and riding out of the deserted town in the cold misty night. Out on the hills, as he breasted the last rise before the long descent toward the Lake, he saw the first shy stirrings of the dawn beyond the far rim of the Hauran mountains and the eerie half-light gleamed upon the white, chill streaks that revealed the glimmering Lake. Soon the sun rose, blindingly bright, blotting out the horizon; and almost at once the long shadows were fleeing from the marshes of the Upper Jordan. With every step away from the Prophet—and back toward that dread sickroom—he found himself becoming more despondent. The strain on his faith was more than he could bear. He could but hope, feebly.

There, at last visible as the mists cleared away, was Capernaum and a little to the right his own home—and his son. Alive or dead? With a sudden sinking of heart, he remembered the actual words of Jesus. "Your son lives." Did they mean that the boy was but *then* alive—with no promise for the future? Had the boy died *since?*

Then, far away down in the distant foothills near the Lake, a group of horsemen could be seen, approaching. A drifting cloud of dust rose behind them—they were evidently riding furiously. A dread fear gripped at the father's heart. Could these be his own servants? If so, surely there could be but one message for him. He was being fetched home. For what reason? Because his son had died? Or . . . ?

The horsemen came nearer. Yes, they were his own servants; he knew the horses from afar. Every step of his own steed was a stab. He could hardly go on. The servants, grave and respectful, drew near, reined in, and salaamed. The words they spoke, with a joyful ring, were strangely familiar. "Sir, your son lives!"

"Is he . . . not merely alive, but well?"

"Yes," they answered, "he is well!"

"When did the turn come?"

And back came the expected answer, so gloriously justifying his faith in Jesus. "Yesterday evening—at seven o'clock—the fever suddenly left him."

The father could not contain his gladness, and galloped back with them, a band of sturdy believers in the new Prophet. His whole household was to follow their lead. Jesus now had a friend and champion within Herod's palace, so that the way was eased for Him to teach freely in the Galilean towns and villages, at any rate for the present.

Trusting His Father, Jesus stayed on in Cana till a messenger arrived to confirm the boy's miraculous recovery—at the very hour when Jesus had spoken His healing word of faith. With this message came an urgent request to Jesus to go down to Capernaum and visit the nobleman's house as an honoured Guest, nay, more, as its Lord and Master! The call for which He had been waiting had at last come; the call to traverse that long descent toward the Lake, tell Peter and the others that the hour had arrived, and begin the Galilean Ministry in real earnest.

(II) TOWARD CAPERNAUM

It was a radiantly happy Jesus that, very early one morning, said good-bye to His relatives (and to young John, who had to return to Jerusalem) there on the hillside at Cana. Mary tried hard to conceal her inner sorrow. Whenever she thought of Jesus she found herself filled with strange forebodings and premonitions. Not so Jesus. He was immensely optimistic. An air of fulfilment, of mastery, of unbounded energy radiated from Him and shone in His eyes as He set off down the hill. As Luke long afterward put it: "Jesus returned in the power of the Spirit into Galilee!"

Cana lay some fourteen hundred feet above the level of the Lake, but the newly paved road by which He travelled—the *Via Maris:* the Way of the Sea—rose, some five miles from the Lake, to a height of seventeen hundred feet above the level of the water. From this bracing vantage point, set in its tonic upland winds, the finest panorama of Galilee could be seen. Here Jesus rested and surveyed His Kingdom; watching the noontide glory of a perfect day. The sun, high in the heavens, *glowed like a Bridegroom leaving His chamber, exulting like a Hero to run His course—setting out!*

Almost the whole of the Lake could be seen from here "—a harp-shaped sapphire set in a ring of emeralds." In front of Jesus frowned the great ravine to the southwest of the Lake, its crags and precipices menacing the traveller; while beyond, the eerie grandeur of the eastern shore, inhospitable and gaunt, could be seen. To the left of the ravine lay the Plain of Gennesaret, fertile and well watered, with Magdala not far from the shore. And see! There was Capernaum—its clustered houses facing the water and rising upon the low hillside behind. To the north Chorazin stood on the higher ground; and, at the head of the Lake, Bethsaida could just be descried where the swamps of the Upper Jordan emptied into the sea. Away to the left, rising proudly on its rocky summit three thousand three hundred feet above the level of the Lake, rose Safed, "the city set on a hill." Beyond it towered the colossal ranges of Lebanon; while slightly to the right Hermon, the mightiest of them of all, lifted its snow-crowned summit high into the sky.

The grandeur of the view was breath-taking in its scope and magnificence. Colour was everywhere: deep blue water, green fields, golden cornfields, white summits far away, set clear against the cloudless sky. "Galilee . . ." The very syllables had for Jesus a limpid loveliness that spelled an endless succession of halcyon days to be spent here in this "Circlet of the Gentiles." On this height Jesus felt He had indeed turned His back upon the austerity and rigours of the Old Covenant, with all its blood-stained history and its grim Prophetic woes, its mistaken conception of God and its imperfect worship. The

very physical contrasts between Judaea and Galilee served to emphasize the temperamental differences in their peoples. The strict Judaeans, living forever in sight of the stark, bare Wilderness, were
hard and cold and cramped. The Galileans, mixing more freely with
the outside world, inherited a more gracious and liberal culture. The
rippling translucent Sea of Galilee was in extreme contrast to the
stark sea of death away to the far south. Here, among these humane
and largely Hellenized Galileans, Jesus was about to enter upon a radiant year of His earthly life—*the Acceptable Year of the Lord,* as
He Himself called it. Before Him now lay a world of light and love,
a smiling, sunlit land whose breezes blew in from an ampler universe.
This was the land of the New Covenant of grace. *Let My Beloved
come into His garden.*

Presently He rose, braced Himself joyously and swung downward
along the far-stretching road before Him; the very road of which
Isaiah, so long ago, had sung: *The land of Zabulon, and the land of
Naphtali . . . by the Way of the Sea, in Galilee of the nations.* Those
multitudinous nations that commingled along the great roads of Galilee—Persia, Egypt, Greece, Rome—all converged upon that white
shore road that ran, just over there, by-passing Capernaum on the way
to Damascus.

The road soon dropped toward the mouth of a mighty ravine—almost like the dread portals of Hades. No words could describe the
eeriness and shuddering horror that overcame Jesus for a short while
as He entered this stupendous gorge. A bubbling brook purled along
beside the roughening road in ever-increasing swiftness as it tumbled
headlong through the chilling shadows of that ghastly ravine. It was
called the Vale of Doves, being the haunt of myriads of doves and
pigeons which were snared by the Magdalenes close by, to be sent
alive in wicker crates up the long and dusty road which led toward the
Temple—and to death.

The walls of this rocky gorge looked like some nightmare dovecote
from the nether worlds, for they were perforated with innumerable
caves and holes, having a grim history. In the days of Herod the
Great, rebels and robbers haunted these caverns, despoiling travellers
through the gorge. Making themselves fortifications in the almost in-
accessible rocksides, they defied all that Herod could do to expel them.

Then he ordered his soldiers to construct great wooden cages which held many fully armed warriors. These were then swung from cranes and winches and hauled up on stout cables till they faced the cave mouths. Torches and straw and smoke and fire did the rest. Not one single rebel was left alive . . . and as Jesus lifted His eyes to those dun-grey rock walls, towering up fifteen hundred feet above the narrow road, He shuddered with a sudden fear. This was indeed the land of the shadow of death.

Yet even here also did the light shine; for the Lord passed through its shades and so out into the Garden of God—the beautiful vine-laden, blossoming Plain of Gennesaret, through whose leafy shades Jesus was soon wending His way, relieved and warming to the sun once more. At last He was by the blue water's edge, and walking along the level strand toward distant Capernaum. Presently He crossed over the streams bearing the waters of the Seven Springs, and so beside a little horseshoe bay with sloping grass-green banks.

Somewhat nearer to the town He passed by the receipt of custom. Handing His coin to the taxgatherer seated there, and walking along the shore road, He scanned the thronging, jostling multitudes always crowding the highway and beaches. Then, at last, He saw him. Who could miss that burly, powerful figure, with the great muscles showing below his rolled-up sleeves? Peter! Yes, and Andrew—and, only a stone's throw farther along the strand, James and John, the two sons of Zebedee and Salome, cousins of Jesus, since Salome was Mary's sister.

Jesus drew near, unseen as yet by any of them. He watched Peter awhile as, intent and absorbed, he and his companion Andrew were engaged in the highly skilled operation of throwing the hand dragnet over the water that was warmed by the flow from the hot springs, where the fish were apt to bask in the shallows. The net opened out wide in the breeze, being weighted with lead pellets round the edges, which flew far over the still water and fell outspread upon it, sinking down in the transparent green depths, to close in on any fish that lay beneath. Then the net was dragged into shore by the fisherman, wading knee-deep in the clear warm water. A happy, kindly smile irradiated Jesus' face as He stood there on the strand in the mellowing late afternoon sunlight.

Then a call sounded over the level water. "Peter"—the Master's own name for him! And Peter whipped round, saw Jesus, threw down his net, and with a roar of welcome was splashing and bounding impetuously toward the shore—and Master and disciple were in each other's arms! Andrew followed and joined them, and, with a hand upon their two shoulders, Jesus strolled happily between them along the beach. "Come," He said, "come with Me—and I will make you fishers of men!"

Another shout—and James and John had increased the little laughing group to five. Their mutual joy was almost too great to bear. Tears were glistening in Peter's eyes. Nevertheless, he just could not help showing off his pride in his Master, for all passers-by to behold. Not, of course, that they knew Who was with him. But you could hardly fail to notice Him anyway. Many turned to gaze after them as they passed along the shore road. They went straight to Peter's house. And at Jesus' request, a message was at once sent off to Chuza, to tell him of Jesus' arrival in Capernaum. Very soon he was rushing in to thank Him in person for the healing of his son; and there was the boy himself, hanging back shyly till his father brought him forward and presented him to Jesus—Saviour and saved standing eye to eye, and the lad won forever.

Nightfall was now approaching, and Jesus was weary with His long walk from Cana, and the excitement of this auspicious day. As for the disciples, Jesus had caught them unready for their call, at least till after that night. They had work to do, if Jesus would let them, having promised to go out upon the Lake at sundown, fishing all night, if need be, in the deep waters out in the central reaches, by moonlight. Jesus bade them go. They must not let Zebedee down. Enough for today. He would be seeing them again on the morrow. And then . . . !

(III) THE CALL OF PETER

JESUS was up early, long before dawn. He knew that this would be a critical day, when He intended to call His friends to full discipleship, and to inaugurate His preaching Ministry, upon which His plans so greatly depended. He crept from Peter's house and made His way rapidly up through the rising streets to the back of the town and so out on to the bare hillside above. Here, as was His habit in crises, He fell down on His knees and poured out His heart to His Father. Somewhere there on the Lake, shrouded in the moonlit mists, His chosen fellow helpers were sailing. On them so much depended—on Peter especially. Jesus sensed His friend's natural gift for unself-conscious leadership. So He prayed for him, that his faith might never fail, that his impulsive exuberance might never lead him astray. Peter was so lovable and so simple, even in his blend of strength and weakness, so human, transparent and single-minded.

Then Jesus rose and descended by a path leading down to a deserted part of the shore. He could hear the soft lapping of the waves, the only sound in a lonely, silent world. The chill deepened as the night began to give place to day. Magically the dawn, dispelling the wreathing mists, rose as if from the mysterious deeps of the Lake. This illusory reversal of natural law revealed a sea which brightened earlier and more intensely than the sky. The level waters, clear and still, collected and condensed the tremulous glimmerings of the dawn till a cold sheen began dimly to gleam like a luminous panel of glass, through which liquid undiluted light was slowly welling up; at first a mere glimmer as of spilled mercury; then a sheet of shining silver, whose chill radiance was softly suffused in the mirroring skies.

After a while the slowly moving points of sails could be just discerned above the black horizon, where the eastern cliffs merged into the mountains of the Hauran, silhouetted against the now-glowing east. The boats were bearing toward the shallows in a little bay near where Jesus stood. To the left, toward Capernaum, He could see other folk astir. Someone passed on the road behind Him and recognized Him as the new Prophet who had so splendidly defied the Temple Rulers. He ran off to tell his friends. Others were already searching for Jesus, having heard of His healing of the nobleman's son. As the sun flashed suddenly over the bleak eastern hills many people were hastening along the Lakeside road toward Him, as He waited for Zebedee's boats to beach. A crowd had already gathered about Him as Peter and the others hauled their boats up the shelving shingle. Someone cried out, "Lord, teach us about the Kingdom! Speak to us, now!"

The two boats were drawn up on the beach; and, seeing how the crowds were pressing upon Him, Jesus made a sudden decision. "Spread yourselves along the shores of the bay," He called out to the people, and turning to Peter (who was a little loweringly jealous of all this swarm of people crowding about his boats, prying into them too and seeing for themselves that they had caught nothing all night long—though he was even now bravely cleaning his empty nets for further work) Jesus called, "Peter!" The beloved voice was calling *him,* and before all this throng. "Peter, could you possibly float your boat again, just a little way out from the shore? Then I could sit in it and teach the people from there, so that everybody could hear Me. . . ."

Then Peter was all aglow with impetuous activity. Strong arms bore the boat seaward until it floated in the shallow water. Jesus stepped in and Peter swung on to its stern as it rode the tiny lapping waves, and there in the caressing breezes he turned the bow round, dropped anchor, and sat down himself to listen. The boat was lifted from time to time as a blue-green wave ran in to shore. The seabed shimmered clear beneath the dancing surface of the water.

Every syllable of that beautiful voice carried far and clear over the level sea.

"The time has come for God's reign to be established upon earth. The Kingdom of God is even now present in your midst. But to enter it you must first change your hearts and minds, and especially your conceptions of God and of His Kingdom. I want you to think afresh as to the way in which He wants you to worship Him. Are you willing to look at life anew—from a new angle, just as though you were, each of you, a newborn child—and to believe in the glorious Good News that I am bringing to you? God loves you, I tell you! God loves you all!"

As the crowd went away along the shore road Jesus turned to Peter, His whole being radiant with joy. "The Kingdom of God is certain to come! It's as inevitable as day following night. Why, it's just as though a man cast seed on the earth—as I have sown it this morning. It germinates of necessity. He can sleep . . . and rise . . . day after day; it'll spring up and grow, all the time—he can't tell why. It's just nature's processes—the earth bearing fruit of itself, inevitably. He has only to watch it grow—first the blade, then the ear, and at last, the full corn in the ear! Then, when autumn is come, he has only to take his sickle and get to work—the harvest will be there, ready for him to gather!"

When, in after years, Peter looked back upon this first Lakeside morning of his Lord's Ministry, he found it difficult to talk about. There was such a beautiful bloom on it, a loveliness that transcended description. Nevertheless, the best was yet to come. For Jesus had suddenly turned to him once more as the last of the listeners disappeared.

"Peter! I want you to weigh anchor—the other boat must be launched too—for I would like to spend this morning with you all, afloat; not here in these shallows, but away out in the mid-sea deeps. Tell those others on the shore to stop washing their nets, for I'm going deep-sea fishing with you!"

Peter was startled, and rather taken aback. This Master of theirs, loved as He was, could not but be regarded as a landsman; how could a Nazarene carpenter tell him, Simon, how and when to fish?

"Master, we have toiled all the night through and haven't caught a single fish!"

But Jesus' eyes were upon him, silently brooking no refusal, and a humbled Peter answered, "Nevertheless, at Your word we will do as You say."

When the others were told they hesitated and stared incredulously. The tackle was piled into the sterns; the boats were run down the beach and floated out into the shallows, and the oars were plied till the ships were clear of the sheltering shores. Soon the sails were hoisted and the land receded . . . far away . . . till, when they were at last in the central deeps and undulating in the slow swell, the nets were once more lowered into the clear, green depths, colder out here in these mid-sea reaches.

Jesus was silent and the disciples waited unmovingly as the boats glided lazily along, and lifted and dipped as the rolling waves bore down upon them from the north, ruffling the surface as it danced in the glinting sunlight.

Suddenly there came a sharp command from Jesus. "Pull in now!" They stared. This was altogether a new side to the Master. But they obeyed wonderingly, and, almost at the first pull, they knew that a great weight impeded their labours. Slowly the nets were hauled in, till the last and heaviest part was drawn up close to the boat's side. But this proved too heavy a task even for the strong arms of Peter and Andrew. Look! The nets were breaking! "Come over and help us," shouted Peter. And in response the other boat, piloted by the sons of Zebedee, sailed ever nearer across the swelling rollers, while Peter and Andrew strained their great muscles to hold on. James and John clambered aboard and clutched the net, and together they soon had it all hauled in. Suddenly there was a cry from the other ship, where Zebedee's hired men were in similar difficulties with a big haul. At last both boats were filled with the bursting nets, and the weight of this vast catch was so great that the sides of the ships were all but awash with the limpid, translucent deep-sea swell.

The tillers were then swung round and the boats headed for home, away in the far distance, some three and a half miles away. Every moment was an agony of suspense lest the boats sink, but Peter and the others had the true fisherman's pluck and would not throw out a single fish. Soon they were nearing the shore, and the foam-tipped breakers rocked the boats as their bows cut obliquely across the mouth of their own little creek. A bigger roller than the rest suddenly tipped the boats, and the warm green water poured in. But they were safe within the shallows now, sheltered by the arms of the tiny bay, the very one where Jesus had taught and Peter had argued with his Master about the futility of going fishing again.

The memory of it caught at Peter's heart. He blurted out his over-wrought and impetuous soul in broken words: "Go away . . . leave me, Master . . . for I am such a sinful man. . . ." His eyes said clearly, "I just can't go along with You. I'm not worthy even to be beside You." Jesus looked at him. Peter's soul, as always, shone clear to its depths—transparent as the deep sea-green waters. That was one reason why Jesus loved him so greatly.

Looking now lovingly upon him, He said, "Do you remember what I said to you yesterday, about your becoming 'fishers of men'? Well, I meant it, for it's true of you all, and you must never forget it. For I know how to catch men, as well as fishes! This may well be your last haul for a long time to come; for I call you, now, to give it all up and to follow Me, as My fellow workers in the great enterprise I started this morning. I need your help, for we must launch out into the deeps of a much greater sea than Gennesaret . . . amidst dangers, disappointments and continual hard work. But we'll be happy, so happy that people will call us, as did the Baptist: 'The Bridegroom and His friends'!" Their eyes lighted up at the thought of the glorious days before them. He went on: "The Message—the Good News that we have to spread—is simple and all-inclusive, life-changing and full of power, the solution of all the ills of the world. And it is this: that God is Father of all, and that therefore all men are brothers!"

(IV) ONE SABBATH DAY, LONG AGO . . .

WHEN Peter was an old man in Rome some of his converts one day asked him, "How did Jesus live? What were His everyday circumstances? Couldn't you tell us, not merely of the crises, the outstanding events, the great sayings, but rather an intimate and connected account of, say, just one whole day in His life? One day, say, in that most happy time of all, when He was beginning His Ministry, the Bridegroom with His friends?"

So Peter gave them—and Mark was there to hear—a complete account of one day's activities; twenty-four hours of Jesus' life, just as He lived it long before by the shores of the Lake.

It was nearly nine o'clock in the forenoon of the first Sabbath that followed the disciples' call—the hour of morning service in the Synagogue at Capernaum. It was a beautiful, new Synagogue, recently built for them by that good friend of the Capernaumites, the Roman Centurion who resided there, although his troops were quartered on the other side of the Lake.

Jesus had been asked to speak to the people at this morning's service, and an enormous crowd had gathered, the Synagogue being crammed to overflowing. The opening prayer with which the morning service always opened was read by Jesus on this occasion.

Blessed be Thou, O Lord, King of the World, Who formest the Light, Who makest peace, Who in mercy givest light to them that dwell in the earth, day by day and every day renewing the works of

creation. Blessed be the Lord our God for the glory of His handi-
work and for the life-giving lights which He has made for His praise.
Selah.

And there was the light of the world dawning upon Capernaum.
The next set prayer followed.

With great love hast Thou loved us, O Lord our God; and with
much overflowing pity hast Thou pitied us, our Father and our King.
Enlighten our eyes in Thy Law. Cause our hearts to cleave to Thy
commandments. Unite our hearts to love and fear Thy name—and
we shall not be put to shame—world without end!

Then followed: *A new song did they that were delivered sing up*
to Thy name . . . by the sea shore. . . . There was a quickening of the
spirit as these astoundingly appropriate words were uttered—there,
within sound of the breaking, cleansing waves. Peter could not help
watching Chuza as they heard the words: *Blessed art Thou, O Lord.*
Faithful art Thou to give life to the dead.

Jesus read from Exodus, choosing an extraordinary lesson which
made many of them feel very uncomfortable: *If a man strikes one of*
his slaves, male or female, with a rod, so that the slave dies under the
blow: if the slave survives a day or two, then the owner of the slave
shall go unpunished; for the slave is, after all, his own property.

Jesus added another quotation from the Law: *Thine eye shall not*
pity. It must be life for life, tooth for tooth, hand for hand, foot for
foot.

Then Jesus paused, to let the full implication of these terrible
words sink in. Was this God speaking to Israel? Was this God's own
Law, God's own character? Then Jesus rose to speak, amidst a deathly
silence.

"You have heard the Law read—supposed to be God's Law, which
you are bound to obey, in every detail, details of slaughter, of ritual, of
retaliation, of pitiless revenge. Now, don't run away with the idea
that I am out to abolish the Law; much less the Prophets. Oh no. I
have come rather to reveal it in its full truth. (And as for anyone
trying to abolish it, it would probably be an easier task to do away
with Heaven and Hell than to delete even one dot or comma from
your Law!) Indeed, I not only accept the Law, but I go far beyond in
My demands. I assure you, that unless your concepts of righteousness

far *surpass* those of the Scribes and Pharisees, you will most certainly never get into the Kingdom of Heaven."

Jesus then went on to deal in turn with the relation of the Law to love in such matters as murder, violence, adultery, oaths, almsgiving and fasting; lifting each to the highest level of morality—as seen in God's sight; in each case revising or reinterpreting the Law according to His own clear-sighted knowledge of God's will.

His discourse—intently listened to—was destined at this point to be rudely interrupted. A piercing, tearing shriek rang suddenly through the Synagogue. A man was staggering to his feet, crying out: "Ea! Ea! What have *we* to do with *You,* Jesus of Nazareth? Are You come to destroy us? *I* know Who You are, the Holy One of God!"

The whole mass of the people rose in terror, as from the back of the building the lunatic rushed forward with pointing finger and distorted features, till strong arms closed upon him and held him fast pinioned, still shaking and straining to get at Jesus. The crowd's gaze shifted. The Prophet had risen from His chair and was coming down through the parting ranks of the people. The lunatic cowered, gibbering, before Him, as Jesus gazed into his demented eyes. A sharp command came from Jesus: "Let him go!"

The crowd's excitement rose as everybody wondered what would happen. The man was free . . . but still, as Jesus, Himself perfectly immobile, held his fear-stricken gaze for a long spell while the people scarcely dared to breathe. Then with a mighty indrawing and outthrust of power, Jesus stretched an arm toward the man. The tearing yells broke out fiercer than ever, as if devils were prisoned within that storm-racked body.

But Jesus, in a voice of thunder, quelled the tumult with a command, "Silence! Come out of him!"

A horrible, convulsive agony tore the writhing body as it turned and twisted upon the floor of the Synagogue. Then, suddenly, it was still. Was the man dead? Or merely exhausted? Everyone craned forward to see, the women in the gallery straining over the balustrade. The group in the centre remained motionless; death facing life, Heaven facing Hell. At last the man's eyes slowly opened, wandered a moment, then fixed themselves on Jesus; and in slow succession, fear, bewilderment, relief and a growing confidence were revealed therein, till a glad smile lighted them and a hand, trembling yet, was stretched out toward Jesus—to be clasped in the strong grasp of the Saviour. The next moment the man rose, sighed with inexpressible relief and passed quietly out of the building with Jesus.

The disciples at once tried to follow them, but the crowd swarmed behind them, and they were hemmed in, amidst an excited mass of gesticulating, chattering Galileans. Those just around Peter as he tried to push his way out into the strong sunlight without, were busy commenting on the strange events of the morning.

"Well, this surpasses everything! We never saw anything like this before. What a power the Man has!"

"As for me, His doctrines amazed me even more than His powers of healing. Talk about new teachings! His were revolutionary—oversetting the Law and substituting His own commands!"

"Yes, I know. But He has such a persuasive way with Him."

"He has far more than that. He has authority. You can't mistake it. Utterly different from the Scribes and Pharisees."

"And yet *they* are the ones who possess authority to teach, and He has none. Queer, isn't it?"

"Not really, when you come to think closer about it. It's just the difference between external and inward authority. The last is the only true kind."

"The important thing for us to remember is that whatever authority He has is obviously ratified from Heaven . . . in that the very devils are subject to Him. You see what that means? Nothing less than that it ratifies His teachings also."

"What? All that criticism and supersession of Moses' Law? Can such a thing be true?"

As Peter listened he was suddenly overwhelmed by this desperately important implication. The connexion between the Teaching and the Miracle was made clear to him. God uses strange means of revealing His will. But this was now crystal clear: that the New Teaching was sealed from Heaven, ratified and confirmed as true. Jesus' conceptions of the Law, of God, were truer than those of the Jewish Elders, truer even than those of the written Scriptures. It was with an amazement passing into awe and wonder that Peter followed after Jesus and at length caught up with Him. Life's values seemed to have been turned upside down by that morning's experiences.

The report of these strange happenings went out at once into all the regions of Galilee, and even farther. It sealed Jesus' reputation as a Prophet.

They soon reached Peter's house, for it was not far from the sea and the Synagogue. John and James had been invited there to dinner together with Jesus. A shock awaited them, however, for Peter's wife came running to them in tears.

"Mother is ill—the fever!"

Peter looked at Jesus, and He at once went forward into the sick-room, where the flushed victim of the dread Lakeside scourge turned and tossed. He stood over her a moment in silent compassion; then took her hand in His own and just raised her up. And lo, the fever had gone and she was well again! Her first thought, good housewife that she was, was for the dinner spoiling there in the oven. She had been helping her daughter prepare the meal when she had been struck down by those terrifying pains and nausea. So, thanking Jesus with a look, she cried, "The dinner—quick!" while a burst of laughter relieved the general tension. So the dinner party was, after all, a success. . . . And then the Sabbath rest fell on the glad household, till the fierce noontide heat of the summer's day gradually gave way before the rising afternoon breezes, and evening's light, calm and mellow, began to filter through the latticed windows, as the golden Sabbath sun sank to its rest beyond the darkening hills. The chequered pattern of the lattices, cast in gold upon the walls, rose slowly up till at length the rooms were shrouded in shadow, and, in the deepening twilight gloom, only the peaks of the mountains beyond the Lake reflected yet the sun's last rays before it was extinguished in the burning waters of the far Mediterranean Sea. Suddenly they, too, were dark, and moonlit night succeeded sunlit day.

The Sabbath was over. Burdens might once more be carried, little jobs and duties done, and journeys undertaken. As darkness fell, the roads, lanes and byways were thronged with hurrying folk, leading the blind, urging forward demoniacs, carrying the halt and paralyzed. It seemed as if all the diseased and suffering of the neighbourhood were making for Peter's house, as well as the whole population of

Capernaum. The noise and babel soon penetrated into the house, and Jesus came out to the crowds and stood a moment or two gazing on the pathetic sight before Him. His eyes were filled with tears—time and again Peter was to see Him in the grip of that intense compassion that burned like a fire within His soul. When the shout that had welcomed His appearance had died down, He went about among that densely packed throng. A word here, a touch there—and another sufferer was healed each time. Some, doubtless, He never reached, who went back sad and despairing; but the greater part of the sick and suffering were healed that late evening. The strain on Him was so great that He was worn out with fatigue and a strange lowering of vitality. So Peter shut the doors and Jesus flung Himself down on His palliasse in utter exhaustion. The crowds slowly melted away, the last footsteps died into the distance, and they all retired to rest and to sleep.

The disciples were early astir the next morning. The dawn lighted up the lattices as they went about their various occupations. They let Jesus rest on. He had been so tired out the last evening. But full morning came, and still there was no sign of the Master and not a sound from His room. There were knocks at the gate. It was someone wanting Jesus. His son, he said, was ill, and they had not been able to reach Jesus last night. Would the Prophet come—only to the door? Peter told him to wait. But soon others came, and before long the street began to fill up with sufferers again. Peter became a little uneasy, and decided to take a look at the Master, and make sure all was well with Him. He crept to the door and peeped in. The room was empty. Where was Jesus? Andrew was called, but he had no idea where Jesus could be. Maybe He'd gone for a stroll along the seashore. John and James had by this time arrived from Bethsaida, whither they had gone home late last night. One of them promised to search the shore road and the Seven Springs and the little fishing creek, while the rest searched nearer home. After a time John returned. No, the Master wasn't anywhere along the coast road, so far as he could see. Someone murmured, "Do you think He's gone back home to Nazareth?" But that seemed unthinkable. He would never have deserted them so soon. The probability was that as He had been so exhausted last night, He had slipped away for a rest somewhere. When noon came and He had not been seen, they organized several search parties, some to go toward Magdala, others toward Chorazin, others to Bethsaida. But Peter had a feeling that He would most probably be found somewhere out on the bare hills at the back of the town. So a few of them struck up by the little footpath that soon lost itself on the grassy uplands. They knew how fond He was of the hills, and how He loved to commune with His Father upon some lonely summit, while the night rolled away before the rising dawn.

As they topped a great hill, they caught sight of the Master, kneeling by a huge stone, His hands clasped before Him and His eyes to Heaven. They were immensely relieved and intensely shy, waiting a while, silent, not daring to disturb Him. At long last Jesus rose, turned, and saw them. Beckoning, He welcomed them with a glad smile.

Peter said, "Everybody's looking for You, all Your friends and the people, too!" At the mention of the crowds He looked pained.

John added, "You must have got up very early."

Then He told them how He had risen a great while before dawn. He could not sleep. He had seen the high moon sailing through the star-strewn sky, from east to west, and still He lay awake, fighting over again the old battle between miracle and preaching. All those sufferers, those aching limbs, those sightless eyes. . . . They haunted Him. And yet He knew that what they needed even more than bodily health was Life Eternal. Was He to be only another Healer, and not the Saviour of men's souls? When the moon had nearly disappeared, He had risen, silently unlatched the door, and stolen out along the moon-shadowy streets, striking uphill and inland, till the last houses were left behind and only the bare hills, looking wan and strange in their dustings of silver, spread far and wide about Him. Here, on this summit—the Lakeside towns but mere shimmering clusters of grey roofs and the Lake itself but a mist-hung blur in the moonlight—He had turned to survey the silver scene and to think of the journey He had taken to reach here, both in body and soul; saw it all in its true perspective; saw also the other towns and villages, there on the other side of the hill. Should He go back again to Capernaum, to the swarming crowds of sufferers and the nerve-wracking ordeal of continual healings, or should He strike down toward yonder village and thence into the broad uplands of northern Galilee, beckoning in the grey distance? He had asked the Father for guidance, and the Father had answered Him. . . .

"Why, aren't You coming back with us after all, then?"

"No. We're all going down there, on the farther side of the hill."

"*Us* did You say?"

"Yes, and the rest can follow on. One of you must go back and tell them to meet us in yonder village, where we'll wait for them. And not a word to anybody, mind you, as to My plans or destination. You see, the whole point of My decision is that I may avoid the miracle working if possible. I want to go into every town and village we come to, so that I may preach there the glad tidings of the Kingdom of God. For *that's* My chief task. For *this* purpose, and not for mere miracle working, am I sent out upon this Divine Mission."

So that was how they all suddenly disappeared from Capernaum —for several weeks, as it turned out. Nobody knew where they were— for a time at any rate. Peter often thought of the boats drawn up on the beach, looking desolate and deserted. But they were glad to follow Jesus wherever He led them.

(V) THE SICK OF THE PALSY

THEN, suddenly, His own city woke up one morning to find He was back again. And not only that: He had been home some days, resting in secret. None of the womenfolk had given Him away. The disciples had quietly rested in Peter's house, glad to get a breather in the strenuous business of following Jesus. Peter had much to tell the women: how they had gone over the rolling hills and across the green valleys, listening to Jesus preaching. The people had seemed so glad to hear the Good News of God and His Kingdom.

Had there been any miracle working? Well, that was the reason why the tour had so abruptly terminated. One day there had come a leper to Jesus, kneeling down before Him and saying, "If only You choose to, I know You could make me clean."

Jesus had been walking close to the gate of a town, where the lepers usually waited for alms. He had looked long at the man, and had then answered: "Well, I *do* so choose! Be cleansed!" actually touching the untouchable as He said the healing words. He had thereupon realized that what He had all along tried (so successfully, so far) to avoid, namely, the notoriety that followed a miracle, was now a possible consequence. So He had sternly insisted on the man going away at once, saying to him, "Now, remember, you're not to tell a soul about this. Instead, you are to go off straight away, and show yourself to the Priest of the village, and give the necessary offering as enjoined in Moses' Law, when you make your notification of being cleansed."

The man had duly gone off; but, in spite of these strict injunctions, the former leper had proceeded to tell everybody about his cure, and to spread the fame of it far and wide. The dire result was that Jesus could no longer openly enter any town but was forced to stay outside in the more solitary parts; and even there the people had searched Him out and had come to Him from every quarter for healing. This had been disastrous for Jesus' plans. There was nothing for it but a moonlight departure from the village and a long trek in uninhabited regions, till He had finally shaken off pursuit; and then a dropping down, by night again, into Capernaum and a period of rest, in secrecy, during which He and His friends could recuperate after their long and arduous tour.

In its way, the tour had been a noteworthy success. The Synagogues had been open to Him—a remarkable proof both of His own natural authority and of the Galilean Jews' toleration, especially in view of His revolutionary teaching, by now widely talked about. Not that there was no criticism. On the contrary, there was a rising tide of controversy among the Church Leaders, following His visits. So much so, that when the news of His return had spread, the leading dignitaries of Galilean Jewry arranged for a meeting of representatives from every Synagogue in Galilee. This august assembly was invited to gather in the Synagogue at Capernaum, and Jesus was asked to attend and explain His views to the Pharisees and Teachers of the Law. This was a Heaven-sent opportunity to express beyond all possibility of misunderstanding His clear-eyed knowledge of God: His supersession of the less inspired sections of the Mosaic Law by His own intuitively known Law of Love: and His strong advocacy of the Prophetic as against the Priestly element in the Scriptures.

Above all, on this occasion, He wished to emphasize His conviction of the forgiving nature of the Father. The Jews were so terribly hard in their views regarding the relationship of sin and suffering. They believed that all bodily affliction was a direct punishment for personal or inherited sin. Furthermore, they taught that so long as the affliction persisted, this continuance was in itself evidential of continued sin. No one on earth had power to forgive sin. Only God could do that, and whether He had or had not forgiven was to be evidenced respectively by the cessation or persistence of the malady. A vicious circle, indeed.

Not that sin did not bring its own punishment with it, frequently to be seen in bodily affliction, but that often the assurance of forgiveness was a prerequisite of moral healing; and only a forgiving love could induce that repentance which alone could cleanse and cure. Jesus saw all these truths clearly; but the Rulers were prejudiced and biased, though what happened at this assembly should have settled, once and forever, the controversy which had for so long worried thinkers. As so often, a casual event of everyday life served to present Jesus with just that very opportunity which enabled Him to propound the truth, and to crystallize it in imperishable fact.

The all-critical assembly was now arriving, and the crowd about the doors gaped at the blue-robed Rabbis as they passed one by one into the building, tickets of invitation in hand. The people of Capernaum were exiles from their own Synagogue today. The doors were at length closed, and the meeting had begun. The crowds, hitherto interested in watching the arrivals, were now about to disperse when their attention was caught by a diversionary incident. Four men had arrived on the scene, bearing between them a mattress or pallet upon which lay, inert and helpless, a poor paralytic. They asked the people where Jesus was and were told that it would be quite hopeless to try to get at the Prophet now, since there was a tremendously important meeting on within the Synagogue which, so far as they knew, Jesus was even now addressing.

But they would not go away. They tried, instead, to force an entrance, but the people were resentful of this intrusion and cried out at them. Foiled there, the four men then laid their burden down and made their way round the great building. There was a set look on their faces. They were evidently not going back with their mission unfulfilled. Somehow or other they would lay their friend before Jesus. They glanced at the outside stairway, leading to the interior galleries and so up to the flat roof; they eyed each other questioningly. One of them ran up, peeped over the roof edge, and nodded significantly. The others went back to the paralytic and told him to be patient. They would not be long. And then they disappeared from sight. The poor sufferer gazed around about him in piteous apprehension. But soon his friends were seen returning, bearing some fishing ropes obtained from the shore near by. What on earth did they want with these ropes—and whose boats had they plundered? But look, they were carrying their friend away between them, making their way round to the back of the Synagogue. Some of the crowd followed out of curiosity. They saw them fixing the ropes to the four corners of the pallet, and this done, ascending to the gallery level, the long ropes trailing from the pallet. One of them clambered onto the roof, followed by another; the four rope ends were passed to them, and while the two remaining men lifted the mattress and guided it upward, those on the roof pulled the ropes in, and lo! the paralytic was hoisted on to the flat rooftop. In a moment all four friends were beside him and passed out of sight of those standing directly below. Some of the eager spectators ran to a little mound farther from the shore and tried to watch again from there. This would be a good tale to go home with. They stared, fascinated, at the drama being unfolded before them. The four men were now busy kneeling and working with their hands, and then rose and faced one another as if at the corners of some aperture— whether a skylight or a quickly and silently made hole in the tiles, the watchers could not tell. . . .

While all this was going on outside, the Rabbis within were still listening to the discourse of the new Prophet. Then, suddenly, someone glanced up at the ceiling and gripped his neighbour's arm, and all eyes were lifted. Jesus halted, conscious of a distraction, followed their upraised eyes, and saw a most strange sight: a mattress being lowered through the roof, a dark mass against the brightly shining sky, while four men could be seen peering over the aperture's edges as they carefully let out the ropes and lowered their burden straight down into the space before Jesus.

Everyone watched, spellbound, while Jairus, the Ruler of the Synagogue, rose to deal with the situation, but he was checked by Jesus' strong hand. At last the long ropes slackened and fell as the pallet reached the floor, and its occupant was disclosed, inert, a living death.

But the eyes of Jesus were alight with a triumphant gladness. This was the sort of faith He had longed for, this persistence, the sheer cheek of it, the ruthlessness—these were virtues only too rare when it came to approaching God. Folk like those peering four, high up there, were the sort who would badger a magistrate till they got their way, fight for their friends to the death, take Heaven by storm—for the right and for love's sake. Jesus glanced up at them and smiled hugely.

Then once more He gazed upon the palsied wreck lying motionless before Him. His eyes searched those listless orbs from whose glassy surface all the zest of life had been withdrawn. He saw clearly why the man was diseased. He knew that, here, sin and suffering did have a very real and terrible relation. Furthermore, He saw that, the underlying cause of the malady being in the soul rather than in the body, only relief of the mind could effect a permanent cure. If the Jews were wrong in ascribing all suffering to sin, they were not so in this particular instance. It would have been comparatively easy to smash through a false logic such as connected guiltless suffering with uncommitted sin. But to smash through a true logic that rightly connected *this* suffering with *this* sin, in order to let in the full sunlight of Heaven—even as those men up there had smashed through that roof to let the sunlight into this Synagogue—that would be a triumph indeed! Jesus now decided to break that vicious circle into a thousand shattered arcs by proving that where sin is repented of—as was obvious in the man's eyes, imploring, and self-accusing—God freely pardons. And not only that, but that His love takes the initiative, being forgiving by its very nature. And Jesus was going to pronounce this glorious truth while the supposed proof of its falsity lay before the people in the still unhealed figure of the paralytic! He would meet the Jews on their own ground, accept, for the moment and for argument's sake, their own premises.

"You say that this man can't be healed till he is forgiven; then, if he be forgiven, according to you he may *then* be healed. Very well, I'll pronounce his forgiveness *first*—let the truth be known without any proof, to begin with, as is meet and right. But when you complain—as of course you will—about My daring to pronounce his forgiveness, then I'll heal him, and so prove not only that he *is* forgiven, but that man on earth has authority to proclaim God's free forgiveness!"

That was the challenge implicit in His thought. Jesus drew a long breath and braced His shoulders—this was glorious, magnificent: doing His Father's work with indisputable authority.

So He turned to the paralytic and said, in a gentle voice, "My son, all your sins are forgiven you!"

At once there was a murmur of criticism, growing in a moment into a horror of blasphemy. What on earth did the Fellow mean by talking about forgiving sin? Only God Himself could do that. The Rabbis began to surge forward in anger. But Jesus' voice rang out, and they stopped to listen.

"I know perfectly well what you're all thinking. You hold that the man can't be forgiven, because he's still unhealed, as you think, of his malady. But he *is* healed of the real trouble, which was in his soul. I see you don't believe Me, so I'll prove it to you. It's just as easy to say: 'Get up, take up your mat and walk!' as to say, as I have, 'Your sins are forgiven you!' So, to prove before you all that the Son of Man *has* power, here on earth, to forgive sins—" with a gesture to the man— "Get up! Now take up your mattress! Now walk out of the Synagogue!"

And at once the man rose up, lifted his bed, and walked away before them all, shouting out, "Glory! Glory!" as he went.

There was immediate consternation among the Rabbis, and the meeting broke up in confusion. Tremendous issues were at stake. The full implications of this healing became increasingly clear as men were able to think them out. Certain facts stood clear. Jesus had proclaimed a forgiving God for Whom physical suffering was abhorrent. He had, furthermore, asserted that suffering was no guaranty of God's displeasure with a man, and that a sinner could be pardoned *before* his suffering was removed. But He had done much more. He had Himself proclaimed this pardon—itself the prerogative of the Almighty and hitherto believed to be evidenced solely by the removal of suffering. He had accepted their challenge—and had gone on to demonstrate that *He*, not they, revealed God's will, by proving before everybody that the man really was healed. This, on their own theory, was confirmatory of His assertions about forgiveness. They thus found themselves in a dilemma. Either Jesus was right in His Teaching, and the traditional doctrines of Israel were hopelessly wrong, or else the miracle was performed by some agency other than the Divine Power. This would require thinking out. . . .

There was yet another issue. Jesus had arrogated to Himself the prerogative of God, in proclaiming forgiveness to a man before his affliction was removed. Either this were rank blasphemy—but, if so, why had not God struck Him dead? And why, still more, had God allowed the miracle?—or else. . . . Was Jesus, then, God's Regent on earth, to dispense His blessings and to proclaim His pardon? *If so, then He was the Messiah*. . . . But that was unthinkable.

What could it all mean? Who was Jesus?

(VI) THE CALL OF LEVI-MATTHEW

MANY a Synagogue was closed to Jesus after this. The Teaching He had given—and demonstrated by inescapable fact—was far more revolutionary than that which the assembly had been called to consider. The shadows had begun to gather beside the Galilean Lakeside, and the emissaries from Jerusalem had queer and ominous news to take back to the Sanhedrin. Nicodemus smiled in his heart when he heard the strange story they had to tell. Yes, this was authority indeed. This Man was greater than he had guessed—and the inward smile turned to solemn awe.

As for Jesus, He faced the future with a plan. A great tactician, as well as a master strategist, He saw that to confine His activities to Church circles would, in these new circumstances, be severely to limit His scope, since His liberty to use the Synagogues of Galilee would be drastically curtailed from now on. Above all, He must, if possible, win the people over to His side. The new Teaching, the destruction of false theologies, the liberation of the Spirit of Love, these aims, so certain now to be thwarted by the authorities, must be championed by those outside Church circles. Alone thus could the growth of the true Church be safeguarded; and it would, furthermore, reveal unmistakably to a mistaken world that this true Church was not confined, either in its activities or its members to "religious" or "pious" persons: that its boundaries were inclusive for brotherhood, not exclusive for ostracism. What was at once needed was the sounding of a battle cry—some decisive call that would make clear, once and for all, that the Kingdom of Heaven was not co-extensive with Israel but open to all the world—and especially to sinners.

Watch, then, Jesus striding down the *Via Maris,* along the crowded water front, preparing Himself for His next move—a bold, a scandalous stroke, nothing less than asking the taxgatherer, Levi, there at the toll bar, to become His disciple. He is going to risk the astonishment, the fury, the contempt of Church circles. He is about to ask Levi to do a tremendous thing: to give up his calling, his livelihood—a very paying one, too—and all his friends, perhaps, for the sake of the cause, for the sake of the New Covenant. Not that Levi knew much about that as yet. But he knew Jesus. The Master was banking on that. It would have to be a personal call to a personal service. Would Levi respond to that appeal?

Jesus was also risking the loss of many of His friends and supporters, people who would think He had gone too far this time. Worst of all, Jesus was risking Levi's refusal. That would be a disaster. So much hung on the taxgatherer's answer; for Jesus needed this man urgently—and immediately. He was the key man in the conquest of the vast hinterland beyond Church circles. His acceptance would open up the way to a huge strategical advance in that his accession to the band of disciples would in itself break through the Jewish caste system and his influence would facilitate the approach to all the outcasts.

Let us have a look at Levi. He is the black sheep of his family. He knows that Jesus is a first cousin, once removed, of his. For his father, Alphaeus, had married Mary, the daughter of Cleopas, who was brother to Joseph the father of Jesus. But his Nazarene cousins have long boycotted him. They have lost sight of him for a long time now, ever since he entered the Roman service. He had prospered, and was now a *Mokhoa,* a specially hated class of tax farmer. The people had good reason to hate these traitors to Israel; for they exacted as much as they could from the Jews over and above the rightful amount due to Rome, a proceeding that suited Caesar since it saved him from paying his tax officials any salary.

Then, one day, came this momentous meeting. Jesus was, of course, in the habit of passing the toll bar, lying as it did on the highway between Capernaum and the Seven Springs near where the boats were kept. Levi had often watched the tall bronzed Prophet coming and going, and frequently their eyes had met and held each other's a moment. There had not seemed any hatred on Jesus' part for the tax-gatherer. One day the Prophet had preached within earshot of the toll bar, and Levi had listened and been deeply moved. He had begun to hate his calling, to think of his cheated victims, for whom there was no legal redress for dishonest exactions. Jesus was obviously loved by the people, but they hated him, Levi. Wealth seemed suddenly sordid, mean. To be loved—especially to be loved by such a man as Jesus—that became his longing.

Then the great surprise of his life was sprung upon him. Jesus was nearing him, along the road, surrounded as ever by a crowd of enthusiastic followers. The Prophet stopped, as usual, at the toll bar. Once more there was the friendly smile, the long and earnest gaze. Then had come the astounding words: "Levi, will you be one of My disciples?"

There was a bewildering pause. Peter looked shocked. The Master was everlastingly doing queer things—talking to a harlot in Samaria, leaving Capernaum that morning a few weeks back just when success had seemed assured. And now!

Then something snapped in Levi's inner world, as his soul broke free from the toils of office, and from the self-contempt of a wavering will. He rose, swept his arm over all the paraphernalia of his profession, and cried, "Yes! Yes! I've finished forever with all this! I'll come, my Master—*now!*" And there and then, with the violence born of sudden decision, and of the fear of retraction, he moved away with Jesus.

The disciples followed uneasily and at a little distance. It spoke volumes both for their self-restraint and for Jesus' influence over them that they followed at all. The people were divided in their immediate reactions. Some saw in this dramatic incident a sign that Jesus hated Rome. "See, He's made even Levi leave his job—for he's broken with Rome at the Prophet's bidding." Others saw in it just the opposite.

"Not so; He's chosen a traitor as His disciple—He must be a traitor Himself!"

Most of the folk there were scandalized beyond words, but some— on the outskirts of the crowd—took heart afresh. This Prophet was not squeamish in His choice of friends. Queer but a good sort . . . not like the snobbish and exclusive Pharisees.

That evening Jesus took Levi entirely into His confidence. There were problems, arising out of this double decision, for them both. Jesus put the case clearly before His new adherent.

"I've lost the support of almost all the orthodox Jews. Only a few, like Jairus here, are brave enough to give Me countenance in their Synagogues. Most of them will be My active enemies from now on— no, not because of you, Levi. I'd lost them already; that's why I needed your help so urgently. It was because I dared to preach a loving, forgiving God, Who would never punish innocent men for inherited sins by afflicting their bodies, nor their souls by refusing them forgiveness when they repented. Well, I've lost these Jews, anyway. Perhaps they had to be lost before the masses of the people could be won. Anyhow, I'm aiming at the masses now. That's where I need your help. Now, your coming to us should be an occasion for merrymaking. I love feasts—why not hazard all on a really bold move? You, naturally, want to show you've not broken with your former friends, even if you've broken with your profession. Well, make it perfectly clear to them that they *are* still your friends; and if you can at the same time find occasion to explain everything to them, all our aims would be met. Now, the ideal occasion for this would be a feast! The best thing you can do in the circumstances is to give a great dinner, and get them all together at it—will you ask Me too? I'll help you to explain, and I'd love to make friends of them all. That would be exactly what I want, and the very thing that you alone could do for Me. Will you do it?"

Levi accepted joyfully, and then looked doubtfully at the other disciples. Would they come too? A moment and they had agreed. They could not let the Master down. Jesus loved them all the more for it. This would be seeking out the lost sheep of the House of Israel, with a vengeance. . . .

But Jesus had yet a word more to say. "Levi, I can't tell you how grateful I am. But, while you're about it, why not go a step—a glorious step—further and make it a feast for *all* the unloved and outcast, even making a point of getting in notorious sinners as well as the lax in the Law? For I am come solely to seek out and to save the lost."

Levi was a rich man. He could easily afford it. It was to be a banquet of friends, to make more friends. It would show the world that Jesus approved of Matthew keeping his friends, and that He, Jesus, also wanted to be their Friend. Furthermore, they would thus be brought into fellowship with their Saviour in the one atmosphere in which they might most easily forget their inhibitions and deep-rooted grievances.

Jesus never forgot this feast nor Levi's tremendous zest in furnishing it with the required guests. First the taxgatherers. Written invitations there, of course. Then a walk along the *Via Maris*. That beggar there—a bad lot? The very man! And that poor wastrel got the shock of his life as Levi turned aside and came toward him and gravely invited him to a great feast to meet the new Prophet. Who's that lounger by the fishing boats? The ne'er-do-well son of the pious Scribe of Chorazin? Ask him too. And the man was so taken aback, almost insulted, that Levi got no answer there—only a sulking silence. (But he turned up on the day, nevertheless.) And that other man who had so often stood in the offing when Jesus was preaching, and who looked so desperately unhappy—rope him in. You can but ask. And don't take No for an answer, either. Compel them to come in! There are still some empty places? Go out into the byways, search the lanes, comb the very hedges, but get a full house. We *will* make a success of our feast!

And so they did. When everyone found that everybody else was accepting, there was a rush to get an invitation. Not only was the feast furnished with guests, but the people even hung about the street outside and crowded into the portico in the hope of squeezing within somehow. The whole thing went off magnificently and was a huge success.

The inevitable reaction from the Scribes and Pharisees came soon enough. They drew aside the disciples the very next day, not daring

to tackle Jesus—His power in retort was already too well-known. . . .
"Why does your Master eat with taxgatherers and sinners?"

But they received no reply. The disciples had learned to leave all
problems to Jesus.

So He made reply, ironically courteous, unanswerable. "Those who
are *well* don't need a doctor, only those who are ill. The men whose
lives I want to change are the sinners, not the *righteous*. . . ."

After this His foes did their best to discredit Him with the people.
They invented new nicknames for Him. "The Taxgatherer's Ally."
"The Sinners' Friend." "A glutton and a drunkard!" But Jesus did
not mind the least bit. Indeed, He was proud to be called the Friend
of sinners.

But one thing that especially incensed the Pharisees was His neglect
of fasting. In this, they could appeal to the example of the Baptist,
who was an ascetic. This time they felt in such good fettle for a fray
that they dared to tackle Jesus Himself.

"About that feast your disciples attended the other day—" even
now they are chary of directly attacking *Him*—"I suppose they had
forgotten it was a fast day? Just so. But these men here—who, by the
way, are disciples of your friend John the Baptist—*they* had not forgotten. Like us, they kept the day properly, in abstinence, not in
drunken carousals."

Jesus' answer was a wonderfully comprehensive rejoinder; for while
it refused to damp the radiance of the gracious personal relationship
existing between Himself and His disciples, it bore witness, in terms
of deepest sympathy, to John's dread fate; and, while looking backward tenderly to His intimate friendship with John it pointed forward
also to His own probable similar doom.

"How can you force the Sons of the Bridechamber—the 'Friends of
the Bridegroom'—to mourn and fast, while yet the Bridegroom is
with them? Nay, so long as He is present with them, they just cannot fast. But the days will no doubt come—as they already have for
these disciples of John—when the Bridegroom will be taken away
from them. It will be time enough, and right enough, for them to
fast—in those days. . . ."

The singing, lyric sunlight of this radiant summer, beside the Syrian sea, was already beginning to be overshadowed by the gloom of twilit dayfall.

The contrast between the Old and New Covenants struck Him afresh as He pondered upon the clash of Law and Love. In ringing tones He gave expression to His explosive, revolutionary thought: "If a thing be outworn, be it cloth garment or leather wineskin, it must be scrapped. It's no use trying to patch old garments with new cloth or to pour new wine into old wineskins. You only lose both the wine and the wineskins, just as a rent mended with new cloth only makes the hole worse than ever. No. New cloth for new garments and new wineskins for new wine.

"It's the same with doctrine. The vesture of the Old Covenant is in tatters. The old wineskins cannot stand the strength of the new wine. I'm not saying that forms are not necessary for the preservation of ideas, but they must be appropriate to the new ideas, being themselves new."

But He added the ironic comment on His own observation: ". . . Though I've noticed how few people, once they've drunk deeply enough of the old wine, ever want to taste the new. 'No,' they say, 'the old's good enough for me!' . . ."

And with that rather satirical comment He closed the controversy.

(VII) IN THE CORNFIELDS

IT WAS a Sabbath in early June. Jesus and His friends were walking through the golden cornfields among the hills surrounding the Lake, where the harvest was much later than in the valleys of Samaria or in the Jordan Valley. The fresh sweet air blew in from the Great Sea to the far west, and the corn dipped and rose in undulating waves, while away below them the blue waters of the Lake glistened in the bright sunlight.

They were returning home to Capernaum from a visit to a hill village near Safed. It was toward evening and they had several more miles to go. They felt hungry, and as they wandered leisurely through the rich wheatfields they let their fingers play with the corn. The full ears ran through their fingers as they passed along. Now and again their hands closed about an ear and they plucked it with a jerk; rubbing it in their palms till the golden berries were loosened, they ate them and enjoyed the white flour within. An idyllic picture . . . a pity there were sour-hearted Pharisees watching them as they walked along. Could it be that these disciples of the new Prophet were actually plucking the ears of corn on the Sabbath? Well, that was allowed, said one of the watchers. Allowed? It oughtn't to be. In any case winnowing or threshing was *not* allowed.

"Get nearer if you can. Yes, did you see? They *are* rubbing the ears in their hands and eating them. And that *is* threshing. Come, let's challenge them—it's a clear breach of the Law."

They hurried and caught up with Jesus and His friends.

"Look! Don't You care that Your friends break the Law? It's the Sabbath day, and see, they're *threshing!*"

"*Threshing?*" answered Jesus, and a mighty laugh echoed over the hills. "What, are you actually referring to the hand rubbing of the ears of corn, and the blowing away of the husks? You really are? Splendid! And, I suppose, as soon as yonder sun has dropped behind the hills over there, what is now a sin will suddenly become perfectly legal?"

Jesus was greatly enjoying Himself. He loved battling for freedom and truth. A broad smile irradiated His features as His amazingly quick and retentive memory seized upon an exactly appropriate citation from the Scriptures.

"Tell Me, you who claim to be experts in the Scriptures, have you never read what David did, when *his* young followers were hungry— how he forced his way into the Sanctuary and accosted the Priest on duty there, who was scared to death? 'What have you got there?' asked David. 'Five loaves? Hand them over to me. My men are hungry.' You will remember how scandalized Ahimelech was and how he did his best to preserve the sanctity of the Temple from this hot-headed firebrand. 'These aren't ordinary loaves,' answered the Priest; 'they're the Bread of the Presence. It's Holy, and only we Priests are allowed even to touch it.' But David got his way, as he generally did. Besides, he was armed, and so were his men. What *could* the poor Priest do? Blasphemous and profane of David, wasn't it? What have you got to say about it? Nothing?

"Well then, I'll tell you what *I* think about it. David was quite

right. His men were hungry, and human need comes before ceremonial correctitude. Besides, even your own scholars allow that, as
David claimed to be engaged in the service of the Lord, his action was
justified.

"Now for *My* men. They, too, are hungry, and it's the same Lord
they are serving! And if the Priests are considered guiltless of any
desecration when they are busy on the Sabbath in the service of the
Lord, ministering in the Temple, so should My men be considered
even more guiltless when they are serving Me. For I tell you, One
greater than the Temple is here now with you at this very moment."

The Pharisees recoiled from Him in horror, but He continued:
"Oh, if only you could realize what the Prophet meant when he cried
in God's name, *I will have mercy . . . not sacrifice!* you would never
have condemned the guiltless. . . . Besides, in any case, the Sabbath
was made for man, not man for the Sabbath! And if serving the Lord
on the Sabbath is allowable, *I* am Lord . . . yes, even of the Sabbath!"
And a wry irony twisted His lips as He uttered these words. Peter
stared at Him in awe and wonder. As they moved forward, leaving the
Pharisees gaping and breathless, there fell a silence of speculation on
the group that followed the Master down the hillside.

But Peter at length plucked up courage to ask a question which he
had at great pains worked out. "Master, do you mean that *none* of the
Sabbath rules apply any longer to *us?*"

Jesus glanced around toward him, and happened to see a plough-
man at work out on the twilit hills—and it was still the Sabbath, the
sun not being set as yet.

"Take that man over there, ploughing. Is he breaking the Sabbath
or not?"

By now they had drawn level with the man and as he turned his
plough at the end of the furrow, Jesus addressed Himself directly to
him. "My friend, if you know what you're doing—breaking the Sabbath laws for a good cause—then you are indeed blessed. But if you
are merely slack and indifferent about religious custom, then you are
accursed and a breaker of the Law!"

And Jesus passed on, in silence, leaving behind Him a staring man,
tapping his forehead significantly.

III

The Lakeside Ministry: The Middle Phase

. . . .

(I) THE CALLING OF THE TWELVE AND THE
GREAT SERMON

DURING this summer the work of Jesus continued unabated, His popularity with the masses of the people growing daily. But His position became increasingly difficult. The people swarmed round because they misunderstood Him; and the religious authorities cold-shouldered Him, largely because they understood Him only too well. Jesus was thus faced by two main facts: His growing popularity with the crowds, largely for the wrong reasons, and the increasing opposition of the religious authorities. However, the first kept the other in check. Nevertheless, Jesus was faced with possible arrest at any moment, especially if the Elders could manage to rouse Herod's superstitious fears. There was—indeed, there could be—no point in trying to make the Pharisees understand His Teaching; for they did understand it, and this was the basis of their opposition. But the people's misunderstanding might surely be rectified, and the sooner the better, since their enthusiasm involved Him in suspicion of revolt; and this meant danger and possible death, almost certain death if He were proclaimed as *their* sort of Messiah—a Warrior King. The only course open to Jesus, therefore, at this juncture was to try to make His Message perfectly clear to the people; in other words, to deflect enthusiasm away from His works to His Teaching.

There was, however, a possibility that even a simple statement of the profundities for which He stood might still be misunderstood. Therefore it became imperative to cover all eventualities, to arrange, if possible, that even if the people misunderstood—and if either they, unwittingly, or His enemies, wittingly, encompassed His arrest and death—His Message would yet be understood to the full by a few

chosen people, who could help Him in His work while He were yet
alive and ensure its continuity if He were to die.

These twin steps, then, Jesus took without delay. He would choose
out twelve special friends from the great body of His followers; planning not only to train them in His Teaching, but to hasten the fulfilment of His Mission by using them as His ambassadors or travelling
preachers. And He planned to issue His great manifesto of the way of
love, of the secret of happiness: the very heart of the New Religion.
From now on, a new note of urgency crept into all His actions. The
Acceptable Year of the Lord, which had opened in the radiance of
spring, was drawing toward its close in the wintry atmosphere of
bleak privation.

He prepared Himself for these decisive steps by a long night vigil
out on the hillsides overlooking the Lake. There, in prayer and meditation, He sought and found communion with His Father, guidance in
decision, power in exposition. He had appointed a rendezvous at
which all His disciples should gather at dawn the next day—a grassy
sward not far from where He prayed.

Then came the dawn; the high clear air of the mountainside bending the grasses and the red cyclamen blossoms, the sun breaking over
the Hauran, the Lake shining silvery far below; the little groups of
friends wending their way up the hill paths, and their Master, on a
grassy knoll before a natural amphitheatre on the mountain, seated
and awaiting with eager anticipation this inauguration of a fresh strategic campaign for the cause of God. At length His followers, a great
crowd of them, settled themselves below Him and prepared to listen.
He explained His dual project: how He was about to choose twelve
men from this vast company, who were to be prepared to drop their
trades and be with Him all the time. Eventually they would have to
go out in His name as His couriers, to preach and to have authority, if
need be, to cast out devils and to heal diseases. He looked round on
that enthralled and eager gathering. The timid and lukewarm, the
cautious, were of no use to Him. He wanted the most manly, the
bravest, for His work. "Lord, can I come?" was written on every
face, and the suspense grew with every moment that passed. Their
hearts thrilled as they listened to the new Prophet revealing His plan
of campaign.

At last Jesus was silent. The moment of final choice had come, and a silence fell on the assembled disciples grouped before Him. Then a single word, "Peter!" and Simon was on his feet in a leaping movement of joy, and stumbling shyly, yet impetuously, over the hillside. Humbly he knelt down before his Lord and Master, while Jesus laid His hands upon him and commissioned him solemnly for the great task. Andrew followed, then James and John, the Master's cousins. Then Philip and his close friend Nathanael-Bartholomew; and Levi and Thomas his friend; another James, and his brother Judas, brothers to Levi; for he had brought his whole family into contact with the Master. Then came yet another Simon and another Judas.

Jesus knew them in time by nicknames bestowed by Himself upon them. There was "Peter"—Rock Man—the first nickname of all. James and John He called "The Sons of Thunder": stormy men of a high spirit and impulsive action. Thomas He called "The Twin." Levi He came to know as Matthew—"the Gift of God." His brother James was called "Tiny." The second Simon "The Zealot"—a reference to his intense nationalism. The second Judas was known as "Iscariot," for he had been born in Kerioth and was the only Judaean amongst the whole band. He told them that His generic name for them would in future be "Apostles," the "Sent-out"; though, as a matter of fact, He often playfully called them "The Little Faiths," a sad reminder of their lack of trust in moments of crisis. And at times He called them His children—a name which young John of Jerusalem liked the best of all.

The Great Sermon

The ordination was by now over. In the distance, swarms of people were to be seen climbing the hillsides. Jesus had arranged, through His closer followers, that the masses of the people of Galilee, and further afield also, should know of His intention to give them a special message that afternoon at this particular spot. He moved down to a more level place, where He could the more easily speak to a vast concourse.

He had, in order to be fully understood, so to present His Gospel that not only was its essential meaning crystal clear, but also easily remembered. He had taken infinite pains in preparing this move, having gone to the trouble of thinking out some of the basic principles of His Teaching in terms of Aramaic metre and rhyme.

The words with which He opened His discourse came in ringing tones, slowly enunciated, carrying to the farthest outskirts of the crowd.

> *Tubehon misknayya,*
> *dedilehon malkuta dismayya.*
> *Tubehon demitabelin*
> *dehinnun mitnahhamin.*
> *Tubehon inwanayya*
> *dehinnum yeretun leara.*
> *Tubehon dekaphenin wesahayin*
> *dehinnun mitmelayin.**

So, *line upon line, precept upon precept,* the people listened, repeated and eventually learned by heart the great principles of His Teaching. He outlined for them the basic elements of the secret of happiness. Each of His opening sentences began with the word *Happy.* The word for Jesus implied a Divine, celestial happiness, an inward radiance of being, expressing itself in a natural charm, God-like in its poise and grace, lyrical in its spontaneity and immediacy. This singing awareness of reality sprang from an innate royalty of being, that knew at first hand the joy of Heaven, that lived to the full with the life of God. Jesus looked around Him at the vast crowds, and told them that if only they would sit lightly to possession, wealth, power, calamity, even to earthly life itself, they would know what it was to live gloriously, abundantly. The sort of men, said Jesus, who were likely to attain to this bliss were those who were humble, meek, single of heart, merciful, strivers after peace, hungry for Holiness—heroes, every one of them. He spoke of "the poor in spirit," but there was nothing poor-spirited about those whom He had in mind; nothing servile about His concept of service. It referred rather to that sincere humility that could relax fully in God's arms and know something of the "rest unto the soul" of which Jesus spoke—and so, too, of the tremendous energy of spirit engendered of that central calm. Only those who had cast out

---

* Charles Fox Burney, *The Poetry of our Lord.* (Oxford University Press, 1925).

self and enthroned God within could smile out to the world with huge and exuberant vitality. There was none so truly serious as your light-hearted adventurer whose gaiety and heroism sprang from a carefree selflessness based on certainty of conviction. Such a freedom neared frivolity. Such a care for causes was so careless of consequence that its most characteristic strength was often manifested in seeming weakness. There was something terrific about a really meek man filled with utter singleness of purpose. He was brave to the uttermost. He had no need of duty's spur. Being moved, instead, by desire, he was entirely free, in that such a one could be trusted to do God's will. No conscript he, truly a volunteer in God's army. The need for outward authority and discipline lessened in proportion as possession of the inward increased.

"Love God—and do as you like!" is perhaps the most profound of all summaries of the Great Sermon. The man who was filled with this Divine afflatus was debonair even with death itself, singing and dancing through life in a very ecstasy of happiness, incorrigibly gay, forgiving, eager. You just could not offend him personally. Being utterly dependent upon God, he was able to see the world as from Heaven's viewpoint—upside down to all earth's values. Moreover, he was rich beyond all avarice, owning the whole world precisely because he had no possessions.

"You look out of your window in the early morning, at the earth, the sky, the sun and the stars. They are all yours for the taking! You can inherit the earth!" said Jesus to those myriad poor and oppressed that thronged the mountain slopes that summer morning. The birthright of the child of God was the freedom of the universe. Flowers and sunsets could never be earned or deserved. They were inherited by those who were joint heirs with Christ of all reality and all happiness. This was the joyous inheritance of the saints in light.

"Light . . ." The word brought before Jesus a throng of bright images and reflections. You could not easily define it, but you could always recognize it. You could not only see it, but see through it and by it; for it was clear, clean and pure, like the sun-filled depths of the mid-sea reaches of the Lake. You see with the eye, though. Therefore the eye also must be clear, and not only so that one might see the light that was without, but that the Light that was within might shine out for all to see: a flaming beacon to the world. Indeed, it would then seem as if "the whole body were full of light." (There were some among those listening to Jesus as He said this, who saw in His own person the best illustration of His words . . . a foretaste of that Light that was later to stream out from Him on the Mount of Transfiguration.) This inner Light, said Jesus, mattered more than all the regulations of the Law or the mysteries of the Temple. Not even the authority of the sacred Scriptures themselves could absolve a man from thought, judgment, decision. The quenching of this inner Light through wilful sin, till it no longer shone of itself—that was the supreme tragedy of existence. Only darkness could front the eyes of such a lightless soul. And how great was that darkness; for when conscience itself was corrupt, how could a man repent and be forgiven? But with the clear-eyed man, the eye was an aperture through which the real truth of the outer world reached his mind undistorted, and through which the inner Light shone clear for all to see. And not only that; but it also illumined all he saw so that its full beauty, and so its real nature—since God made all things good—was clearly seen. Beauty and significance were but the perception of the truth of things —the glory without being lighted to clarity by the glory within. The senses of man should be channels of grace, not opaque barriers. It followed that only the pure in heart could see God, just as the sun, as both seen and illuminated was only a reality to those whose eyes were clear-sighted. For through the eye the Light within mingled with the light without, and thus the two aspects of the one light burned in a blazing unity. Only the true poet could be the supreme realist; for he alone could see life clearly and see it whole.

Jesus, standing there in the sunlight as the day wore on toward evening, was revealed as the greatest poet of all time; for He alone could see the world about Him in all its glory. The flowers, the birds, the fields, the waters—and, above all, the pathetic masses of humanity— they were all lighted up, glowing and gleaming, though with darkened shadows attendant upon brighter highlights. "He who wonders shall reign," He told them, "and he who reigns shall rest. . . . Look, then, with wonder at that which is before you." Alone in this regnant wonder, this re-creative rest, could truth and beauty unite in love.

Looking on His followers gathered there, Jesus thought of them in terms of His own sense of vocation. *"You* are the light of world!" He cried, albeit He realized, half humorously, that many of them successfully concealed that light. "Bring out your goodness—give it a chance to shine!" And as He pointed away to the north and every head was turned toward where Safed stood high and clear on its hilltop, He cried again, "A city set on a hill just cannot be hidden! So let your light shine out before everybody, that the world may see your happiness and glorify your Father which is in Heaven!"—even as He Himself shone, sun-bright, fire-warm, for all to see and see by. For He was, literally, light-hearted, as no man ever was before or since, though of all ordinary men St. Francis came nearest to his Master.

Above all Jesus bade men give up worrying. "If you're trying to serve God, you won't have time to bother about material things; you'll leave those to God, Who cares for you. No one can serve two masters; he's bound to love one and hate the other, especially when they're as opposite as are God and Mammon. So it follows that you should never be overanxious about your livelihood—what you're to eat or what you're to drink, nor yet for your bodies, what you're to wear. Surely life itself matters more than food and likewise the body more than the clothes it wears! Look at the birds up there in the sky! They know nothing about either sowing or reaping or gathering into barns. Yet God feeds them; and think how much more you matter to God than birds. Consider: can worry add a single moment to your lives' span? If you can't even do a little thing like that, why worry over anything at all? Look at these lovely flowers all around us. Think, if you can, how they grow. They know nothing about toiling or spinning; yet I tell you that even Solomon in all his glory was never robed like one of these. And if God so gloriously clothes the wild flowers which today bloom, and tomorrow are thrown as fuel into the breadoven, isn't it obvious that He will care even more that *you* are clothed? O you *'Little Faiths!'* Never worry, then, or go about asking 'What shall we eat?' or 'What shall we drink?' or 'What are we to wear?'—the sort of things the Gentiles are forever worrying about. For your Heavenly Father knows perfectly well that you do need all these things. No. Make His Kingdom and His righteousness your chief aim in life, then all these other things will be yours as well! So don't worry about tomorrow. Let tomorrow's worries look after themselves! After all, today's troubles are quite enough for the present! So just ask God for your needs and leave everything to Him. Seek and you will find. Knock and the door will be opened to you. For everybody who asks receives, and the seeker finds. Yes, whether good things or bad things, everyone in the end gets what he really wants. Doors are always opened to the persistent knocker. Take yourselves: many of you are fathers of children. Now, if your little boy asks you for bread, will you offer him a stone? Or if he asks for some fish, will you hand him a snake? Or if he wants an egg, will you hand him one from which a scorpion jumps out when it's opened? Well then, if, in spite of all your sins, you yet know perfectly well how to give good gifts to your children, how much more readily will your Father in Heaven give good things, even the best gift of all—His Holy Spirit— to those who ask Him!"

Look at Him smiling there. He is thinking (as He nearly always was) of God, and of God's goodness. In simile after simile He rubbed home the nature of Divine love; the nature of the Father. It was best expressed in the concept of excess—as was inevitable when Infinity is revealed to finity. Love knew no limitations, exhibited no favouritisms. God's love was a plenitude of pressure upon every human soul. Like the sunshine and the rain, God's best blessings were potentially shared alike by all. There was no high-watermark to love's inundations. When God gave, He gave royally, as became a King. There was no measuring out of the gift of the Spirit. It was offered "pressed down, shaken together, and running over," like the grain in the market place. Moreover, the action of forgiveness was not something dependent upon a preconditioning repentance—although its final apprehension might be. It was rather an outgoing a vital dynamic, taking the initiative in a great campaign of reconciliation.

What *could* one do with the sort of man who, when he heard that justice had been twisted, the verdict was against him and he had been ordered to be sold up—with not even a coat to his back—only laughed and cried, "Wouldn't they like my cloak as well?" Yes, and meant it. Was there not, too, something debonair about the man who, being smitten, turned the other cheek? Or who, when impressed by Rome's legionaries to do forced labour for a mile, asked: "Can't I do another mile?"—with a huge disarming grin?

There were no rules in the Kingdom of God; no justice, no duty; only love, grace, fellowship. For within this gracious personal relation which was the heart of true religion everyone would think and act only in terms of the family. Neither the Father nor the Son—nor yet any true son of any true father—could feel conscious of duty where love dictates. Goodness became, instead, natural, inevitable, spontaneous.

So the Master outlined His lovely Gospel of grace, grace that includes charm and charity. Himself the living embodiment of grace, He revealed the graciousness of God, and bade all men live in a state of grace . . . which meant living in the overplus of love: a love active, dynamic, bursting, aching, till goodness came easily to the soul, till all care was lifted, because men floated on the floodtide of the grace of God. Not in careful correctitude but in spontaneous casualness would love best reveal itself. Love could only think in terms of Infinity. He told that great crowd: "I want you all to be perfect; even as My Father in Heaven is perfect." For He longed for all men to share in God's joy, in God's rest, in God's super-abundant life. To share in all this, they must be God-possessed.

Moreover, only when a man so surrendered his soul to God could he become most fully himself. For the God within him was the only real part of him, and only in so far as he lost himself in God's service would he gain in fullness of personality. Jesus saw love in terms of the lover—the *Lover of souls*. In very truth He was so filled with God that He *was* God to the full; God in human form, in those days and in those circumstances acting always as God would have acted. And because God does not change, so what Jesus was then God ever was, is, and always will be. The life Jesus lived on earth was the Life Eternal, timeless, spaceless, deathless. His feet were firm upon earth, but His heart was in Heaven. He loved, as none other ever did or could, the beauties of earth, but only because He saw in them the beauty of Heaven. The blue Lake, that high mid-summer loveliness, the fleecy clouds and the wheeling birds, the far mountains, palpitating with the haze of distance and reeling away into infinity—no one in all that vast crowd loved them as Jesus did, as the glowing sun fell westward over the golden uplands of Galilee.

But for the people themselves, He Himself was the most lovely

vision of them all. They were long to remember Him as they saw Him
that day, bathed in the glow of the late afternoon sunlight. And many
felt that as they slowly wound their way homeward down the twilit
hillsides, a new-found peace and a new freedom had entered and triumphed in their souls. All their cares were uplifted in the Everlasting
Arms. They had seen Heaven on earth; been in touch with bedrock
truth, truth which no storms of circumstance could endanger or dis-
place. Their eyes were dazzled as with the sense of infinite light . . .
limitless, about, above, within. And somehow, this light radiated
from and centred in the Man Jesus; for the light of the knowledge of
the glory of God had shone forth in the face of Jesus Christ.

(II) THE CENTURION'S SLAVE

THE summer months slipped by and autumn drew on, waxed in
glory, and waned into winter. It was a comfort to Jesus that Jairus,
the Ruler of the Synagogue in Capernaum, remained true to Him in
spite of the opposition of the Jewish authorities. He was a broad-
minded man, looked at askance by the more orthodox Jews on account
of his friendship with the Roman Centurion who had built the Synagogue as a gift to the town. It was regarded as deeply offensive to
sensitive Jewish minds that Roman emblems should have been used in
its ornamentation. The little effigy of the Ephesian temple gave especial offence. But the Centurion took little heed of their scruples, knowing he had a good friend in the Ruler and that the people were grateful to him for his gift. He himself was attached to the Roman garrison
based on Gadara, on the other side of the Lake, but preferred to live in
more gracious surroundings in Capernaum. He was a rich man who
had grown to love the country wherein he was posted, tolerant of its
beliefs, and willing and able to be its munificent friend. He had been
especially interested in Jesus, observing Him as from a detached viewpoint. He liked the new Prophet's straightforwardness, His disciplined authority of manner, His courtesy and innate breeding. In
short the Fellow had quality. You could not mistake it. Power under
control—that summed Him up. And He certainly could heal.

Then one of the Centurion's slaves fell ill, grew rapidly worse, and

was like to die. A good fellow, too. Under his brusque manner the
Centurion hid a kind heart, having no use for the overbearing ways of
many Romans with their slaves. Treat them properly—no pampering,
mind you, but decently and humanely—and you got far better service
out of them. And here was the fellow dying. Couldn't let him pass
out without an effort to save his life. Physicians were little use. A lot
of quacks. But there was this new Prophet—a Healer, so everybody
said. A Jew, of course, with all their ridiculous prejudices, he supposed. Better get hold of the Elders of the Jews, and ask them to approach the Prophet. At once, too. The man was obviously dying.

So the Elders came to Jesus and asked Him earnestly to come and
save the slave's life. They added, "The man for whom we speak is
fully worthy of your help; for, as you may know, he loves our nation,
and it was he who, at his own expense, built us our Synagogue."

Jesus at once answered, "I will come and heal the slave," and went
along with them immediately.

The Centurion was on the look-out to see whether his entreaty had
had any result. Catching sight of Jesus approaching with the Elders,
he at once turned to some friends who were with him in the house,
asking them to hurry with another message to Jesus.

"I can see the Prophet in the distance—He's evidently coming here
as I asked Him to. Run along and tell Him there's no need for Him, a
Jew, actually to enter this house if He doesn't want to. In any case,
I'm not good enough to have Him under the same roof as myself. Tell
Him just to *order* the slave's healing. He'll be obeyed, I'll warrant.
Say, if you like, that I'm a soldier, used to being obedient—and so to
be obeyed in turn. If I say to one of my men, 'Go!'—well, he goes.
If I say to another, 'Come!' he comes all right. If I ever said to this
very slave who is so ill, 'Do this!' he's always done it. Jesus will like
that, I know. He'll understand me, I'm sure. He's got discipline written all over Him. You can't miss it. And now be off quickly."

As the Centurion turned away, his friends noticed a tear in his eye
as he glanced with deep concern at the sick slave lying there in his bed.
Nobody could fail to see how dear the slave was to him.

When the message was given to Jesus, He turned to those that followed Him, saying, "Talk of this man not considering himself
worthy, just because he's not a Jew, to speak to Me or let Me enter his

house! Why, I tell you in solemn truth, I've never yet met with such a wonderful faith—no, not even in Israel! He outsoars all the Jews that ever I met for sheer splendour of faith!"

The poetic imagination of Jesus was fired at this. He saw in the Roman the forerunner of a great host of believing Gentiles, saw, too, in universalistic vision those that were outside the Law not only favoured of Heaven before many contemporary Jews, but equal to the greatest figures in Israel's long history.

His voice rose in exultant conviction: "I tell you, many shall come not only from the west, but from the east and the north and the south, and shall sit down beside Abraham and Isaac and Jacob, in the day when all the Patriarchs and Prophets shall celebrate the Reign of God. . . . And outside, in the darkness, amidst the weeping and wailing of the outcast, will be gathered many sons of the Chosen Race—perhaps some of you that are gathered around Me even now."

Then came His final words, to the Centurion's friends: "Go your way. Even as the Centurion has said, so shall it be done!"

And those that were sent, on returning to the Centurion's house, found the slave healed. The self-disciplined Commander of the world of Spirits had been obeyed. Rome and Heaven saluted each other in a mutual understanding.

(III) AT NAIN

SHORTLY after this, Jesus and the Twelve were journeying toward a town called Nain, situated on a hill not far from Mount Tabor. It was about twenty miles from Capernaum and some seven from Nazareth. Quite a number of youthful enthusiasts accompanied Jesus besides His disciples. They were on a preaching tour, and everyone felt that they were sharing in a great adventure, as they thronged about the tall, blue-robed Figure that was their beloved Master.

As they drew near to the town, climbing the hillside, they heard in the distance a weird wailing, evidently a funeral procession, making its way toward the burial ground halfway down the hill. Soon the cortège appeared, and the wailing—florid, metallic, nasal—rose in volume. It happened to be the funeral of a young man, the only son of his mother, and she a widow. Jesus and His friends respectfully drew aside to allow the long and tragic procession to pass slowly by. *Behold, I set before you Life and Death.* There was the Bridegroom, the young Prince of Glory, with His friends: the Lord of all good life, meeting, face to face, with death in its most tragic form. A great crowd followed the cortège. First came the orator, proclaiming the virtues of this only son. Then the women, wailing and beating their breasts. The bereaved mother—her attire showed she was a widow—immediately followed the bier, a wickerwork receptacle on which the dead man's body was laid, with face uncovered, though bound about with a napkin, and with hands folded upon his breast.

It was the sight of that bowed and shambling mother that so moved Jesus that it was all He could do not to burst into tears. He found Himself starting forward impulsively, running to her, laying His hand on her shoulder and saying, "Don't weep!" But she was stupefied with grief and hardly heard, much less comprehended His words. Then Jesus moved authoritatively toward the bier, and laying His hand upon it actually stopped the procession, a daring thing to do.

Then His voice, commanding and thrilling out upon the still evening air, startled the crowds, rapt and wondering, as He cried, "Young man, I say unto you, arise!"

That cry, before its echoes were lost in the valleys around Tabor and Little Hermon, was heard in Hades, and called back a spirit from the land of the shadow of death. Before the people's astonished eyes the dead man suddenly sat up and his voice could be heard muttering incoherently. Peering over the edge of the bier, his eyes, framed in the white headcloth still, and expressing successively despair, fear, incredulity and an amazing joy, stared down upon a bewildering scene: the tall Stranger, the thronging crowds, then his mother. Then Jesus took him by the hand, helped him off the now lowered bier, and led him to his mother, whose tears of grief were turned to tears of joy; hysterical, fumbling hands felt their way over her son's face and tried to pull off the headcloth.

Then the two crowds, that following Jesus and that forming the latter part of the funeral procession, merged together and began to move up toward the town, glorifying God and crying, "A great Prophet is risen up among us!" and "God has visited His people again!"

(IV) TEACHING BY PARABLES

THE fame occasioned by this miracle distressed Jesus, in that once again it proceeded from a wrong motive and was based on a false estimate of values. It was the Good News of God that Jesus was so anxious to give the people, not mere physical life or health. He had tried the method of teaching by easily remembered rhymes and precepts. It was now that He decided to try yet another method. Folk might remember a telling image or a dramatic story when precepts were forgotten.

He was once again seated in Peter's boat, preaching to the people massed on either side of the little shelving bay near the warm springs not far from Capernaum. Peter, sitting in the stern of the boat, was caught as in a spell as he listened to Jesus' voice.

"Do you remember," He was saying, "how I once told you, here, that I was so sure of the rapid spread of My Gospel that I likened it to the sowing of seed? I said, 'Once it's sown, you can lean back and watch it grow—it'll spring up inevitably while, day after day, you sleep and rise, and soon you see the results.'"

A dreaming sadness shadowed His face as He continued: "But I soon found that things didn't turn out quite as I had hoped. The fields that then I saw in imagination 'already white to harvest' are still unreaped. Look! There's the sower again, over there on the hillside, at work for next year's harvest. Now watch him closely."

All eyes were turned to that lonely figure on the rising ground behind the shelving shores, all unconscious of his immortality, casting his seed in great circular sweeps of his hand from the seed bag at his waist.

"Do you see how some of the seed falls on the footpath that crosses the field? Now watch. . . . See the birds wheeling round behind him? Ah! Now they are settling on the footpath, as I thought they would, gathering up the seeds. Now the sower is going over some stony ground. Not much is likely to grow there. Too little depth of soil. It will most likely shoot up quickly, but when the hot spring sun gets on the young blades, they'll be scorched and withered, because they'll have no depth of root. There! Did you see that handful flung among the thorns? Next spring, when the thorns come up again, they'll grow much faster than the corn and will stifle it, so that it'll never bear any crop. Nevertheless, *some* does fall on good ground, but even then the yield will vary. Some will show an increase, say thirtyfold, some sixtyfold, some—just a few here and there—may even bear fruit a hundredfold!"

Jesus' eyes searched the crowds on the beaches around Him. Which of them would yield the full harvest? It all depended on how eagerly they were listening and taking it in. So He added, in deeply earnest tones, "Whoever among you has ears to hear with, let him listen carefully. Yes, and always be careful, too, as to *what* he listens to." And with these words His discourse ended. But He looked very sad.

That same day, as evening approached, He suddenly said to His disciples, in a pause of His discourse: "I'm tired. Let's cross over to the other side!" Soon they were sailing, in sweeping tacks from side to side, toward the shadowed brows of the eastern cliffs, beyond which the moon was slowly rising.

As the western shore receded, the disciples, finding themselves alone with Him at last, decided to ask Him a question which had been troubling them all day. "Master, tell us, *why* have You been speaking to the people today in parables?"

As He did not answer at once, Peter added, "You see, we want to know whether it is so that You can give them nice easy little tales while You give *us* the real Secrets of God?"

"Yes," said another, "are You trying to hide the truth from them or—shall we say—wrapping it up in story form because that's all that they can understand?"

This was so near the truth that Jesus paused before replying. Yet, on reflection, He realized that they were utterly mistaken. They actually thought that He had been speaking in parables *so that* the people might be prevented from fully understanding, for fear the truth might be cheapened. He was desperately disappointed and a little on edge.

"So you think," He replied, "that you alone are to have the Secrets of God—and that I am purposely hiding the truth from these . . . 'outsiders,' shall we say, by obscuring it in parabolic form? Why, *of course* that's My intention—to keep My meaning from the mobs! Isn't that exactly what God meant to do when He cried to Isaiah of old:

> *"Go ! Tell this people:—*
>   *'Listen—and go on listening—*
>   *but be careful never to understand. . . .*
>   *Look—and go on looking—*
>   *but make sure you never see.' . . .*
> *Yes, make the minds of these people dull—*
> *make their ears deaf,*
> *and close up their eyes . . .*
>   *lest by any chance their eyes should see,*
>   *and their ears should hear,*
>   *and their minds should understand . . .*
>   *for, if so, their spiritual health might possibly be restored,*
>   *and they would even run the risk of being forgiven. . . .*

"Is the terrific irony of this *really* lost on you? Do you honestly mean to tell Me that you *don't* know why I'm talking to the people in story form, that, in fact, you failed to see the point of this particular parable? If so, how do you think you're going to understand *any* parable?

"Well, then, here's the meaning of *this* one: What the Sower sows is the Message of God. Those who receive the seed are those who hear the Message. As for the seed 'on the footpath,' this represents those who hear, but don't really listen or understand, so that Satan quickly snatches away the Message, *lest they should believe, and so be saved,* you see. In the same way, that 'on the stony ground' represents those who are quick off the mark and accept the Message with enthusiasm. But, having no deep roots, their conversion doesn't last. For directly trouble or persecution comes their way on account of the Message, they immediately fall away. Another group is represented by the seed sown 'among the thorns.' These listen to the Message; but worldly worries and the snares of wealth and all the other passions come in and choke the growth, so that it becomes ineffective and sterile. On the other hand, that 'on the good ground' stands for those who honestly and from their hearts listen to and take in the Message, welcoming it and so bearing fruit, perseveringly; though, as I said, the yield varies with each person—'some thirtyfold, some sixty and some —a hundredfold!' "

As He was speaking, there suddenly shone out from the shore, far over the water, a brightly golden speck of light, as some cottager lighted up before going to bed. The reflection of the light danced in the darkening waters, as the gloaming drew on into night.

"Why," He exclaimed, "look at yonder lamp shining so brightly! Are the cottagers going to put it under a bowl? Or under a bed? But it hasn't gone out. . . . Why, they must have put it on a lampstand— so that everybody in that house may see it and share its light! So don't imagine that when I wrap up My meaning in story form I'm doing it to hide it! I only so do it that it may be the better disclosed.

"But, above all, do be desperately careful *how* you listen; for who-ever grasps but one point is already on the way to grasping more; whereas whoever fails to get hold of one thought will inevitably lose the next that follows as well. So, again, I say: whoever has ears to hear with, let him listen carefully!' "

(V) STORM AND CALM

1. *The Sea*

By now night had fallen, and they were out in the mid-sea reaches of the Lake. Jesus had wearily settled Himself down on a cushion that lay in the stern of Peter's boat, the rise and fall of the lengthening swell lulling Him to oblivion. The disciples glanced at Him lying there. He was fast asleep. They were careful not to awaken Him, sensing His need of rest. The boat rose and fell in the swell as the long smooth rollers bore down on them from the north. Soon their billowing undulations were perceptibly gathering in range and power. The air grew suddenly chill, as it blew off Hermon's icy heights and whistled through the mountain gullies till it whipped the waves into frenzy. The mountain gorges acted as funnels for the snow-chilled air from the whole Lebanon range, which blew down the Jordan vale, especially at sundown, to fill the vacuum caused by the rising exhala-tions of the day's torrid heat. There was hardly time in which to lower the sails before the full fury of the tempest, howling through the gorges, tossed the little boat from crest to trough till the waves were not only breaking over the boat but beginning to fill it up.

The disciples, trembling with fear, looked at Jesus, sleeping through it all. How tired He must have been! It did not come easily to Peter to admit himself beaten in a storm on the Lake. Especially hard was it to call upon a landsman for help. But, as he glanced once more at Jesus he knew that their only hope lay in Him—He had such strange powers.

"Master!" they called. But there was no response. Yet another huge wave broke over the ship with sickening impact.

"*Master!*" they cried, several of them together, almost into His ear. As He at length roused Himself, Peter shrieked, impulsively, "Don't You care if we drown?"

And He arose, with a slow, God-like majesty and an immense calm, till, erect in all that furious, lashing rain and wind, His garments clinging, slowly His arm was raised and He rebuked the winds and the raging of the sea, saying, "Peace! Be still!"

And the waves miraculously sank, the wind ceased to blow, a sudden silence fell upon the waters, and there was a great calm. . . . The disciples shrank back into themselves as they witnessed this overwhelming proof of His power and majesty. A *Man?*

Seeing them so frightened, He smiled, saying, "Why are you all so scared? Where is your faith? O you 'Little Faiths!' "

But they could not smile back; and the rest of the voyage was sailed in silence, while the still, unruffled night-bound waters, beginning now to be dimly burnished by the light of the moon, now rising behind the yet visible wrack of the storm, were unstirred by even the laziest swell, the sails hanging limply from the mast. And Jesus, there in the stern, seemed to that clustered, awestruck group in the prow, as remote as the stars that began to shine out from the clearing sky.

2. *The Mind*

The disciples were yet trembling with fear. They had been face to face with nature in her most terrifying and sublime mood, and had witnessed their Master's mastery over all elemental forces. Little did they realize that they were now to experience an even stranger and more sublime event, when a far more appalling cosmic storm of the spirit would be in turn mastered by Him Who was Lord not only of earth, but of Heaven and Hell also.

All unknown to the occupants of the shoreward-drifting boat, a man, gigantic in stature, was crouching stark-naked in a rock tomb on the mountainside, watching, in the slowly brightening moonlight, the approaching ships, the running down and furling of the sails, the prows cleaving smoothly through the shallowing water, the huddling group, the white-robed Figure in the stern. Echoes of a mighty cry had come to him from out the rain-lashed darkness of the Lake, followed by a sudden stilling of the storm. Whose voice had it been? Someone even stronger than he, come to master him? As the boats grated on the shingle, far down below him, he began to clamber precipitously down the steeps, intent on challenging these intruders into his domain. Had they not, often, been sent to capture him? Had they not clamped the cold, heavy fetters upon him, chained him to a ring in the rock face, thinking that iron could master him? But he had shown them his strength, and only sundered fetters and severed chains had remained as witnesses of his demonic power, while far above, he had watched and yelled defiance at them all, as they cowered to examine the shattered discards of his dominion.

The disciples had hardly drawn up the boats on the beach before the maniac with a bloodcurdling yell rushed down the steeps and on to the foreshore. Their hearts almost stopped beating from sudden fear and shock. But Jesus acted with incredible swiftness. His alert reaction to that avalanche of yells and waving limbs was magnificently decisive.

His voice once more thundered forth upon the still night air. "Come out of the man, O foul spirit!"

The man flung himself down prostrate before Jesus, crying forlornly, "Jesus, O Son of God most high, what are You going to do with us? By God, I adjure You, don't torture us! Have You come here to torment us . . . *before the time?*"

Jesus saw that fear possessed him utterly—fear of captivity, fear of Himself, fear of the devils which he believed possessed him, fear of the Divine Avenger, Who one day would consign him, devils and all, to everlasting torment. There could be only one way of healing such a case—for Jesus' first commanded exorcism had not yet cast out the fear in the man's soul. He sought for a point of contact with the man's individual personality, something that would focus his mind and draw it away from the devil fixation to a return of personal consciousness.

"Tell Me, what is your name?" He asked.

But this man's true self was hidden, trampled into unrecognizable shape by a complex of multiple consciousness. He could only answer, "My name is—Legion!" a belief owing its origin to the Roman Legion, six thousand of them when at full strength, who often encamped upon the crest of this very mountain. In the man's imagination, he was possessed by an army of evil spirits—a strong man armed, indeed. But a stronger than he had come upon him, and his realization of Jesus' strength only brought more fear to confront him. He foresaw Jesus' conquest of the devils and, in consequence, an even ghastlier fate awaiting himself. By now he had led the way, backing from Jesus, to the top of the hill. As he gained the summit, he flung himself once more before Jesus, begging Him not to send the devils "out of the country, out of earth itself, and down into the abyss." He looked over the cliff edge at the leaden waters, and recalled the terrors of the recent storm: how he had clung in desperate strength to the cave walls as he had watched the great piled-up thunderclouds rolling down from the north, blotting out the low-set dayfall, and bringing with them the tempest of wind and rain, the flashing of lightning and the Olympian laughter of the thunder roll. He had watched the sea being tossed up by a waterspout and whirled into an eddying funnel of foam, churning and sucking and hissing, as if the bottomless pit had suddenly opened up before him and all the foul obscenities of darkness were disgorged and vomited up. Then had followed the sudden calm; the sealing of the waters over that dread abyss, sucking down all those living, lashing horrors into the lightless depths of Hell.

Just as the man's demented imagination had seen Hell opened in the storm, and all the scaly horrors of the seabed in the churning waves, even so had Jesus seen, in the man's mind, the foul obscenities of the spirit world rising to view and writhing in torment before Him. Soon they, too, would be cast into the abyss bound, drowned and sealed up forever.

Then it was that the demoniac suddenly saw a huge herd of swine feeding in the now clear moonlight, rooting, jostling, squealing. To his Jewish mind these swine were unclean, foul, forbidden. They were gradually moving nearer toward the cliff face, which fell away so steeply that the eye could not see any of the actual declivity but saw beyond the sheer edge of the colossal drop only the moonlit waves a mile or more out to sea.

Then it was that a solution, a release, opened up before the madman. If only he could persuade Jesus to send the devils out of him and into the swine, then he himself would be saved and the devils destroyed. So he fell on his knees before Jesus, imploring Him, "Send us into the swine! Into the swine!"

Jesus saw that the man's cure was being gradually effected. Already the demoniac realized that the will of Jesus was stronger than even all the devils within him. There was also a growing perception of his own personality, as distinct from those of the devils who he imagined possessed him.

Jesus knew that there was in fact but one cause of the man's dementia—fear. But He also knew that if only the man could be persuaded that the devils had really left him, he might be cured permanently. So He silently nodded assent to the man's entreaty.

At once the maniac started up, rushed toward the herd, waving his arms wildly, and shrieking, "We are coming into you—into you!"

There was a scuttling and wheeling of swine, a gathering, hurtling, headlong stampede, a riot of rending screams blent with maniacal laughter, a man brought to a sudden halt at a precipice—staring down into space, and a clean-swept mountain side, gashed with scores, each one a black line in the shade of the moonlight, as if some huge clawing beast had spread its talons in a wild slide over the cliff edge. And then, as the disciples listened breathlessly, came from far out of sight, away below, a ghastly cacophony of bestial, choking cries and a faint sound of invisible splashes and watery hisses—then silence.

As for the maniac, there before him as he peered over the precipice, was proof, glorious and incontrovertible, of the reality of his own cure. Had not the waters closed over the shrieking devils and sealed them up forever? The spell was broken, and he was delivered. In unutterable relief, he turned and flung himself upon the ground before his Deliverer, a sane man again. Someone covered him with a cloak, and Jesus put His arm around him in comforting strength.

Then Peter, who especially loathed swine, as he thought a good Jew should, felt deep down within himself a strange scruple about the destruction of the herd. He tried to argue with himself by asserting his Scriptural prejudice against swine. "Master . . . the swine perished, didn't they, because the same devils that were in the man entered into them?"

Jesus considered this for a moment, and nodded silently.

For, He reflected, Peter was in a sense perfectly right. They *were* the same devils: fear, panic, terror. But Peter was busy nodding his head sagely. The beasts were unclean. The Scriptures said so. They were fit only for the abyss.

Meanwhile, down there in the moonlit walled city of Gerasa, about a mile away, the sleepless and the restless were stirred to sudden apprehension as, from afar, came a bloodcurdling chorus of bestial cries that rent the still night air and was followed by a complete silence. Soon those living near the northern city walls heard a cry from without, a thunderous drumming on the barred gates, and then a stumbling running along the quiet streets till it died away into the distance. The breathless swineherd who had watched the swine's destruction was soon beating upon the shuttered doors of his master's house and telling his terrible tale to an outraged audience.

The dawn was just breaking as the furious citizens, led by the herdsman and the angry owner of the swine, were streaming through the gates on their way up the mountain road toward the scene of the tragedy. The herdsman was excited with his new-found importance. "It was up there. Can you see the scarred earth on that high slope? It was there they rushed down. Not one escaped. They were on that rounded hill before the devils entered into them. Look, you can still see their carcasses floating in the middle of the Lake. I was watching the swine, when I saw the madman near a tall Man that seemed quite unafraid of him. I heard the maniac beseech the Man not to send the devils out of him and into the abyss, but into the swine instead. And He sent them; and they all shrieked and stampeded and perished. Of course He may have gone by now. He was just beyond that boulder over there. We shall know in a moment. No. He's still there! Yes, the madman too—looking quite sane! Do you think the Prophet will run when He sees us coming?"

But there was no sign of any attempt to escape, though the disciples for a moment started away in fear. But they held their ground when they saw Jesus so calm and unruffled. The men from the city began to be a little uneasy. These were uncanny regions in more senses than one.

Then one more coarse than the rest spoke up. "Clear out, You! We don't want You here. Get back where You belong—over the other side of the Lake, I suppose."

Jesus eyed the boorish face gravely, till the speaker's eyes fell and he began to back hastily away. Another voice cried out, "There were two thousand swine in the herd. What do You mean by destroying other people's property?"

Jesus, without a word, turned and walked calmly down the mountain path, followed by the former madman, and at a greater distance by the disciples and the crowd, more frightened than angry as they beheld the maniac looking sane and the tall Prophet who had cured him.

The former madman clung desperately to Jesus' arm, crying out, "Don't leave me alone with them! Take me with You! They've tormented me so often—oh, don't leave me!"

But Jesus, by now on the shore, bade the disciples, by a gesture, launch the boats, at the same time detaching Himself from the former madman's clutch. He turned to address him.

"You are Mine, forever! You are safe now, for all Eternity. I have a work for you to do—for Me. Look at those crowds! No longer be afraid of them. There must be some friends among them who will care for you. Go home with them; they'll look after you. And tell them, and all Decapolis, what great things God has done for you—how He had mercy on you and made you whole."

Jesus could not take him over to the other side of the Lake. To do so might be once again to jeopardize His own chance of converting the people through His Teaching, rather than through His Miracles. But here in Decapolis it was different. It was not in Herod's territory. He Himself was not likely to be preaching here in any case. It was for Him only an area of escape and rest, to be sought for its lonely reaches, not for its cities. So, as the man bowed his head in silence, Jesus turned away (but there were tears in His eyes) and embarked; and the boats drifted out to sea and the sails were slowly hoisted, and the crowds moved off. But the man would not move. His eyes gazed out over the level waters at those receding boats now becoming but black dots and brown wings against the far, misty horizon . . . till the Beloved Figure in the stern was one with the boat, and the boat was at last lost in the level shimmer of haze. For a long time he stood there, upon the lonely shore. Then long after all trace of the boat was lost, he turned away with a deep sigh, but with a new light of sane, purposeful resolution shining in his eyes, and moved up the hill path inland.

He had a task to carry out for his Lord. He would accomplish it to the full. So it happened that when next Jesus visited the regions of Decapolis He had not only one firm friend, but many supporters to welcome Him.

(VI) JAIRUS' DAUGHTER AND THE
SUFFERING WOMAN

IT was full morning when Jesus and His disciples arrived back on the other side of the Lake.

News of His return was soon flashed round the town and reached two homes. One was that of Jairus, the chief Ruler of the Synagogue. He was in dire trouble, and Jesus could not be found. His only daughter—just at the age when a Jewish girl said good-bye to her childhood—lay dying. "Did someone say Jesus had returned?" And the father was out of the house and rushing toward the shore.

Making his way through the surging crowds he at last saw the Master, and falling down at His feet besought Him greatly, "My little daughter is even now at the point of death—she may be now dead—but come with me, and lay Your hands upon her, and I know she'll recover and live!"

Tired as He was, how could Jesus resist such an appeal? So He arose from where He was seated teaching, and at once went with Jairus. They had some little distance to go and the multitude followed and thronged Him, being especially excited at the expected cure of the child of so well known a man as Jairus. In the midst of the throng about Jesus was a woman striving to get near enough to Him to touch His garment. For she said within herself, "If only I can just touch His clothes, I know I shall get well." At length she just managed to reach out her hand and touch for a brief moment the border frieze of His outer robe of blue cloth.

Two things happened immediately. She felt in her body that her sufferings were at an end, and Jesus knew that power had somehow gone out of Him. He at once stopped dead in His tracks and turning about He asked, "Who has touched Me?"

"Who touched You?" the disciples laughed back. "Why, everybody's touching You! And then You ask, 'Who touched Me?'!"

But He continued to stare about Him to find out, if He could, who had touched Him, Jairus all the while in an agony of controlled impatience. Then the woman, when she saw Jesus' eyes upon her, came shyly forward, very frightened and trembling, and falling down at His feet told Jesus what she had done. Then He replied, "My daughter, your splendid faith has made you well. Go in peace, and from now on be free of your complaint."

Peter afterward heard from his wife all the gossipy details of her illness as told by the woman herself. "My dear, twelve years I'd suffered—no one knows what I've gone through, nor the number of doctors I've been to, nor the money I've spent—every penny I had went on it, and all to no good. I wasn't a whit better—worse if anything. . . ." Mark was very interested when Peter told him. He felt he could quite see the woman—a real character.

At last the interruption was over and Jesus and those vast crowds surged slowly forward once more. Jairus wished those hordes elsewhere. They would have moved so much more quickly had the streets been clear. He thought of his wife, saying to herself, "How terribly long he is fetching the Prophet!" Could he have seen, she was at that very moment bending over the prostrate form of her little daughter, lying so still upon the bed. She was listening and, in terror, feeling . . . but no rise or fall stirred the white coverlet on the still breast. She was dead . . . and a smouldering, irrational resentment inflamed the mother's heart against her husband. Had he not been so keen to fetch the Prophet, he need never have been away when his daughter died. And still he had not come. Indeed, so long a time had by now elapsed since the child's death that the mourners were already arriving, relatives and friends swelling the growing crowd about the Ruler's home. Even the professional flute players had found out about the tragic death in this important household, and were already at the door with the wailing women who accompanied them in funeral processions. The agonized mother sent out a messenger with a bitter, satiric message for Jairus. Jesus saw the servant shouldering his way through the press toward his master, and the dreaded words fell from his lips: "Sir, your daughter is dead. I am also to add: 'Why trouble the Teacher any further?' "

The grave irony was not lost on Jairus in this, the most bitter moment of his life. He looked at Jesus waiting there. Yes. His wife had been right. Why trouble Him any "further"—whether in time or space? There was an illimitable distance separating the soul of his little child from any man still treading earth. Whether he were Prophet or charlatan no longer mattered. Jairus closed his eyes in an agony of despair.

But Jesus touched his shoulder, and His voice was very low. He could hardly speak for emotion.

"Don't be afraid. Just go on believing."

He made a quick decision. The impeding crowds must leave Him. Then He beckoned to Peter and the sons of Zebedee and went forward with all speed, being now not far from the house.

As they turned the corner of a street the raucous noise of wailing and the shrill piping of the flutes could be heard. How He hated all this morbid fuss, this loathsome obsession with bereavement! Wherever the carcass was, there were always the vultures gathered together.

"Give place!" He shouted abruptly. "What do you want to make all this noise and uproar for?" The caterwauling ceased of a sudden and the people turned to stare at the newcomer. "Clear out, all of you!" He cried. He was terribly angry. Peter had never seen Him look more angry—not even on that day when He cleared the dealers out of the Temple. But His voice when next He spoke was quiet and gentle. "She is not dead . . . only asleep."

A shout of ribald laughter greeted the repetition of this by those who had overheard it. Jesus in reply turned everybody out of the house, relatives, servants and all. And taking the child's father and mother, He went into the room of death, followed by His three disciples. There lay the white body and the closed eyes . . . so like sleep. He bent over the bed, took the frail hand, so cold and limp, within His own strong grasp; and there in that shadowed room, with only believers about Him (for by now the poor mother had let slip all her fretfulness) He gathered up strength in silent prayer. Then He spoke but two words, soft syllables that Peter never forgot.

"Talitha kumi!" ("Little girlie, rise up!")

And, wonder of wonders, the little girl stirred, rose, stretched, opened her eyes and smiled at Him, and then gravely got off the bed— still hand in hand with Jesus and He led her to her mother.

"Please don't tell anyone about this," He begged them earnestly. "Give her something to eat," He added with practical sympathy.

There were tears in Peter's eyes. He could not repress his emotions. "Talitha" meant "Little lamb" and Isaiah's words came into his mind: *He shall gather the lambs with His arm. . . .* Would death be like this? A sleep and an awakening . . . to find Jesus bending over one and one's hand in His? And would one rise, still hand in hand with Him—and walk into the sunlit glory of the Resurrection?

(VII) REJECTION AT NAZARETH

ONE day the mother of Jesus was amazed to see Him outside the door of His Nazareth home with a company of His friends and smilingly bringing them all inside the living room, to Mary's embarrassment. She was overjoyed to see Him, but the presence of these—"disciples" did they call them?—betokened no return home for good, such as she had so longed for. Well, she must make the best of it. It was good to have Him home once more, even if it were only for a flying visit, as He made clear. His brothers, when they came in, looked wryly at Him and went quickly out again. Mary's heart was ill at ease. She felt once again the pricking of the sword.

As the Nazarenes went to the Synagogue on the next Sabbath day, there was but one subject of conversation among them. Jesus, the carpenter, was actually going to preach today.

So here He was, back again in the Synagogue where He had, as a

Boy, learned to love the Scriptures and to pray to His Father. But this time He was to preach, not to listen. He glanced around at the congregation. Familiar faces were there, grown a little older, and looking more critically at Him than of old. The attendant was handing Him the roll of the Prophet Isaiah. He unfolded it and chose His text, His favourite passage, reading it first in the original Hebrew, and then freely paraphrasing it in Aramaic to bring out the full sense, as was customary. His voice carried to the ends of the galleries.

> *The Spirit of the Lord inspires Me!—for He has consecrated Me*
> *to proclaim the Glad Tidings to the wretched,*
> *to heal the broken-hearted,*
> *to proclaim release for all prisoners,*
> *to set free the oppressed,*
> *and to announce the Acceptable Year of the Lord!*

He had been about to read the next sentence but suddenly forbore. Then, folding up the roll, He handed it back to the attendant and sat down.

The eyes of everyone in the Synagogue were fixed upon Him, as they sat back to listen intently. How would He open his address? They had expected thrills, but never such a shock, such a thrill, as He achieved in His superb opening sentence.

"Today," He began, *"today* is this Scripture fulfilled in your own hearing!"

They were a little slow to infer the full implications of that tremendous claim. But they realized that He was saying something terrific. Nevertheless, one couldn't deny His charm. There was power and personal magnetism in His bearing and voice, a commanding authority in His gestures, which made you listen, whether you liked it or not. He could certainly talk.

But where on earth had He learned Hebrew? And where had He picked up all this wisdom and oratory? Above all, what did His claim mean? For by now they were beginning to realize the astounding role He was assuming, there in the Synagogue. Their wonder increased all the more when they heard Him assert that to raise a soul from spiritual death was far more important than to raise a child from physical death, as He had done at Capernaum. ("So that story was true, then . . . or so He claimed for Himself. If so, what was the significance of His being able thus to perform such miracles? Did it mean . . . ?")

A sense almost of panic stole over His listeners. They found themselves shrinking from so towering a personality. And with the advent of fear came the sharp reaction of dislike, even of revulsion. Who was He to set Himself up above His betters? Was He not only Jesus the carpenter—the Son of Mary (up there in the women's gallery), the Brother of James and Joseph, and Simon and Judas, over there? "Yes, and we know the sisters too. Nothing we don't know about the whole lot of them." They were deeply offended at Him.

Jesus quickly sensed their disapproval. "I know what you are thinking," He countered, "but don't forget the proverb, 'Familiarity breeds contempt.' After all, a Prophet is not entirely destitute of respect, save, of course, in His own country, and among His own relations, and in His own home. . . ."

These bitter words were heard in an appalled silence. James was thunderstruck and furious, and glanced up to see his mother cowering as if struck. A moment after she was sobbing into her veils, bowed and broken. What could she do to reconcile her Firstborn with her other sons? She had meant it rightly when she had tried to dissuade Him from continuing His Mission. Who could have foreseen this white-hot eruption of the fires deep within His soul? She could not guess that the measure of both His loyalty to His Mission and of His love for her was to be found in this very bitterness of heart.

The crowded congregation was shocked and angered. Who was He thus to sneer at His own town, and at His own folk and friends? Once again He sensed their thoughts.

"No doubt you are in turn applying to Me yet another proverb: 'Physician, heal thyself!' You are thinking: 'We've heard a lot about Your fine doings in Capernaum and elsewhere; but let *us*, here, have a chance of seeing something of Your powers—if these stories be true.' Maybe you've heard rumours of a widow's son raised from the dead at Nain, or of some leper healed at Chorazin. Well, there were many widows in Israel in the days of Elijah—poor widows too—when no rain fell for three and a half years, with a consequent famine over all the land. Yet to not one of *them* was Elijah sent, but only to a widow

living at Sarepta, not far from Sidon. You see, it was not only Israelites who were favoured. . . . Again, there were many lepers in Israel
in the time of his successor, Elisha; yet none of *them* did the Prophet
cleanse: only Naaman, another Syrian!"

This angry, sweeping universalism, almost amounting to pro-Gen-
tile propaganda, stung that massed crowd into fury. Jesus faced them
for a moment in challenging defiance, well knowing that the sole reason why He had never felt able to perform any miracle in Nazareth
was due not to absence of need or to unwillingness on His part, but
to the people's lack of faith in Him, making release of power all but
impossible. Save to heal a few sick folk, He had a sense almost of
impotence in Nazareth. The mighty works that the people demanded
as a sign of His status could not be vouchsafed to a mob of sceptics.

The crowd, in turn, faced Him—this impostor, this upstart brag-
gart, this traitor to Israel, with all His sarcastic talk about the town not
being good enough for Him, and all this ranting about God's choosing
other races. Besides, deep down in their hearts was the gnawing, blind
fear of the abnormal and supernatural. Then the tension broke, the
mob surged suddenly forward, seized Him, dragged Him out of the
Synagogue, and, all restraint lost, hustled Him up the hill behind the
Synagogue, someone having shouted, "Let's throw Him over the cliff
top onto the refuse tip!"

The disciples, there on the edge of the crowd, powerless to help,
and, to speak truth, terrified to reveal themselves, never knew exactly
what did happen. One moment it had seemed that nothing could have
prevented His death. The next, they saw Him walking in unhurried
majesty through the midst of the crowd, that parted before Him and
stood as if petrified while He moved away, followed by the disciples
in hastening fear. . . . His "hour was not yet come." That was all He
would say about it. . . .

So it was that Jesus for the last time trod the hillside above His
home town, the dreaming place of His Childhood, the solace of those
seemingly interminable eighteen years of waiting. As for the Nazarenes, returning uneasily to their homes, their Saviour had passed
through the midst of them and gone His way, never to return.

Back there in Nazareth, Mary crept about trying to avoid avoiding
eyes, drawing her widow's veils ever closer about her, and growing

visibly older and more frail every day. She would repeat over and over again: *God be gracious to Thee, My Son. . . .* and *Remember the Lord Thy God, that the avengers of blood destroy not any more, lest they destroy my Son.*

(VIII) A VISIT TO JERUSALEM

SOON after this, Jesus, unaccompanied by His disciples, went up to Jerusalem to the feast of Purim, about a month before the Passover. He stayed, as usual, with His young friend John. He deeply loved the poetic, mystically inclined youth. His training at the school of the philosopher Philo in Alexandria had fitted him to understand Jesus better than most of the disciples. Also he was highly respected in Jerusalem, being an aristocrat and well known to many of the Sadducees and especially to Annas and Caiaphas. But his friendship for Jesus had strained these ties. Nevertheless, he always welcomed the Master to his home whenever He was in the City.

One Sabbath morning Jesus, with John, was passing by the Baths of Bethzatha—one for the people to bathe in and another for the washing of sheep—when they decided to go inside, and pass through them on their way to the Temple.

John pointed out to Jesus the five porches surrounding the circular bath, in which lay many invalids and lame folk—beggars, nearly all of them—who existed mainly on the charity of passers-by. They were waiting, explained John, for the bubbling up of a spring which intermittently broke and "troubled the water." The popular belief was that an Angel descended into the bath at these times, and it was believed that whichever invalid stepped in first after the "troubling" began, would be healed. Evidently the spring was of great therapeutic repute.

As they passed along John pointed out to Jesus one particular beggar, lying inertly on his mat, his head sunk down on his breast in a torpor of despair, save when his eyes languidly lifted to watch some possible sympathizer from among the visitors to the Baths.

"He's a queer old fellow. He's lain here so long that he's all but lost the use of his limbs, always the same and always telling the same tale. People say he's been here for thirty-eight years now. He tells

everybody that he's always the unlucky one. He can never manage to
get first into the water when the spring bubbles up. No one ever
gives *him* a hand; it's always such a mad scramble, and he gets left
behind every time. Probably he scrapes a bare existence from the charity of the Pilgrims at festival times through his one set story. He'll tell
it You if You ask him."

Jesus eyed the man with a quizzical look in which tender compassion and a kindly humour were blended. He moved over toward him,
and His eyes were twinkling and a slight smile played over His mouth.
"Do you *really* want to get well?"

The man eyed Jesus suspiciously, then launched into his set piece.
"Sir, I have nobody to carry *me* into the pool when the water bubbles
up, and while I am doing my best to get there by myself, somebody
else always gets there before me."

Jesus and John exchanged smiles. But now the Master was determined to act; to break through this vicious circle of complacent frustration—even though it meant depriving the sufferer of his one luxury, the opportunity for exhibitionist self-pity.

The voice of Jesus rang out sharply. "Get up! *Get up!* Now lift
your mat! Now walk away!"

The astonished invalid looked at Jesus in awe and fear. No charity
forthcoming from Him, evidently . . . and He looked as if He meant
business. To his own intense surprise he found himself trying to obey
Him—*and succeeding!* He managed to struggle to his feet, found he
could stand, grabbed his mat and was off and out of sight, amid the
startled astonishment of the other beggars grouped there.

Once outside the Baths, he shambled hurriedly down the narrow
streets carrying his mat. The exercise of his limbs came strangely to
him, and the future use of them suddenly became an urgent problem.
He realized that he would be forced to find work—none too easy a
task for an elderly man after thirty-eight years of idleness. As he
shuffled somewhat ruefully along he felt scared at being forced to face
life anew so suddenly.

Some Pharisees, returning from attendance in the Temple, were
coming toward him down the street. They stopped and pointed, scandalized. The Sabbath day—and here was a man actually daring to

arry his mat! This sort of thing must be stopped at once. They hur-
ied across the street and accosted the delinquent.

"Don't you know it's the Sabbath?" they cried. "You've no right
o be carrying your mat!"

"Don't blame me," answered the man, furious to have this extra
worry on top of all his others. "If you want to blame anybody, blame
he Man Who told me to take up my mat and clear out."

There was no gratitude on the man's part for having been healed,
and no wonder on the part of the Pharisees, who evidently knew him
of old, at his cure. They did not ask, "Who was it who cured you?"
but instead, "Well, who was it, then, who dared to tell you to carry
our mat?"

"I haven't the faintest idea," snapped the man. There the matter
might have ended and the man have shuffled out of sight forever, had
not Jesus happened to catch sight of him later in the Temple, whither
he man had gone in order formally to legalize his cure. The Master,
in His radiantly friendly way, immediately moved over to him.

"Well, you're splendidly fit and strong now, but there are worse
hings than mere bodily infirmity. See then that you make the best
use of your remaining years, lest an even more pitiable fate befall
ou!"

The man stared back, unanswering. So *this* was the Stranger who
had caused all the bother—so annoyingly vital and energetic and enthusiastic, interfering in other people's business, and getting honest,
innocent persons into trouble. Without a word he turned on his heel,
and went straight to the headquarters of the Pharisees, and there made
formal charge.

"I want to make a statement. Some of your members blamed *me*
or carrying a mat on the Sabbath day. I told them not to blame *me*,
but the Person Who told me to do it. When they asked me Who He
was, I said I didn't know; nor did I, for the Man had slipped off—and
o had I, for that matter. Anyway, I've just seen Him, now, only a few
seconds ago. He's in the Temple at this very moment. I'll take you
o Him!"

They soon found Him, and charged Him with Sabbath breaking.
His answer was profound beyond all fathoming. Had not God cried:

I will work, and who shall stop Me? So He, in God's name, cried, "My Father does not stop working because it's the Sabbath—nor will I!"

Their conception of the Sabbath rest was not only founded on a wrong idea of the Sabbath, but still more basically upon a false notion of rest. For true rest implies unimpeded activity in obedience to the highest law of one's nature. There should be nothing negative about the Sabbath. It was the day when true religion should get its fullest opportunities, when God's work should be most fully done.

The Jews were livid at His answer, mainly because it was in turn so unanswerable. He added, "In any case, none of you honestly and fully obeys the Law. Now, tell Me—why do you want to kill Me?"

They laughed at Him. "You're mad! Whoever thinks *You* important enough to kill?"

"Well, I've only just performed one good deed on the Sabbath, and yet every one of you is staggered by it. If the rites of worship can be observed on the Sabbath so that the Law can be obeyed, why on earth are you so furious with Me for healing a man on the Sabbath? For goodness' sake, give over judging by appearances and drop all this shallow thinking. Judge justly. Get down to the truth!"

After this, it was genuinely unsafe for Jesus to remain in Judaea, because it was nothing less than the truth that the Jews *were* trying to kill Him. So He went back again to Galilee.

(IX) JESUS AND JOHN'S DISCIPLES

MEANWHILE, in the castle of Machaerus, on its precipices thousand of feet above the Dead Sea, John the Iron-Hearted languished in the dungeon hollowed out of the rock. The fetters were not only enchaining his body; they had begun to constrict the free range of his imagination—even of his hopes. The cruelties of long imprisonment had begun to sap his tremendous vitality. He had always been so free, living in sight of the stars and in company with the great hills. But now the constant immurement had dimmed his eagle eye and his soul's muscles were beginning to atrophy.

At last a terrible doubt uprose and confronted him there in that darkness. Had his intuition been correct? Had he been truly God inspired in proclaiming Jesus as the Messiah? Or was he mistaken in all his hopes, in all his work, so that not even the consolation of a task fulfilled could be his?

Only rumours reached him of the happenings in far-off Galilee; rumours brought to him by those few disciples who had not yet left him for Jesus—or from fear of being associated with so notorious a prisoner. . . . They had been doubtful themselves of Jesus. What had He done? He had certainly defied the Priests, but there had been no challenge to, or even condemnation of, the hated Roman rule. John recalled the convictions burning within him when he had proclaimed Jesus—the anticlimax by Aenon's Springs; the lack of authenticating signs since then.

For what were the sure signs? What had he seen in prophetic vision there by Jordan's banks? A Man of Spirit and of Fire: a Being through Whom blew the winds of Heaven, fanning the flames that should set fire to the earth. Or, to vary the metaphor, a Figure, fan in hand, astride the threshing floor of the world's values, thoroughly cleansing it and gathering the wheat into His garner, and, like Elijah of old, calling down fire from Heaven to burn up the chaff with unquenchable flames. Another vision he remembered, of One wielding a great axe, hewing down the unfruitful trees, lopping the high ones of stature and casting them into the fire. Always the fire, the fan and the axe.

But now where were the axe, the fan and the fire? Had he, John, the successor to Elijah, proclaimed a dreamer, a weakling—yet another Pretender to Israel's Throne? There was the possibility that Jesus was not that kind of Messiah at all, but the Suffering Servant of the Unknown Prophet, the Lamb of God, dying that Israel might live, even as he, John, had once dreamed. But even this image was assailed by the reports of the conviviality of Jesus. Was He not called "a glutton and a drunkard"? John just could not make it all fit in. He must have his doubts set at rest.

He turned to his disciples: "Go at once into Galilee. Find Jesus, wherever He is, say I sent you, and ask Him, 'Are You the Messiah—or not?'" And with a gesture of dismissal, the two disciples were sent on their mission.

They eventually found Jesus at a hill village to the southwest of the

Lake. He was thronged, as usual, by an enormous crowd of people consisting largely of the sick and demented. Awkwardly they approached Jesus and plunged at once into the darkness and deeps of John's terrible doubts.

"Our Master, John the Baptist, has sent us here to ask You a question. Are You the One that should come? Or are we to look for another?"

Jesus made no immediate reply. For a moment or two the shock was almost more than He could bear. The one man on earth, whom, more than any other man living, He admired, was disappointed in Him. The gulf, so vast as to be almost unbridgeable, between the very greatest of the Prophets of the old dispensation and even the humblest enthusiast of the new way of love, yawned before Him in all its stark horror. And, meanwhile, here were the crowds, hearing that John doubted Jesus, thus confirming the misgivings of the Zealots—the party most dangerous to Jesus' ideals. What could He answer? To say, openly, "I am the Messiah" would vitiate His Mission. Conviction of that great basic fact must come by persuasion, never by force. Self-testimony was worthless. Experience alone could witness to truth. So it was that He was once again thrown back upon the great Prophecy of Isaiah: as before in the Wilderness and again at Nazareth. God had called Him not to overawe by signs, nor to command great armies in the hour of victory, but to go about doing good, saving souls, revealing the love of God for men. Not in a literal sense had the Prophet prophesied of Him that He would *bring out the prisoners from the dungeon and them that sit in darkness from the prisons.* If John would be sure of Him he must know something of His work of grace, of the radiant faces about Him, of His way of love. So He could make no immediate answer. That could only come by way of witness. Silently, therefore, He quietly went on with His work of healing and forgiveness, and at last the day neared its end and His work was done for the moment. The disciples of John were now equipped to bear personal testimony to Him. He could now reply to them in the only way in which true reply could be made.

"Go your way now, and tell John what you have now seen and heard for yourselves—how I am indeed fulfilling the Messianic Prophecies of Isaiah: for *the eyes of the blind see, the lame man leaps as an hart, the lepers are cleansed, the dead are raised to life again,* and, above all, *the poor have the Glad Tidings preached to them!* And you might add just this: Blessed is anyone who is not ashamed of *anything* about Me. . . ."

And with that, the two disciples of John departed and were soon lost to sight, speeding across the Plain. It looked to the crowd as if John were at last turning against Jesus; and thereby the value of John's initial testimony would be more than lost in the reaction. Yet so great was His magnanimity that Jesus chose this very moment in which to defend John and praise him up to the skies. It would have been so fatally easy for Jesus to drop a hint of John's failing powers, of his pathetic loss of faith—and then His own Self-esteem would have been reinstated and the doubts of the listeners put to rest in a revived enthusiasm for Jesus at John's expense. But Jesus was too big for this kind of petty fractiousness. He remembered how great John had been when, in his turn, it would have been so easy for him to disparage his ascending Successor.

Besides, had John really doubted? If so, how could he have expected *Jesus* to give a satisfying answer? Even in his seeming doubts he knew that Jesus alone could resolve them; that though Jesus' credentials were seemingly suspect, yet Jesus alone could vouch for those credentials!

Jesus sensed all this, even before John's messengers had passed out of sight. And as the torrent of eulogy poured from His heart, His disciples not only saw to the full the glory of John, but also something of the infinitely greater glory of Jesus. He troubled not to defend Himself. Instead, He defended the doubter from his doubt. And never in all the world's long history was a friend better defended. That John could doubt Jesus was answered by the affirmation that Jesus could never doubt John.

"Tell Me," He cried to the crowds, "what did you go all the way into the Wilderness to gaze at?"

Jesus produced a coin of Herod Antipas. He pointed to the device engraven upon it, showing a reed waving in the wind; a fitting emblem of the weak-willed king.

"Did you expect to see—a reed swayed by the wind?"

There was a roar of laughter at this.

"Come, what *did* you go out to see? A man—" pointing to some courtiers from Herod's palace of Tiberias—"arrayed in soft robes? No. Those who are gorgeously dressed and live in the lap of luxury are to be found *in* royal palaces, not down beneath them in the dungeons. Well, what did you expect to find out there in the Wilderness? A Prophet? Yes, indeed. Only much more than a Prophet; for this is the one of whom it is written: *See! I send My herald before Thy face, to prepare Thy way before Thee!* Yes, I tell you in most solemn truth, there never was a greater man born than John!"

Yet the gulf remained. John, in spite of his solitary grandeur, his heroic stature, was yet "on that side of Jordan," like Moses of old, looking toward the Promised Land but never himself entering in, a Prophet prophesying of the Kingdom but not the Prophet of the Kingdom. So Jesus, loyal to the truth, even in His flaming eulogy of John, could but preach the New Covenant while paying glorious tribute to the greatest figure of the Old.

"And yet," He cried, "even the least *within* the Kingdom of God is greater than the greatest without. It is true that the Law and the Prophets led up to the Kingdom, ending with John, who was the Elijah who was foretold would appear. But from John's time till now the Kingdom—and its Glad Tidings—has been preached and is even in your midst, a reality, working and effective, here and now, in your immediate presence! And the humble and meek, the merciful, the pure in heart, and the peacemakers—these are taking the Kingdom of Heaven by force—the only true force in all the universe—that of love!" He looked round appraisingly at the soldiers and taxgatherers in the crowd, and added, "Yes, and the Kingdom *is* being besieged and battered, and *anyone* presses in, storming it—yes and capturing it!"

On hearing this, all the people—but especially the taxgatherers—upheld the justice of God, being themselves baptized with John's baptism; whereas the Pharisees, through refusing his baptism, had frustrated the purposes of God regarding themselves. Jesus sensed this division among His audience, and with a flash of oratory turned it into a tremendously telling exposure of the implied criticism of both John and Himself. John's heroism and His own quietism were both under fire from critics here in the crowd. Well, He had a word to say regarding these grumbles.

The people were as disdainful of the older, ascetic ideals as of the newer conception of a God of grace.

"As for *this* generation," He cried, "to what can I compare it? I know! They are like children playing in the market place." (His mind retraced the years, and He was back in the market place of Nazareth, playing with John and the other boys at their favourite game of "Weddings and Funerals," Himself the Bridegroom and John the friend of the Bridegroom.) "Sulky children, refusing to join in their companions' games. No wonder the latter cry to them: 'We piped for you, but you would not dance. We sang dirges for you, but you would not weep!' John the Baptist was a stern ascetic, rigorous, severe, a hermit and a recluse; and of *him* they said, 'He's possessed by a devil.' And I, the Son of Man, come now before you as an ordinary man, loving the good things of everyday life, social and convivial, and you exclaim: 'He's nothing but a glutton and a drunkard!' And you add: 'A Friend of taxgatherers and sinners!' as though that were an indictment! Never mind. Wisdom is vindicated by *all* her children."

When John heard the report of his disciples—of the grace of Jesus, of His healing power, of His sublime teaching, of His friendship for the outcast and the friendless—surely his soul crossed the great gulf separating the Old and New Covenants, and entered into the Kingdom, leaving behind forever the hinterland of expectation. For him upon earth there was laid up the doom of death. *For after this cometh Night. But vice shall* not *prevail against wisdom!*

(X) THE ANOINTING OF JESUS

WITHIN hearing of Jesus as He denounced those who "lived delicately, and in Kings' courts," was a notorious character, Mary of Magdala, better known as "The Magdalene." She had also heard that He was indeed the Friend of sinners. Standing there on the far edge of the crowd, by her side a suitor for her favour, she had been attracted almost against her will to this tall, spiritual-looking Prophet of Whom she had heard so much, in a roundabout way, through the family of Chuza having cried His praises throughout the court of Herod. Seeing Him for herself, so truly courteous, yet so strong and compelling, she could not help contrasting Him with the courtiers—effeminate and cossetted—who were always vying with one another for her favours. Jesus had Himself just compared them, damagingly, with the austere Prophet of the Wilderness. She had glanced at the beringed and perfumed young man at her side as Jesus uttered His denunciation, and was amused to see him hasten away in confusion. But Mary had stayed on, and a sudden revulsion of feeling had swept over her even before the terrific laugh at the courtiers' expense had died down. She had been led to compare those loose-living, rich, vicious fools with the virile, clean-limbed Prophet with the beautiful face. He looked so pure, so true. And when the crowds were at last dispersing many wondered at the preoccupied bewilderment with which she wandered listlessly back to her lovely, luxurious house.

And then had come the day of Simon's feast. Simon was a well-known Pharisee of Magdala. Several of his friends had conspired together to test Jesus' reaction to an invitation to dine, this time not with taxgatherers and sinners, but with reputable officers of the Jewish faith. In an informal atmosphere they would be more able to find out exactly what He was after. Of course, there could be no question of making Him in any sense the guest of honour. It was obvious that He would be sufficiently honoured by the invitation.

So, when Jesus entered his house, Simon was studied in his discourtesy. Jesus noticed in amused silence the absence of the customary foot washing, of the kiss of welcome . . . noticed, too, the rush—but thinly disguised by seemingly accidental edgings—to get the best places at table, those near the host. He Himself took the lowest place, at one of the curving ends of the *reclinium,* nearest the entrance to the courtyard. He glanced round at the other guests, rich men, all of them, by the look of them, one or two seemingly relatives of the host so like were they to him in feature. They talked to one another in a strained and uneasy atmosphere, seldom drawing Him into the conversation. That was as well. He preferred to be silent and to watch.

Meanwhile, Mary of Magdala had been through Hell: the Hell of remorse and despair. The memory of the home at Bethany swept over her. She thought of her brother and sister, Lazarus and Martha—her own name never being mentioned between them—of the shame of her sins, of her parents and what they would have thought had they been alive. The infinite difference between the spotless purity of the Prophet and her selfish, shameful lovers; the image of the woman God had intended her to be, of what she might yet be if only His Love could have free play in her soul: these thoughts overwhelmed her in a flood of bitter, cleansing tears. Was it too late? Would He pardon—or condemn? She had not yet realized that it was the certainty, intuitively known, that He would both condemn and yet pardon that called to her irresistibly.

The hours went by in an agony of suspense, while all Magdala wondered at her sudden absence from the streets. Her lovers could make nothing of her. There was one with her now, wondering petulantly at her preoccupation, at the misery in her lovely eyes. Once more he tried to gain her attention by giving her now, instead of later, as he had intended, the costly sealed vase of rare perfume he had procured from Egypt, a thing of beauty, delicately carved from marble quarried at Alabastron on the Nile—a porous stone, through which the scent emitted its fragrance, the seal being left intact, lasting thus for years, providing the vase were not broken. But Mary took the gift listlessly, saying no word, her mind far away.

Then it was that her soul broke bounds. Desperate, distraught, she suddenly leaped to her feet, leaving her lover bewildered and angry, watching her rush out into the street, still clutching her vase of ointment—running, crying, in a very whirlwind of passion.

She had heard that Jesus was to dine that day at the house of Simon the Pharisee. So it came about that that respected Jew found, to his infinite scandal, that his house was invaded by the most notorious sinner in the town, no other than the Magdalene herself. She entered swiftly, glanced round wildly, saw Jesus as He reclined at the low horseshoe-shaped table, and with one bound had thrown herself at His feet. The guests turned angrily and stared at the astounding sight. There was no sound but Mary's uncontrollable weeping, her tears falling over Jesus' outstretched feet. She bent low to kiss them passionately. Then, her lovely eyes swollen with weeping, her golden hair falling loose about her shoulders, her robe dishevelled from her breathless speed of running, she raised her head and gazed into the eyes of Jesus; gazed long and searchingly, soul to soul uniting. She was redeemed in that moment of utter self-giving and abandonment.

Then suddenly the tension was broken. She became conscious for the first time of her precious burden, and fumbled, desperate in her haste, at the waxen seal in the neck of the vase. At last it was broken, and she was busy pouring the perfume on Jesus' feet. Unconsciously she felt that she had to express her devotion in action, by some gift, forgetful that she had already given Him her heart. Then, looking down at His feet, she realized that the commingled tears and ointment needed wiping off. Looking round and finding nothing handy with which to wipe them, she took hold of handfuls of her lustrous hair and dried His feet and repeatedly kissed them.

By this time Simon had risen in his place, a terrible look on his hard face. Staring at the impostor, he found that he was even angrier with Jesus than with Mary. That this Man—pretending to be a Prophet, too—should allow Himself to be defiled by this sinner was an outrage to Israel, and a sure proof that He was no Prophet, since a true Prophet would, of course, have known what sort of woman it was that touched Him.

But Jesus was now ready for Simon, His left hand restraining Mary from running away, and His lips parting for His terrible indictment. But the words came slowly, suavely, almost casually.

"Simon . . . I have something to say to you."

"Then say it, Rabbi." But Simon cursed himself for his civility.

"There was once a moneylender who had two debtors. One owed him fifty pounds, the other five. As neither of them could pay anything, he freely and graciously forgave them both. Now, tell Me, which of them, do you think, will love him most?"

There was no getting out of that one. "He, I suppose, to whom most was forgiven."

"Quite right, Simon—you've answered perfectly correctly! He to whom most was forgiven." Jesus let this sink in a moment.

"Well, Simon, you see this woman? When I entered your house, you gave Me no water for My feet nor any towel to wipe them with. But she has bathed My feet with her tears and wiped them dry with her hair. You never gave Me any kiss of welcome, but she, ever since she came in, has hardly left off kissing My feet. You never anointed My head with oil, but she has poured this perfume over My feet. This, Simon, *this* is the reason why her sins—which, I know full well, are many—are freely forgiven. For she loves greatly; whereas he who thinks he has but little to be forgiven loves but in a little way."

Then turning to Mary, He said, "All your sins are forgiven. Your love has saved you. Go and be at peace!"

So it was that the Magdalene was saved. And because she just could not bear not to be near Jesus—and because she knew her soul to be safer so—she tried to sublimate her passion by excessive activity, seeking out all the women who loved Him, especially those richer sort who were friends of Chuza's family (since, at Jesus' wish, Mary was received as a believer) and organizing them into a band of helpers. . . . There was Joanna, of course, Chuza's wife; and Susanna and a number of others, who gave freely of their money and personal service for the Master and His disciples, even going to the extent of following them about on their journeys for a time. . . . But this was, fortunately, but short-lived. Mary was naturally indolent, and, even in this period of enthusiastic action, she generally managed to make the others do most of the work. After that, reaction again followed, and she became quiet and preternaturally calm, like the sea after Jesus had stilled the storm—leaden, dull, and motionless.

But that was after He had disappeared from the Lakeside and she found herself without any occupation or anyone upon whom to lavish her affection. Then it was that she did a lovely thing, and went home to Bethany; and Martha and Lazarus did an even lovelier, and welcomed her. But not till the sunlight of His renewed presence shone upon the still waters was the great deep of her soul fully revealed.

(XI) THE APOSTLES' PREACHING TOUR

BACK in Capernaum, Jesus reviewed the Ministry of the past months, with a view to further action. The rejection at Nazareth had been a shattering experience for Him. The dangers that had ever threatened God's Prophets in past ages had, in His case as well as in that of the Baptist, proved to be as real as ever before. At any moment and without any preliminary warning He might be cut off out of the land of the living, His Message as yet largely unheard and certainly not fully understood, and His Mission unaccomplished and in large part frustrated. The capital had long been dangerous. It now looked as though Galilee were becoming equally hostile.

But reflection soon proved that this hostility came from the ruling factions, not from the people. The multitudes were about Him still, pathetically bewildered, yet turning to Him with eager willingness from the arid scholasticism of the Scribes. He saw them *even as sheep having no Shepherd.* There they were, *multitudes, multitudes, in the valley of decision* awaiting leadership and guidance. He Himself, travel and speed as He might, could not hope to reach every town and village; and time was precious and opportunities were being wasted owing to the lack of any organized distribution of preachers. Looking upon His disciples, He formed a new plan in His mind, to be speedily put into execution, if at all. The Apostles had now been ordained some months. They had learned something of His outlook, of the content of His Message, of His methods in dealing with men. His new step was the logical outcome of that ordination. So He made a stirring appeal to their loyalty and devotion.

"The harvest truly is plenteous," He told them, "but the labourers are but few. So let us pray to the Lord of the harvest to send out reapers into the harvest fields."

Then He unfolded to them His plan. As winter gave way to spring, He wanted them to go out two by two, for comradeship and mutual support, on arranged and allotted journeys, covering, as far as was humanly possible, the whole of Galilee. He paired them off as discreetly as He could: the two sets of brothers, Simon and Andrew and James and John; Philip with his friend Nathanael Bartholomew; Thomas with Matthew; the other James with Lebbaeus-Thaddaeus; and Simon the Zealot (or Nationalist) with Judas from Kerioth, also an ardent Nationalist.

"I want you to hunt out the lost sheep of the flock of Israel, and, as you go, tell everybody, 'The Reign of Heaven is near!' I give you power to heal the sick, to cleanse the lepers and to cure madness. But take no payment for any such service—for, after all, you've never had to pay, have you, for any blessing *you* have received from Me? I would go further: don't even take any money at all in your purses—neither gold nor silver nor copper, not even a wallet. No change of linen or sandals, just a staff only, if you want one. And don't set out with any food in your satchels. After all, the labourer in the harvest deserves his rations.

"And whenever you enter any town or village, enquire for some really good man—a disciple, if you can—and then make his home your headquarters till you leave the place. As you step into a house, salute it with the customary 'Peace be to this house.' If by any chance you should be turned away or the people refuse to listen to you, make it perfectly clear to them what they are missing by shaking off the very dust under your feet when you leave, as a warning to them."

So it was that they set forth on their journeys, He Himself going alone to teach and preach in a few chosen cities not included in their itineraries. The main import of His charge to the disciples was that they should travel light, for speed was of the utmost urgency.

IV

The Lakeside Ministry: The Final Phase

. . . .

(1) THE TRAGEDY OF MACHAERUS

WE return to the Baptist's two disciples hastening along the road toward Fort Machaerus, first descending the Jordan Valley, with every step finding the air becoming more sultry as the road struck deeper into that fiery rift, until at last they turned southeastward and upward across the Judaean Wilderness where it led over toward the Dead Sea; and then they saw, unmistakable and dark, the frowning bastions of Herod's grim stronghold far and high above them. Somewhere within those massive walls their master was eating his great heart out and anxiously awaiting their return.

As they drew nearer to the castle they noticed an unwonted stir and signs of full military occupation. They passed much traffic on the steep and stony roads, whereon the horses, hot and straining, were pulling covered loads up the almost precipitous hillsides. Soldiers could be seen on the ramparts and at the mighty gates, manning the bastions on either side. What was afoot? They were soon to learn; for Herod's lawful wife, the daughter of Aretas, King of the Nabataeans, had fled to her father on learning of her husband's adulterous union with Herodias, his brother Philip's wife. Aretas, being very angry, was even now preparing to wage war against Herod. In order to forestall any approach from the south, Herod had moved his court to Machaerus, his strongest bulwark against invasion from that side, so that a personal survey of its fortifications might be made by himself and his high captains. Rather than leave behind him in Galilee any important official, who might thus be tempted to presume on his master's absence, he had brought all the chief civil administrators south with him. Herodias had refused to be left behind, so that the

174

whole court was here for the time being. Its members loathed leaving sunny Tiberias for this gaunt fortress set high amid the crags of the Wilderness.

The two disciples were soon admitted to the dungeon where their master languished. They brought, he found, no specific answer to his question—only their personal testimony to Jesus' activities and His own reference to them. John was thus forced to use his own judgment, even as they themselves had been thrown back on witness rather than on authority. But he never heard of Jesus' eulogy of himself. For that he had to await access to the spirit world. Then he knew and rejoiced.

It was Herod's birthday, and a great feast had been arranged to celebrate the occasion. Everything for this banquet had to be dragged three thousand four hundred feet up from the Jordan Valley. But tyrants must be served and their whims gratified. So the horses sweated and the slaves worked till they were ready to drop, and the banquet, even here on this bleak outcrop of black rock, was at last prepared.

But John went hungry. The sense of his presence down there was beginning to irk even Herod, who was afraid of the Prophet. As for Herodias, she was at the end of her patience. Her hatred of John had fanned itself into a blazing fury by all this preparation for war, all this cost, this misery in the Wilderness. The consciousness that it was all caused by her illicit union with the King aroused a resentment that was visited upon the denouncer of that union. Was there no way (thought Herodias) in which those accusing lips, that echoing voice, could be silenced forever?

The noise of revelry rose higher and higher, and the lamps were lighted as the sundown shrouded even this peak in the shades of night. Wine flowed freely, and the King drank copiously. The clash of brimming cups, the ribaldry of besotted minds, the hissed whispers of scandal, filled the stale air; and as the slaves glided in and out on their replenishing errands, suddenly the King rose.

"I have a new sensation for you tonight, to cap our celebration," he cried, swaying as he spoke. "Salome, the daughter of my Queen, has promised to dance for you!"

After a moment of hushed incredulity the guests applauded riotously. For a Princess of the ancient Hasmonaean line of Priest-Princes to dance before the King's guests was indeed an unheard-of condescension. Many wondered what motive the Queen could have had in allowing it. She was known to be shrewd and cunning. Something was afoot . . . but Herod was unsuspecting.

So Salome, a young girl in her teens, came in, half naked, sensual, leering, foul, but beautiful and alluring. The flutes and drums began their whirling melodies and insistent rhythms. The sensuous gyrations became ever more and more abandoned as the music rose and hurried to its climax. The King and his guests gazed, spellbound, filled with a rising lust.

Then suddenly the music ceased, with a clash of cymbals, as the dancer flung herself prostrate before the drunken King. The guests shouted their applause till, at a gesture from Herod, they were silent, as his voice, thick with the fumes of wine, roared out, "Bravo! Ask anything you like of me, and I'll give it you!"

Salome glanced, frightened, at the curtains behind which her mother was, she knew, waiting. Herod, noticing her hesitation, called out boastfully, "I swear to you—do you hear?—I'll give you anything you like to ask, even were it the half of my Kingdom!"

The guests reeled back, amazed and thrilled, and the girl slipped out of the Hall to consult her mother. Holding the curtains to behind her, she whispered breathlessly, "What shall I ask?"

"The head of John the Baptist!" came the hissing reply. The girl rushed back through the curtains to the King, before he cooled down or regretted his offer. Silence fell on the half-circle of tables as the curtains parted to let through the gauze-clad girl. Her lips were white, and a terrible pallor, heightened by a feverish flush in either cheek, made her dark eyes glare from their sockets as the ghastly words fell, one by one, from her parted lips.

"I want you to give me . . . here, at this very moment . . . on a dish, the head of John the Baptist."

The King heard the words in staring silence. His blood was frozen by this ice-cold cruelty. He was struck sober as if by a blow. He looked round at last upon his terrified guests. They turned to stare at him instead of at Salome. Would he go back on his sworn word? He saw their implied censure if he forswore himself. Herodias had planned it well. She knew the essential weakness of her paramour. He would think more of his oath than of his real wishes. Silently the King motioned to a soldier standing to attention near the door. Silently, too, he went out; the door was again shut; and suspense, gripping and strangling, reigned in the Hall. Minutes went by, no one moving or speaking.

Then the door reopened and the soldier appeared, holding a great silver dish outstretched before him, on which lay the bleeding head of the great forerunner. The girl took the dish and carried it in silent triumph through the hangings which swung to behind her and settled into immobility again.

So was Herodias satisfied at last. As the guests rose in a body to glide nervously from the Hall, they left the stricken King still crouching in his chair, his eyes hidden by his hands.. Behind the tapestry of the arras Herodias was gloating over the head of the man who had defied and condemned her. Those lips were silenced at last. Those piercing eyes were sightless now, though the lips were parted as if to speak, and the eyes were open yet. The words "It is not lawful for you to have her" yet echoed in her brain, and would haunt Herod till his dying day.

Those closed curtains swung to upon the close of a dispensation. The last of the Prophets was dead.

(II) THE FEEDING OF THE MULTITUDES

THE news of the Baptist's murder spread like wildfire throughout Palestine. The people were intensely excited and resentful. They were as tinder ready for the spark. Jesus heard of it directly from the disciples of John and burned with anger, so that when His own disciples arrived in Capernaum, hastening home in little groups as they heard of the tragedy, anxious to be with Jesus and to receive His guidance in this crisis, they found their Master distraught and tense. Though they were glad to be back, if only to form a bodyguard about their Master (for the dangers inherent in His Ministry had enormously increased), they were sorry to have to relinquish their tours. For success such as none of them had in his heart expected had rewarded their work. They soon found themselves talking to Jesus about their experiences—and dwelling mainly on their healings and exorcisms rather than on their teachings. Jesus' cousin, John Zebedee, grew quite excited over some unpleasant quarrel he had had with a rival exorcist.

"Master, one day during our mission we saw a man actually casting out devils in Your name! So naturally, we told him to cast in his lot with us; for, after all, he wasn't an Apostle! But, would You believe it, he refused to join us, preferring to go his own way? So we promptly put an end to his insufferable presumption by forbidding him to use Your name at all."

James nodded in righteous agreement. Jesus looked long at them. They were always impulsive—not in the blundering, lovable way of Peter, but in a more fiery manner. Not for nothing had He nicknamed them "The Sons of Thunder!" But He rebuked their stormy spirit. In this new crisis His cause would need every potential follower. So He told them, "Don't ever do that again, for I'm sure no one who could do such great deeds in My name could possibly be likely to speak evil of Me. In any case, whoever is not actually *against* us is on our side!"

Soon news reached them from Chuza, who had come back to Capernaum to prepare for Herod's own return—he was expected, he said, in the near future—that the King had heard of the Apostles' tours and of the spread of Jesus' fame thereby. Herod was nerve-wracked and almost crazy. He kept crying, whenever Jesus was mentioned, "It's John the Baptist, risen from the dead . . . and that's why these miraculous powers are working in Him."

So they told him that if only he could get a sight of Jesus, that would prove that He was not John. But by the time Herod had arrived back in Galilee Jesus was no longer in his province. He had to wait till the Trial of Jesus before ever he saw Him.

Prudence counselled withdrawal on the part of Jesus and His disciples, and private grief made such a move doubly necessary. Jesus felt an almost unbearable need to get away from the crowds, to breathe the more bracing air of the heights on the eastern shores of the Lake . . . to find time and leisure to think out anew His plans, and, above all, to avoid the incensed multitudes who were looking only for a new Leader to rise in wrath against Herod. Besides, He and His men deserved a rest, for they were tired out with the strenuous zest and speed of their respective missions.

So He turned to them and said, "Come away, all of you, to some lonely spot, where we can get a little rest. . . ." There was absolutely no chance of that while they were on this side of the Lake. The crowds were never absent, so many continually coming and going that they hardly had time in which to snatch their meals.

So the boat was once more launched, and the crowds were left behind on the shore. There were mutterings of disappointment, even of anger, at this withdrawal of Jesus.

"We must do something to teach Herod—and Rome, too, whom he serves, the traitor!—a lesson he'll never forget. John must be avenged. Fancy serving up that loved head as an extra birthday dish to please that beast Herodias! We must see to it that this Jesus is not lost sight of, just now particularly. He's the very Man—the only Man! Is He not a miracle worker? Can He not raise the dead? What if He were to call back John from the grave? What if He *lifted up a standard for the people—His reward with Him and His work before Him?*" Should it be said of them, standing there on the shore as the brown sail dwindled to a mere speck in the midsea levels, *Our hope is lost . . . We are clean cut off?* No, they would force events to a crisis. There was much excited chatter; then someone started to run—northward. Others were after him in a flash. Shouts were heard: "They're off to find Him! Look, they're going round by the coast road and over the northern bridge! Quick, there's no time to lose!" And there was a general stampede and rush; the roads through Capernaum and Bethsaida were thronged by hurrying crowds, eager and excited and drawing others in their wake every minute. Here was mass hysteria—a new factor in the Gospel story. Rebellion was in the air.

But of all this rush and excitement Jesus and His friends were blissfully ignorant. They were looking forward to a few days' real rest on the less-frequented side of the Lake. Jesus directed Peter to make for a lush plain, rising up at the back into the hills; a lonely spot and well watered, on the east side of the estuary of the Upper Jordan, not far from the newly built town of Bethsaida Julias, which Herod Philip had erected in honour of Caesar's daughter—and incidentally to secure the rich plain that lay behind it. It was one of the most fertile places in Galilee. Here the grass was green almost all the year round, so moist was the soil. It would be a good place for a picnic meal. Jesus was glad to have the company of young John of Jerusalem—He loved him so much that he eventually became known as "the Disciple whom Jesus loved"—he had come up from the capital owing to the Baptist's death. He told Jesus he would have to be back in the City before the Passover, which was quite near now.

Jesus and His friends disembarked on the lonely shore and walked across the grass-green plain, crossing its many overflowing brooks and climbing some way up the rising ground where the foothills of the great Hauran mountain range began to rise from the plain. After a while they sat down to rest and to talk. Someone stretched out an arm and pointed away to the northwest. All eyes followed his, and then they realized what he was staring at: an immense crowd coming toward them along the seashore, evidently looking for Jesus. They knew in a glance that the crowd had come from Capernaum and the other Lakeside towns, shining clear in the spring-cold sunlight across the silver levels of the Sea. The disciples were for escaping them and retreating further inland behind a summit where they could not be seen.

But Jesus had compassion on the multitude. "After all," He said, "they're just like sheep without a shepherd. The Baptist is dead. They have no leader. They are coming to seek one. Shall we disappoint them? No. I will lead them!"

So, as soon as the crowds came up, Jesus proceeded to teach them. The discourse was a long one; so it seemed to the disciples, anyway. They longed to resume their broken holiday, to be once more alone with their Master. The day wore on, afternoon merging into evening, and still Jesus went on teaching the people. He even healed some of them that had some minor ailments of which they complained. There seemed no limits to His energy today. The disciples were irritated and restive, and it certainly looked as though one of them would be forced to interrupt His discourse if they were to get any rest. It was bad for Him, too. Besides, they were terribly hungry—having eaten all their own provisions during the long day's listening. But they had to be careful, for fear of offending Him. They well knew His sensitiveness to others' hunger—especially that of the masses of the people. So they approached Him after a while, during a pause in His teaching, and suggested to Him: "The time is fearfully late, and this is, after all, a very lonely place. So please send the people away, so that they may get something to eat in the farms and villages round about—for it's too far away for them to get anything down there in Bethsaida."

But Jesus saw through them. He knew perfectly well that they were really meaning "It's high time the people cleared off, anyway." So He answered, "There's no need for them to go away. . . . Let us feed them ourselves!"

Philip turned in protest, eyebrows raised questioningly.

Jesus, noticing, ruminated gently, "The only question is, where are we going to get enough food for all these people to eat?"

"Exactly!" Philip replied, "Why . . . thirty dollars' worth of bread wouldn't be sufficient for them to get only a snack each!"

"It would take fifty dollars' worth of bread to feed all these crowds," chimed in another, "and do you really mean to tell us we've got to go all the way to the town and buy all that amount of food and bring it all back here again, and then feed all this crowd?"

"Never mind," Jesus answered. "Just tell Me how much food you *have* with you, among you, of course. Yes, I mean it. Look in your satchels!"

This seemed so futile that it was hardly worth answering. Besides, they knew perfectly well that they had nothing at all, having eaten their provisions, each of them, while listening to Jesus' discourse. Somewhat sceptically they obeyed Him. But Peter hated having to answer "We've got . . . nothing," especially as Jesus was faintly smiling.

But while the pretended search had been going on, a little lad of Bethsaida, an acquaintance of Andrew and Simon, had been steadily edging his way, boylike, to the front of the crowd, to be nearest Jesus. He had been sent out for the afternoon by his mother to amuse himself as best he might, his picnic tea with him. He had busied himself for a while tickling for fish in the shallows near the fords; then, wandering farther along the beach, he had noticed a vast crowd in the far distance on the further edge of the Plain of Butaiha and had drawn near to see what it was all about.

Hearing Jesus call for any food from the disciples' satchels, he now came forward to his friend Andrew, saying, "I've got some barley cakes in my satchel. Look! I've got some fishes too!"

Andrew was touched and led him to Jesus, saying half apologetically, "There's a little lad here who says he's got some barley cakes. How many is it, sonnie? Five? He's got some fishes as well—two, he says. But what use are they among so many?"

But Jesus' eyes lighted up with a sudden resolution. "Five cakes and two little fishes, eh? That's fine! Bring them over to Me." And the boy shyly handed them to the tall, smiling Stranger. The Master was in high spirits. He was delighted with the little boy's offering. He will show what can be done with a lad's snack meal. He will teach the people, and especially the disciples, that the increase of God comes best not by revolutions and cataclysms, but by a right use of what we already possess. To him that has shall more be given, and he shall have in abundance.

A sharp command followed. "Make the people sit down." He was not satisfied with that. "Arrange them in orderly groups—fifty over here, a hundred or so over there, another company there by that rock. Get them all decently seated and settled."

When the disciples had carried out His orders, Peter noticed how the groups, dressed in their highly coloured wrappings, looked just like garden beds filled with bright flowers, especially when seen against the vivid green of the grass and the deep blue of the rippling sea beyond. Away to the far west the hills of Galilee were darkening as the red sun dropped to rest, and over all was a golden glow—almost as if one's soul had broken through into the eternal, timeless world of the Spirit.

Then Jesus took the five cakes and the two fishes, and looking up to Heaven He blessed the food and gave it to the disciples to give to the multitude. Miraculously there was enough for that great multitude, and when they had all had sufficient He bade the disciples go down to the beach and fetch the fish baskets to gather up the fragments that lay on the ground. All twelve of the baskets were filled before they had done. Then, rising, He cried in a loud voice to the people, "This is a covenanting meal, shared by you and Me in order to bind us together as brothers forever. We have eaten the same food and drunk the same spring water, so that we are now allies, even to the death. As for Me, I here and now bind Myself to aid and befriend you, even to the loss of My own life. You shall swear the same to Me." There was a roar of assent.

The excitement was intense. This well-known ritual was immediately recognized as the Sign and Seal of Khuwy, the Brotherhood— the most potent of all the rites of alliance. The bread so shared would, they believed, never leave the heart of a true and loyal covenanter; for a covenant so entered into could never be renounced. From henceforward Jesus was their pledged Leader and they His pledged followers. The ritual significance of the meal was seized upon by the crowd with tremendous enthusiasm. They failed entirely to see that Jesus was trying to bind them to Him and to be their Leader solely in a spiritual sense. Instead they cried, "Messiah! Messiah!" and "This is *really* the Prophet Who was expected to come into the world!" The acclaiming plaudits echoed from the hills as the whole mass of the people shouted their slogans and cheered Him.

Then there was a mad rush to seize Him and carry Him shoulder-high to a bouldered summit and proclaim Him as their King instead of Herod. He and the disciples were borne backward as the people surged with them up the hillside.

He saw in a flash how greatly He had failed to judge the reaction of the people to His lovely sacramental action. This was the very thing that He most wished to avoid. It would prove fatal to His whole Mission, infuriate His enemies, giving them a real grievance against Him, besides drawing the hostile notice of Rome. So, in a lightning decision He drew on all His innate authority and faced that impetuous, insistent crowd. Twice now He had been jostled and seized, once by enemies at Nazareth and here by friends on the Butaiha Plain—equally dangerous, both times, to His Cause. Never was He greater than now, when, putting aside earthly Kingship, He, alone against thousands, by sheer power of will and personal authority, managed to still the storms of passion, to tame these wild, zealot spirits, and to persuade the majority of the people to go quietly back to their own homes, crestfallen, disillusioned but obedient. A few hung about on the Plain, unwilling to leave the scene of so much excitement. But even they offered no opposition when at length He turned and walked with His disciples upward toward the mountains. But the shore suddenly became inhospitable and unfriendly, still and lowering with the aftermath of passion, as His figure at length disappeared behind the shoulder of a hill.

Once away from the crowds, Jesus felt an overmastering constraint to be alone; to pray with His Father and lay all this anxiety before Him. So He gave command to His disciples to depart and embark in the boat, telling them that He would join them later somewhere near the shore by Bethsaida. Reluctantly they obeyed Him, fearful of leaving Him with so many wild zealots abroad.

Arrived down by the shore, they made ready the boat, working in silence with many a glance at the distant hills. The air struck cold. From somewhere beyond the mountains of Lebanon a low rumble was heard ... very far away, deep and threatening. It was followed by an even more intense silence, as the afterglow of the northern sunset was suddenly eclipsed by a gigantic stormwrack, fretted with golden fire and hiding even Hermon from sight, as the shadows piled up and blotted out the day.

(III) THE WALKING ON THE WATER

UP in the solitude of the hills, Jesus could see things in their true perspective: the near-by immediacies against the limitless eternities. From these bracing heights, the Lake and land of Galilee could be seen in the blacks and greys of the rising moonlight, while to the far west a thin saffron streak on the horizon marked the resting place of the sea-drowned sun. The storm was drawing closer, the wind rising, the air growing colder every minute. Away to the north, sheet lightning silently lighted up the summits of the mountains, their peaks a moment silhouetted against the sheen and then lost again in even more impenetrable darkness. At times the distant menace of slowly nearing thunder rolled down from the remote proud hills of Lebanon, and soon the zigzags of forked lightning flashed out over their looming immensities, as if, in a stark, vivid moment, the jagged outline of some vast rock face was loosened from immobility into the freedom of the spirit—the sword of Eden in the hand of God, sundering, searing and piercing even to the dividing of joints and marrow.

Jesus sought and found comfort in the storm. There, high up in those barren hills of the Hauran, face to face with a great crisis, and resolving it, as ever, in communion with His Father, it seemed that a cosmic contempt of man's puny hostility swept those Lakeside towns, while Heaven's affirmations echoed in the reverberating thunder rolls, as the piled-up clouds moved in majesty over the darkening hills. The mystic solemnities of eternity were re-enacted before Him in the exultant rhythm of those flashes and thunder rolls—the Spoken Word and the acclaiming plaudits, paeaning in glory among the hills.

The Acceptable Year was all but ended. The Bridegroom would soon be going into a far country. The crowds had finally failed Him, His enormous popularity proving the fatal bar to all His lovely Galilean dreams. Beyond the troubled waters of the Lake lay the dear, familiar towns and villages which He had loved so well, the scene of His most glorious works and of His most memorable preaching—much of which had been misunderstood. The people had proved that they wanted Him, wanted to be loyal to Him, to offer Him their services, their lives, if need be—*but in a false cause.* The crisis of the Wilderness was upon Him once again; but this time there was no temptation. And as the lightning flashed, the wind whistled and the shuddering thunderclaps rolled and rumbled among the hills, the Christ remained inexorably true to His convictions, while His enemies were massing against Him and the partisan crowds were departing, disillusioned and resentful. Meanwhile, His friends were somewhere out in that grey, rain-swept trough that hid the Lake.

For the disciples were in deadly peril. They had been blown right out of their course and were labouring with oars to keep the boat endways to the rolling waves, sails being out of the question. And all the time they were being driven farther and farther out into the mid-sea perils. They had done their best to remain inshore as long as possible, expecting to pick up Jesus somewhere on the shore near to Bethsaida, till the darkness and rain hid the beaches and the rising wind had buffeted them ever more and more southward in the central deeps of the sea. The long hours had gone slowly and perilously by, and they were now well nigh exhausted with rowing.

It was in the last hours of the night that a shaft of moonlight shone out from between two great storm clouds, and lighted upon the Lake.

Jesus, from His high vantage point, stared hard and long at a tiny speck just visible a moment in the centre of the sea. A little boat—could it be Peter's? An intense intuition told Him the truth, and with a shock He realized anew the infinite preciousness of that little boat-load of men—the Ark of the Church. Now that He had been forced to end His Galilean ministry, the future of all His Mission and message lay with that tiny group there in peril on the sea. They alone were to perpetuate His message, understanding it to the full. He knew that the events of this last evening would be sure to reach Herod's ears, and Rome's. From henceforth He would be a hunted man. In a day or two the spies would be out after Him and a price upon His head. And there were the disciples, the fate of the universe hanging upon their immediate safety, in deadly danger of drowning.

In a flash of realization He was striding, running, leaping down the craggy mountainside. Soon He was at the water's edge, His eyes fixed on the centre of the Lake. It was once more black with impenetrable darkness, broken only by stray flashes of sheet lightning from the now more distant storm, lighting up the little craft for a brief moment—almost hidden by the turmoil of the waves. "I will not leave you comfortless. *I* will come to you!" And with His eyes set inflexibly on the spot, far out to sea, where the boat had last been seen, Jesus, without premeditation and trusting blindly to intuitive impulse, moved, straight as a line, out upon the cold swirl of the waters. Gripped in the throes of intense nervous tension and exalted by desperate intention, His body, all but somnambulant, was levitated with the Divine Afflatus and upborne by the waves. His material flesh was so etherealized that He looked almost like a disembodied spirit as soundlessly He glided over the water.

Small wonder that the disciples shrieked when they caught sight of Him and thought it was His ghost that they saw—and He dead, killed by that frenzied mob that they had left behind on the shore.

Their shrieks brought Him to sudden awareness; but His courage held and He did not sink—and His voice came clearly to them over the water. "Be of good cheer! It is I. Don't be afraid!"

Peter, however, still wondered if it were a departed spirit speaking to them across the chasm separating two worlds, and in his answering love and courage cared not if he crossed that chasm, provided he reached his Master. He hailed Him across the gulf: "Lord, if it's really You, bid me come to You—now, over the water!"

The voice replied, "Come!" and immediately Peter was clambering, insanely, gloriously, over the ship's reeking sides into the giant, swirling waves, and striding out, with something of Jesus' own courage, onto the water. And in that wild and magnificent moment the water upbore him, even as it did Jesus.

But if he thought to rejoin his Master, whether in life or in death, the ice-cold water and the buffeting winds and waves were terrifyingly real, and drew him back to earth and its dangers, and he found himself crying out, "Lord, save me!"

Instantly Jesus stretched out His hand and caught him, saying, "O you Little Faith! Why did you doubt?" So Peter humbled himself under the mighty grip of God and was saved.

Only then were the others willing to take Him and Peter into the boat; and, as once before, the wind suddenly dropped and the waves smoothed themselves into a calm, and amazement fell upon them as they drifted in silence. They had survived one terrifying experience— a peril of the body—only to face another—a terror of the supernatural.

By this time they were, though they had not realized it, quite close to the shore near Capernaum, Jesus having traversed almost the whole seven miles' width of the Lake before He came abreast of the drifting ship. The voyage, awe-filled in every way, was suddenly over, and they were disembarking on the shore. But from now onward they felt Jesus to be more remote, more majestic than ever before. That chasm yawned ever wideningly between Him and them, for they had begun to see Him as He truly was—and is and ever will be.

(IV) THE BREAD OF LIFE

THOSE who had hung about the Plain of Butaiha and been forced to shelter from the storm in Bethsaida had returned at early dawn in the hope of finding Jesus. While they waited, several boats from the other side of the Lake beached on the shore, carrying many who were bent on the same quest. They asked those they found already on the shore where Jesus was. They were told that as no boat was there when daylight came and as the disciples had gone off in the only boat that had been there yesterday, Jesus must therefore be still on that side of the Lake. So there was a general search for Him, many ascending the hills where they could get wide views of the country further inland. As He was nowhere to be found, it was concluded that He must somehow have got across to the other side again, probably having walked round by the shore road, though no one had seen Him.

So they crowded into the boats and crossed the Sea in further search for Him, making for Capernaum as the most likely place in which to find Him. Thus when Jesus had disembarked with His disciples, He was soon besieged by two crowds, that from His own town and neighbourhood and that from the other side of the Sea, some of whom, when they saw Him, went up to Him, asking, "How on earth did You get here? When did You cross the Sea?"

But Jesus in reacting from the strange exaltation of last night, was facing the inescapable fact that the hour of His greatest popularity had also been the hour when the crowds least understood Him—when He had been forced decisively to reject their advances. They were, He knew, hopelessly materialistic in outlook.

Sombrely He spoke to them. "You have been looking for Me not because you understand the signs I work, but because you ate the loaves and fishes and had a hearty meal."

He turned away, but was immediately followed and importuned to explain what exactly *was* His own interpretation of the sign He had performed. Their natural guess that it meant the acceptance of Kingship had been proved wrong. What then did it really mean?

But He was still thinking of the enthusiastic search and of their reasons for it. Moodily He told them, "Spend your energies, not on the sort of food that perishes, but on the imperishable food of Everlasting Life; the food that the Son of Man alone can give you; for on Him hath the Father set His seal. . . ."

Yes, indeed, thought young John; for as wax takes the impress of a seal, so was Jesus the express image of the Father.

By this time it had begun to rain, and they all moved off to the Synagogue, which was still open to Him through the good offices of Jairus. Once inside, the people returned to the point at issue. "What was wrong in our trying to make You our Leader?" they asked Him earnestly. "Surely we don't need any further sign than that which

You performed yesterday? What more *could* You do in order to make us see and believe in You? Was it not comparable with Moses' gift of manna in the Wilderness—as it is written: *He gave them bread out of Heaven to eat?*"

But Jesus replied, "What Moses gave them was *not* the true Bread from Heaven; for the true Bread of God came down from Heaven to give Life to the world."

"Ah, Sir," they sighed, "evermore give us *that* Bread!"

Then He gave them His real answer: *"I* am the true Bread of Life. Whoever comes to Me shall never hunger, and he who believes in Me shall never, never thirst. For I have come down from Heaven that whoever believes in Me should have Eternal Life."

The Jewish Elders were infuriated by this claim to be "the Bread of Life." They kept asking, "Isn't this fellow Joseph's son? We know all about His parentage . . . quite enough to laugh at this ridiculous talk about 'coming down from Heaven.' "

Jesus turned on them. "Don't be forever muttering among yourselves. In most solemn truth I tell you that whoever believes in Me already *has* Eternal Life! I am the Bread of Life. And as for the manna in the Wilderness, your ancestors ate indeed of that; but they died, nevertheless. But if anyone eats of the Bread that I shall give Him, he shall live forever! Listen, and I will tell you the inner meaning of the sacramental meal we partook of together yesterday. You will remember that you and I shared the food and drink, and so became blood brothers, bound to one another even to the death . . . as if we had shared the same flesh and blood together. I tell you, My flesh is *real* food and My blood is *real* drink. Whoever eats My flesh and drinks My blood remains in covenantal union with Me, and I with him. In the same way as I live by the Father, so he who feeds on Me shall live by Me."

This was altogether too much for them. "This is ridiculous," they complained. "It's impossible to understand. How on earth can we eat this Man's flesh? Who can listen to such teaching?"

They could make nothing of His answer. He evidently wanted the covenant—without the Leadership.

Jesus looked round on them. It seemed that He just could not make the people understand. If He taught abstract truth they called Him a dreamer. If, on the other hand, He spoke to them in terms of imagery, they took Him literally and then accused Him of being a materialist! He saw that even His disciples were puzzled.

"Does this seem so utterly incredible to you?" He asked them. "Which am I most likely to be talking, literally—or spiritually? The only possible source of the life I speak of is Spirit, not matter. Why, of *course* the flesh, as such, confers no benefit at all! All I have been saying to you is symbolic, sacramental, living; not literal, material, dead." And He added, "But there are some among you, I know, who just *will* not believe." (It was, indeed, hard, just when He was uttering the most deeply spiritual truths, to be accused of favouring—cannibalism!) "So those of you who cannot—or will not—accept My Teaching might just as well be honest about it, and say so."

He watched in silence to see what would happen. Then His critics began silently to leave, followed by the greater part of the crowd. He noticed with dismay that among those who got up and left were some who had professed to be His followers. He knew that He had lost them for good. When the last to leave had at length disappeared through the portico, He looked round on His disciples, scanning their faces. Bewildered Peter, with the questioning, wistful furrows in his brow; the ardent "Sons of Thunder," out of their depth, puzzled; and lastly, Simon and Judas, firebrands both of them, Nationalists, haters of Herod and of Rome, rebels born: what were their thoughts? Hopes had been raised to unimagined heights, only to be dashed down again, amid vapourings of mystic symbolism.

Jesus swept His arm round upon them all in a gesture of permissive dismissal. "Would you also like to leave Me?"

Peter could stand it no longer. Not that He understood the talk about eating His flesh, but that he himself so greatly loved Jesus, that he really did not care what He talked about, providing He was there in the flesh with them. Then he thought of the many great sayings he had heard uttered by Jesus—words that had in them a liberating, cleansing power. Impulsively he blurted out his love and need of Jesus.

"Leave You? To whom else could we go?" He had left the Baptist to cleave to Jesus. There was no Successor to Him—nor ever could be. "Besides," he added, "I know that Your Teaching—" he remembered how Jesus always stressed that—"tells us about Eternal Life."

And so Jesus was left with His little handful of men; for even Simon the Zealot and Judas of Kerioth stayed on—a wonderful tribute to their Master's magnetism, as also to their sorely tried loyalty, so nearly at breaking point, but it held. From now onward Jesus had lost the crowds. It was all controversy after this; dispute, persecution, even outlawry. For a few more days we must watch the opposition gathering ever more strength to itself, as the last sands of the Acceptable Year trickle away in darkness and bitterness and disillusion.

How glad Jesus was at the Apostles' decision to remain loyal can only be dimly guessed at. His heart was eased and uplifted.

These few were His true blood brothers. The covenanting meal *was* true for them as well as for Him, its symbolism a reality. The bond had held.

John had to return to Jerusalem at this point. It was good to know He had a close friend in the capital—someone who really understood Him. But they had all continued with Him in His trials. For this He was deeply grateful.

This loving loyalty was in tragic contrast with the defection of many of His former followers. Jesus, in thinking over the worsening of His cause and its prospects, realized that He was now facing not only indifference or even defection, but open, devilish hostility. He voiced His thoughts aloud.

"You remember I told you the Parable of the Sower, and of the varied fortunes of the seed, how some was trodden down, some picked up by birds, some choked by thorns? Well, now I've got a new story for you. For I can now see tares among the wheat. They look much the same, to begin with. But after a time their real nature appears ... and then it is that the labourers in the fields come up to the Owner of the field and ask permission to pull up the tares. 'Didn't you sow *good* seed in Your field?' they ask Him. 'Where then do these tares come from?' He answers, 'An enemy has done this!' Then they ask Him again, 'Would You like us to go and pull them up?' But He replies, 'No, for you might uproot the wheat as well.' "

His eyes rested on the disciples lovingly, and upon Judas especially.

" 'No. Let them both grow together ... for a time, anyway, until the harvest. And at harvesttime I will tell the Reapers to gather in the tares first, and tie them in bundles to be burned, but to bring all the wheat into My barn.' "

When the people had departed, the disciples, worried that He might be personally referring to any of them, asked Him to explain the Parable.

"I think you know what I mean. The Sower of the good seed is the Son of Man. The field is no longer Israel only—but the world! The good corn represent the Sons of the Kingdom. The tares are the sons of the Evil One. The enemy who sowed them is the Devil. The harvest—which once I looked forward to as coming so soon—is something which must now wait till the end of the world. The Reapers are no longer yourselves, in this world, but the Angels of God in Heaven. Just as the tares were gathered and burned in the fire, so will it be at the end of the world."

His eyes rested on the far horizon showing through the latticed windows, where the sun was setting in a blaze of fire.

"The Son of Man will then send forth His Reapers, the Angels, and they will gather out of His Kingdom all who cause evil and all that practise iniquity—and throw them into the fire! There shall be wailing and gnashing of teeth. But then also shall the righteous shine out like the sun in the Kingdom of their Father! Take heed to this— *all* of you, that have ears to hear with."

There fell on the company a sense of tragedy as they heard this terrible revision of the Parable of the Sower. The even greater contrast with that first lovely Galilean Parable—of the Sower who had only to sow the seed and could then sleep and it would grow naturally and inevitably as quickly as a mustard seed grew—cast a gloom over them all. At first, too, He had marvelled at the people's unbelief and misunderstanding. But now that this bright optimism had been lost in disappointment and this wistful wonder had been choked by disillusionment, it seemed that the smoke pall of tragedy had indeed smothered the flame of His faith under the piled-up wreckage of His broken hopes. But it was to burn within the pall ever more fiercely and into ever greater conflagration and toward a greater confidence in *ultimate* results; and as postponement and frustration hindered the consummation, so would His faith in final victory grow to its full stature in the last great cry from the Cross: "It is finished!"

(V) TRADITIONS

THE enemies of Jesus meanwhile were busy fomenting trouble. They had decided to fasten their next accusation on a ritual omission in the covenantal meal.

"Tell us," they complained, "why do Your disciples eat without first washing their hands—so breaking the traditions of the Elders?"

Jesus might well have treated the whole complaint as a trifling absurdity, but there were deeper issues involved. For Jesus as well as the Jews had been pondering anew over the significance of the Butaiha feast. What that feast had symbolized was the truth that as food is of no value till it has been assimilated by the body—become truly part of it—even so is spiritual truth of no avail till it be a man's possession—of the very stuff of his soul. The steps in the argument were logical and clear. The shared food became part of each man's body, so that they had something in common in their bodily make-up. Even so their ideals might be shared and they become brothers. And as all ideals were in the last resort personal or else unintelligible, so for a man to assimilate Jesus' ideals and thoughts was tantamount to sharing Jesus' personality—in a figure, eating His flesh and drinking His blood; whereas this talk of unwashed hands was only yet another proof of their concentration on unessentials and their by-passing of essentials. He was furiously, bitterly angry. He refused directly to answer them. Instead, the lightning of His irony flashed out over them.

"Yes. Isaiah was splendidly right when he made his fine Prophecy about *you! These people honour Me with their lips, but their hearts are far from Me. Vain, then, is their worship of Me—for the doctrines they teach are but mere human precepts!* For you ignore *God's* commandments, and cling, instead, to man-made regulations. Excellent, isn't it, to set aside what God commands in order to maintain your own 'traditions!' For instance, Moses said: *Honour your father and mother,* and again: *Whoever curses his father or mother must be put to death.* But *you* say that a man has only to say to his father or mother, 'This money which was intended for your support is now "Korban," that is, "Dedicated to God's Service," ' then that man is thenceforward freed from any further liability to his parents. In this way you make utterly void the will of God in the purely selfish interests of your man-made rules—devised for the enrichment of the Temple authorities, of course. And this is only one among countless other similar 'traditions.' "

He was so angry that He called the whole crowd to Him, bidding them gather round Him—and about these Jerusalem hypocrites. He was now to utter the most liberating word in all the long history of religion, to cut as with a sword all the taboos, observances and regulations that did not affect the heart and character, laying down in one sublime sentence the basic principle of true religious morality.

"Listen to Me, all of you!" (He was so flamingly furious that His voice carried to the ends of the street.) "Nothing that enters into a man from outside can defile him. It is what comes out from within a man that alone can defile him."

He swept the crowd with a passionately earnest gaze and added, "If anyone has ears to hear with, let him hear *this!*"

There was a surging stir of anger on the part of the Pharisees. But having said this—starkly, unelucidated, take it or leave it—Jesus turned away and went inside the house. Within those shut doors the disciples anxiously asked their infuriated Master, "Do you realize how terrifically angry those Pharisees were at this saying of Yours?"

Jesus flashed round on them, all the righteous wrath of many years of pent-up rebellion bursting out in the fierce saying: "Did I say, of the tares planted by the enemy, 'Let them grow up together with the wheat, lest both be uprooted?' Well, *now* I say—*every* plant not planted by My Father shall be uprooted! Blind guides! And if the blind lead the blind, well, *both* shall fall into the pit."

But Peter again asked Him, "What exactly *did* You mean by that saying of Yours that so upset the Pharisees?"

"Don't *you* understand either? Are you also totally ignorant? Can't you see that whatever food a man eats is no concern of his soul? It doesn't enter his heart but his stomach, and is thence ejected—not affecting his character. . . .

"No. It is what comes *out* of a man that alone can defile him, for from the heart come all the evil motives that can ruin a man's soul: sexual vice, dishonesty, murder, adultery, lust, malice, profligacy, jealousy, slander, arrogance, recklessness. These are the things that, coming from the heart, defile a man."

Herein Jesus gave His final interpretation of the sacramental meal. That was the last utterance of His Teaching Ministry. He had realized that something more was needed: an answering sympathy, a readiness to receive—a power to assimilate and imbibe His own personal characteristics. Ethics were of themselves powerless; and love was personal: part of a person, directed from a person to a person and becoming in turn part of that person.

This antinomianism of Christ was so revolutionary that the Priests were faced with the necessity of discrediting Jesus publicly—if they could. It is more than probable that they had heard of His reluctance to perform miracles to order, or indeed, to perform them at all save in the service of urgent human need. They therefore decided to demand of Him a "sign from Heaven," and if, by any chance He performed one, to attribute it to devilish power. A refusal on His part would serve their purpose, however. It is significant that those who challenged Him included emissaries from Caiaphas, the Sadducaean High Priest. Jesus heard their demand in patient silence, the crowd eagerly watching the contest. He sighed deeply, being troubled in spirit, and then gave His unequivocal answer: "Why are you forever asking for a 'sign'? This is an evil generation, requiring 'signs.' I tell you, no sign shall be given you!" The finality in His voice was like the clap of a drum. And with that He left them. There was nothing more to be added to that flat refusal. Right was right, and needed no buttressing. No "signs" could either add to or detract from that ultimate and eternal fact, attested by the heart and appropriated by the mind. Only gross materialists sought after tangible proofs of spiritual realities.

(VI) JESUS AND HIS FAMILY

I

To trace out the cumulative and converging causes of Jesus' withdrawal to the Lebanon, we must return to Nazareth and enter once more that shadowed anxious home, from which the sunlight seemed to have been permanently withdrawn. Mary was daily becoming more and more bowed with uneasy forebodings. Ever since that terrible time when last her Son had visited the house, her life had been full of silent suffering. Truly the sword had pierced her heart. She seldom, if ever, went out in the streets. She could not bear to enter the Synagogue. The eyes of the Nazarenes were hostile and scornful. Even her sons smouldered with wrath against their Elder Brother. Silent and taciturn, they went about their business, or, led by James, braved out the stigma attaching to Jesus' kindred by attending Synagogue in a defiantly orthodox manner, as if to dissociate themselves from His heresies. Within doors, little was said. His name was never mentioned—it would have set tinder to the flint of their wrath. Sinkingly Mary's heart wavered beneath the burden of her griefs, for she loved all her sons.

Then had come the terrible news of the Baptist's murder, ghastly in its horrifying details. It had swept like a desert wind through the land, fanning the smouldering flames of patriotism into a holocaust of hatred and revenge.

Rumours also reached Nazareth, confirmed by returning and disillusioned Zealots, of a sudden and violent Lakeside uprising—and, of course, Jesus was at the centre of it. The people had even attempted to crown Him as their King—a completely mad proceeding, foredoomed to failure, though folk said that its failure was solely due to Jesus' own faintheartedness and lack of enterprise. Either way, thought the Nazarenes, He was hopeless.

This news was doubly dangerous, for Jesus personally and for His family, in so much as the attempted insurrection, with Him at its centre, would inevitably stir up the authorities—Rome and Herod, and their attendant Sadducaean satellites—besides angering the people. By the former He would be arraigned as a rebel, by the latter for not being a rebel. And all the while, the Pharisees, watching these exciting events, saw, with smug satisfaction, their most dangerous enemy getting Himself further and further into trouble.

There was only one thing to be done, thought James—to lay hold on Him before Pilate or Herod did, and to clap Him in the madhouse cells or smuggle Him away somewhere, far out of reach.

At length James and his brothers laid their views before their

mother. To her their plea was that only thus could Jesus' life be pre-
served and the family name be restored to honour. The former argument alone weighed with her, and at last she bade them set out on
their tragic errand.

But they demurred at this. They knew something of the force of
their Elder Brother's resolution. If Mary would not go with them,
they would never carry out their mission. Only she would be able to
persuade Him to give up His crack-brained schemes and go away. And
if He were to refuse to fall in with their plans, then the only remedy
lay in forcibly restraining Him. And even to get at Him at all, it might
be necessary—surrounded as He was by a bodyguard of followers—to
plead that His mother was wanting Him privately. So they told Mary
that they wanted her to add her entreaties to theirs—they knew how
deeply He loved her. . . .

The plan worked. She glanced at them in pathetic and poignant
suspicion and, after a long, tense silence, agreed to go with them. She
would rather be near Him, anyway.

So, early one morning, just before dawn, the pitiful little procession started out: Mary on an ass, with a daughter to attend her, James,
gaunt and rugged beside them, and Jude and Joseph and Simon walking behind. It were well for them all to be there; and they had se-
creted a strong rope among their belongings, in case it might be
needed. Those long, aching miles were a measure of their tragic misunderstanding; for by every step that Mary neared her Son she was a
thousand miles farther off from Him in Spirit. But there was worse
to come at her journey's end. A pitiful little procession? Nothing like
so pitiful as when it shall return and traverse the long uphill road
again.

II

Little did that plodding family know that Jesus was at that very
moment in the midst of a battle with His enemies. He had never
been angrier. There had been brought to Him a man who was both
blind and dumb—an extreme case, in that the man was almost certainly deaf as well, since dumbness, in most cases, is accompanied by
deafness. Jesus had been swift to respond to this mute appeal. Then,

hearing the man speaking and observing that he was also able to see, the multitude marvelled, saying, "Can it be that this Jesus is the Son of David? After all, nothing like this was ever seen in all Israel's long history!"

This was exactly what the Pharisees most feared—the inference from Jesus' Miracles of His Messianic Mission. Their counterstroke must be also swift and drastic. It was impossible to deny the miracle; therefore their only course (and it was quickly and brilliantly chosen) was to ascribe His powers over disease (and so over "devils") to Devilry; so that, while admitting all His mighty works, they might use them as evidence against Him, thus invalidating at a stroke all His credentials and exposing Him before all the people as an incarnation of Satan. The power (they would argue) to work His Miracles came either from Heaven or from Hell. That they came from Heaven was impossible, since He repudiated the obligations of the Law—God's Law. Therefore . . .

The inexorable logic was unanswerable if one reverenced the Law.

So they cried out: "This Fellow never casts out any demon save only by the power of Beelzebub, the Prince of Demons. Indeed," they went on, "He is Himself possessed by Beelzebub!"

This, the most awful accusation ever made against Him, roused Jesus as never else in His life, not so much on account of Himself, as because it was the direct negation of the one sure ethical basis. For it repudiated goodness and completely reversed the whole scale of values. This was the sin against the light: the soul itself crying, "Evil, be thou my good!" The words of Isaiah rang in Jesus' ears: *Woe be to them who call Evil good, and Good evil, who mistake Darkness for Light and Light for Darkness.*

After a silent pause, as the full significance of the ghastly indictment overwhelmed Him, that Master Mind grappled with this crisis and took command of the situation. His thoughts, as always in His swift poetic nature, shaped themselves in a flash into pungent brevity in which irony and humour came to the aid of His devastating logic; for He at once found the only logical answer to their own inexorable logic.

"Come over here, near to Me," He told the Pharisees, and waited till they obeyed. Then He swept them with the lightning of His wit.

"How *can* Satan cast out Satan? If a kingdom be divided against itself, that kingdom cannot stand. If a family be divided against itself, that home is finished." (And all the while His family was nearing Him along the coast road.) "So, if Satan has risen in arms and made war against himself, then that's obviously the end of him. He's finished and done with! So much, then, for your charge that I cast out demons by the Prince of Demons."

But He had not done with His enemies yet. That keen brain had fastened on a telling image, and even as He was speaking the metaphor was being shaped and applied. His voice was cuttingly calm and considered.

"Evil entrenched in a soul is like a strong man armed. No use anyone trying to break into that stronghold, release the captives and plunder its spoils—unless He's sure He can first overcome and bind the strong man. *Then* He can spoil his citadel."

(And all the while the brothers were drawing nearer with that hidden rope with which to overcome and bind Jesus, because they thought *He* had a devil.)

Jesus continued: "When the strong man, fully armed, successfully guards his keep, his possessions are intact. Nevertheless, when a stronger than he shall come upon him and master him, then all his trusted armour will be useless and his goods will be plundered and his captives delivered."

Peter, keeping, as ever, his eyes on Jesus (Who was looking lovingly at the healed man) could not but feel that here was Someone stronger than even Satan; One Who made one feel that love was stronger than hatred. But Jesus was wondering what would become of the man; and, still more intently, what became of those who were helped spiritually by Himself. Did they all remain whole, clean and purified in afterdays? Or . . . ?

He went on: "Not that that is always the end of the story, unfortunately. There are times when a foul spirit, having been cast out of a man, roams through waterless places" (water was regarded as inimical to devils) "seeking rest and finding none."

His voice was very stern. "Hear what the foul spirit says. 'I will return to the home I left.' When he comes there he finds it swept and clean, all ready for him, awaiting his return. . . . But what happens *then?* Now watch the foul spirit. He goes off to bring back with him seven other spirits more foul even than himself, and they all go in and dwell there; and the last state of that man is worse than the first."

His mind was still dwelling on that ghastly saying of theirs that He performed His Miracles through the agency of Satan.

"I tell you, therefore, that the things that men say will one day be brought up against them before the judgment seat of God. And how *can* you be forgiven if you cannot repent—if the very light that is in you is, in reality, Darkness?"

This awful judgment, so logically inevitable, lay from henceforward over the heads of those Jews who had committed the supreme blasphemy of calling goodness evil. Their own natures had slammed-to the doors of Heaven and shut them out forever from the sunlight of God's presence; having, instead, the understanding darkened, being alienated from the life of God through the ignorance that was in them, because of the blindness of their hearts.

"As for Divine pardon, I here and now solemnly declare to you that there is *no* sin which shall not be freely forgiven if only men *can* repent of it. Yea, *all* their sins shall be forgiven unto the sons of men if they can but repent. Yes, *and* all blasphemies with which they may blaspheme God; save that, by the very nature of things, men *can't* be forgiven for blaspheming against the light within them."

He did not want them to dismiss these solemn words by ascribing them to personal pique—to the fact that it was He Himself Who was offended by the accusation of the Pharisees.

"As for Myself, why, anyone may say anything he likes against Me, the Son of Man. God will forgive him for it. But whoever atrophies his own conscience, continually denying its validity and rejecting its commands, cannot ever have forgiveness, neither in this world nor yet in that which is to come, for the light within is quenched in darkness. He is guilty of an eternal sin."

As He looked round on that vast crowd, searching their faces and wondering who would remain loyal to Him, He realized as never before that only the out-and-out disciples were of any use to Him in the dread fight against entrenched evil. The gloriously inclusivist saying, uttered so short a time before, was now tragically inverted, as that last flash of His first radiant optimism was turned into the bitter, heart-

breaking cry: "He who is not *with* Me is against Me! Whoever re-
fuses to gather with Me—scatters!"

For this was, indeed, the testing and sifting time of discipleship:
when following Him meant following One Who was branded as
Satan and cursed with all the curses of Hell.

III

It was at this very moment that the message suddenly came to Him:
"Your mother and brothers are outside wanting to speak with You."

Here was a fresh crisis, for He knew full well what they had come
for. His recent sojourn in Nazareth had made that crystal-clear. The
intense pull exerted by His mother's wishes was measured by the
fierceness with which it had to be resisted. For there could, literally,
be no going back now. But it was all the harder for Him in that her
pressure was exerted (and more powerfully by her mute presence
without, after her fruitless journey, than by any words she might have
uttered) just at a time when, to a large extent, His own will coincided
with hers. For He had been forced to repudiate the people's acclamation of Him, and He was, in any case, already contemplating withdrawal into the safety of the Lebanon hills. Even now a voice called
to Him: "Turn away! Go back with them and escape! . . . The people
are not worthy of You. They even mock Your God-given powers,
branding Your deeds of mercy as Satanic. Leave them alone—to
God's justice!" Yes, He knew He could do nothing now with these
Priests. He knew also that He needs must withdraw into the hills.
And yet He had to show His mother and brothers that He was *not*
giving up His final aim of converting the world to God . . . that this
withdrawal was but a strategic retreat, a building up of hidden re-
serves, a preparation for the final offensive. He had, thus, to be immensely stern with Himself, lest those combined prudences lead Him
to rationalize reaction into an angry break with His Mission. It would
be so fatally easy to throw it all up, and go home with His family,
amid the tearful relief of His mother and the reasoned commendation
of His brothers and friends. And it would be a return to the fold of
Israel. Herod probably would leave Him alone. Rome would not
bother with a failure. Besides, He was so dreadfully tired physically.

Against all these considerations He had only His innate conception of God's plan for Him and the world. It was His own faith against the combined claims of reason, "religion," and now of affection. He had to tear His way through all the mazy trammels which sought to bind Him to Nazareth, to Israel, to life itself. Even if it meant hurting Mary to the quick, He had to cut loose from all those invisible cords of love and prudence. Only a foul spirit would now cry, "I will return to the home I left." He would not give up His enterprise. His men were there beside Him, those on whom He relied for the implementing of that vast undertaking. They had elected to stay with Him when the prudent deserted. Never had He loved them so deeply as now.

Extending His arm over them, He answered the messenger: "Who is My mother? Who are My brothers? See! Here they are, around Me! For whoever will do the will of God, the same is My brother, My sister and My mother."

Some impulsive woman, hearing that His mother was outside, cried out, "Blessed is the womb that bare You, and the breasts that You sucked!"

But He replied, "Blessed, rather, are they that hear the word of God speaking to them—and obey it!"

There, in the street, the family waited, huddled together, disconsolate, anxious. At last the messenger was seen to be threading his way through the crowds again. They looked eagerly beyond him for a sign of Jesus, but only the man came forward. What was this that he was saying—this that had caused James and his brothers to start with incredible surprise as they asked the man to repeat the message? What could Jesus mean? Was He mocking them? Mary was suddenly so tired that she all but collapsed. What was Simon doing with that rope? No, no, let us go home. Now, yes. Come, James, or I shall die. . . .

With burning hearts and eyes blazing with wrath, her sons led her away, sunk now into benumbed stupor, broken in heart, defeated. As they trudged hopelessly along the shore road again, she knew that every step bore her farther in spirit from her Son and from that remote world of His from which she was now barred out. . . .

It was like to a dead woman that crept about the house back there in Nazareth—now only a pale ghost, a bloodless wraith, of the flaming singer of the Magnificat.

Lo, He was near me, but I saw Him not. He sweeps on . . . but I behold Him not. Who can hinder Him? Who dare ask Him: "What are You doing?" But were I to summon Him, He would not answer. He would not even listen. . . . Were it a trial of mere strength, lo, He is so strong! Were it a matter of law, how could we arraign Him? Never mind. I care no longer about life. What does it matter? . . .

(VII) THE FINAL BREAK

THE Galilean Ministry was all but over. The Acceptable Year had already run its course, and only a few short hours remained before the once radiant Bridegroom would have forsaken His own city and be sailing on the Lake for the very last time. Already He was acquainted with grief. Soon, very soon now, He would be a Man of Sorrows, a lonely, hunted Figure, outlawed from Israel. For Herod had received reports of the Butaiha uprising; and Rome was watching, eagle-eyed, though as yet the Governor had not been troubled with the news. After all, the thing had fizzled out.

On the next Sabbath Jesus was teaching again in the Synagogue. It was the last time that Jairus and the Centurion were to see Jesus within its walls. The Pharisees had, as was almost usual now, arranged a plot to trap Him into an illegality. What they needed above all was a definite charge upon which they could proceed against Him as a breaker of the Law. So there, just under the eyes of Jesus, was set a man with a withered hand. It was an obvious frame-up. Besides, this particular crisis was fraught with especial significance. He had just been accused of performing His miracles through the power of Satan. So, even if He did perform this test healing, He would not only be breaking the Sabbatical Law (He had done that many times before, anyway), but He would lie open to a yet more telling indictment—that their imputation of Satanic agency was fully justified in that God Himself would never empower a Prophet to break His own Laws.

But Jesus, as always, raised the whole miserable controversy into the realm of unanswerable ethic. He cried to the man to come forward, and then asked the Pharisees, "Tell Me—you who are so zealous for the Law—is it lawful to do *good* on the Sabbath?"

They could not answer this, for the Law expressly allowed certain good actions to be done on the Sabbath. He went on: "Well then, tell Me, which is more right on the Sabbath—to help or to hurt—to save life or to kill? Now, what would *Satan* do?"

Then after looking round Him with a sweeping glance of anger, He told the man, "Stretch out your arm!" He obeyed and lo! it was completely restored. At once the Pharisees left the Synagogue in a body, mad with fury, and immediately held a conference with the Herodians in order to find some way in which they might kill Him.

There was only one course open to Jesus after this, if He wanted to accomplish His Mission and preserve His Message. The Apostles needed to be trained in His ideals. Prudence and wisdom counselled withdrawal to some area outside the jurisdiction of Herod and beyond the reach of spying Jews.

So it was that the next morning Capernaum woke to find the town empty of its Prophet and His disciples. Search was everywhere made for them, questions asked of everybody. But no one had any information to offer. They had all gone . . . where, nobody knew.

And in Nazareth a mother sighed . . . and a band of brothers discarded a coward from their family.

ACT THREE

. . . .

The Christ of Hermon

I

A Syrian Summer

. . . .

(I) TYRE

JESUS and the Twelve were sailing on the mid-sea waters of the Lake. The mists had enveloped Capernaum and the western shore; and, the northeast coast not being yet visible, they seemed to be gliding on a shoreless ocean, pewter-coloured, calm, silent. The Twelve were as yet unaware of their Master's intention. They noted only that He was very silent this morning and that His eyes were fastened on the shores of Capernaum till they were lost in the haze. Why this sudden and secret departure, so early in the morning? Where were they off to? Was it to be a day's holiday? If so, what about provisions? Someone glanced round and searched in his satchel. The others shook their heads in negative agreement.

Then a low voice broke the spell. "Look, would you believe it, we've brought no food—only one loaf among the lot of us."

They looked at the Master significantly and a little awkwardly. They had not forgotten their shame when, so recently, their empty satchels were exposed before a huge crowd.

But Jesus was far away in thought. His mind was filled with the terrible events of yesterday. The pressing crowds had become a horror to Him after His mother had departed. He had been so near to giving way and sobbing out His sorrow, kneeling at her side, as so often He had done as a Boy. But to have broken down then would have been to abandon His Mission altogether. So He had let her go instead. But the crowds remained. How He had longed for the blessed anonymity of darkness, so that, lapped in its sweet privacy, He might be alone with the understanding stars. Up there, in the central hush so far above earth's din, there was no hatred, no succession of tragic days— only eternal rest.

What was that? Food? A lack of it? Were they thinking of break-fast? What did men know of the true food from Heaven? Or of the poisons of Hell? He spoke His thoughts aloud.

"Take heed . . . and beware of the yeast of the Pharisees, and of Herod."

The disciples were, indeed, at sea. "Yeast?" they muttered, be-wilderedly. "What on earth can He mean? Is it because we've for-gotten to bring any bread?"

But He was now fully roused from His dark reverie. "Bread? Who's talking about bread? Are you still intent on being literal-minded? Don't you understand even yet? Are you still blind and dull of heart? You've got eyes—can't you see with them? You've got ears—can't you hear? Besides, have you no memory? Do you mean to tell Me you have really failed to see the meaning of the covenanting feast of brotherhood—how there'll always be enough and to spare for everybody in the Kingdom when all hearts are loving and unselfish? Tell Me—how many baskets of scraps did you fill up after the feast over there?"

Still bemused, they answered, "Twelve."

"Well, can't you see the significance even now? I'm thinking in terms of spiritual, not material, food—of its influence for good or evil, of doctrines and ideas."

But they were silent and uneasy still, as the boat glided forward over the smooth limpid water. But, in spite of His dismay at their obtuseness and all the tragic wreck of His hopes for Galilee, He would not give way to despair. The good would win in the end, though its working might be invisible. The talk about yeast had given Him the exact simile for which He had been searching. His eyes lighted up as He again spoke His thoughts aloud.

"Yeast . . . the yeast of the Pharisees and of Herod. Yes—and of the Gospel! For the slow spread of the Good News, the gradual ex-tension of the Kingdom, is like the yeast that a woman takes and kneads into a bushel of flour. It can't be seen. You wouldn't know it was there. But all the time it's working invisibly and secretly till it gradually leavens the whole. Then suddenly it bubbles up—and the loaf is ready! That's how My Message will work in the world!"

Leaving their boat with a friend at Bethsaida Julias, they at once struck northward along the course of the Upper Jordan. They were now in the territory of Herod Philip, and outside the reach, therefore, of Antipas. They were free to relax and expand . . . and plan. But mere safety was secondary in the purpose of the Master. The somewhat leisurely progress of this present trek northward masked the most urgent and tense move He had yet made. For one could not hurry the training of the Twelve, the gradually deepening influence of His personality, the impregnation of the minds and souls of His men with His ideas. These things, vital and urgent, took time to develop, to grow and mature.

The disciples were a little frightened at the new streak of severity in their Master's mood and words. They found themselves watching Him with darkening, suspicious glances. Besides, these uncouth pagan regions were no place for zealous Jews. There was, furthermore, the feeling, hard either to accept or reject, that He was turning out to be a coward. One day they asked Him point-blank whether He intended always to refuse the crown of Israel.

There was immense dignity, a majesty of stature, in Him as He answered, "No. One day I mean to be King, and not only Israel's King but King over the whole earth!"

This was splendid, for it meant victory over Rome. Excitedly they asked Him, "*When, Lord?*"

But He did not answer at once. Then He said, "The times and seasons rest with God. Mine hour has not yet struck."

They were forced to rest content with that, cryptic though it might be. With burning hearts and with many a long backward glance they trudged onward and up into the foothills of the Lebanon range. The keen mountain air was restoring their natural spirits and reinvigorating the frayed nerves. Jesus, with every step, seemed to gain in poise and vigour; but He was often silent still, almost as though He were deliberately storing up strength for some decisive battle yet to come.

The road they traversed rose nearly seven hundred feet in nine miles, and the flow of the river was at times tumultuously rapid. Soon the stream broadened out ever wider and wider till it was lost in the Waters of Merom, a vast mere, bordered with sedge and marsh. Away in the distance, tier on tier, rose the great hills, with Hermon's snow-strewn summit towering over them all. Before they reached Caesarea Philippi they turned aside to the northwest and struck across country toward the coast. Here was some of the very finest mountain scenery in the world. It was well watered in the vales, which were very fertile, filled with orchards and flower-bright with oleanders, their blossoms softening the lines of the jagged cliffs and the steep banks of the rivers. Everywhere rose, far above them, the great hills, often jutting precipitously over colossal ravines, which yawned some fifteen hundred feet or so below them. Luxuriant woods and rushing streams commingled together as they climbed and scrambled along the winding gorges, threading their tortuous way through many a leafy tunnel or under cascading waterfalls, when they made long detours that followed the line of a wady.

At length, from a height, they saw, vast and deeply blue before them, the Great Sea, beyond its white thread of coast line bordering the maritime plain. Here, on the summit of the last ridge, they lay down awhile and drank in deep breaths of the sea-salt air. Was Jesus, then, really going down toward Tyre—clearly visible a little to the right along the northward road? Peter's eyes lighted up at the sight of the many ships putting in and out of the world-famous port, but to enter the city was not the sort of thing that a strict Jew would do. Judas and Simon the Zealot felt so strongly about this as they reluctantly followed Jesus down the hill that they at length plucked up courage to ask Jesus whether He were really going into the city. He nodded, looking quizzically at them.

"But surely, Master, your Mission is only to the House of Israel, isn't it?"

"Am I never, then, to teach the Gentiles?"

"Well, it seems different, somehow, when they seek *us* out of their own accord, to be taught. But have we any right to go to them, to seek *them* out in their own evil habitations?"

Well they knew that Tyre had the reputation of being one of the wickedest places in the world.

"Am I not sent to the lost sheep—to seek them out and to find them?"

"Yes, Lord, but only to the lost sheep of the House of Israel!"

Jesus looked long and sadly at them and fell silent again, for His own thoughts were weighing their patriotism against His universalistic dreams. There, in the distance, was the great city, world-renowned, prosperous, reeking of sin. Should He preach there? But He so needed a rest. Besides, the main purpose of this journey was the training of the Twelve, which was daily continued, not so much by direct precept as by the subtle influences of mind on mind and soul on soul. In any case, the prosaic necessity of replenishing their stocks of food made an entry into the city all but inevitable.

It was beautiful beyond words to express, with a magnificent harbour enclosing an island connected with the mainland by a gigantic causeway built by Alexander the Great, scores of white temples, theatres, palaces, and at its back the wonderful backcloth, when seen from the sea, of the Lebanon range. Its merchants dealt in *emeralds, purple dyes, embroideries, wine and white wool, bright iron, cassia and calamus; lambs, rams and goats; spices, precious stones, gold; bales of blue cloth; chests of rich apparel, bound with cord and made of cedar*. There was also a considerable traffic in wild animals, the poor caged beasts being swung from cranes into the ships to serve the lusts of Rome, Corinth and Athens in the blood-soaked arenas where their terrified eyes would at last close in death.

The city was immensely ancient. Herodotus said it was two thousand and three hundred years old when he visited it, four centuries before Christ. It had been the centre of the Baal worship against which the Hebrew Prophets had so consistently struggled. The bestial perversions inherent in this worship had survived the actual decay of belief in Baal, and, though human sacrifice was no longer allowed, Tyre and Sidon had become the focal points of all that was most vicious, luxurious and perverted in Hellenic life. They were also the centres of the manufacture of the dye made from the murex (shellfish) which were ground down to yield the world-famous Tyrian purples and crimsons, the factories being operated by human labour in conditions of agonizing cruelty. Indeed, human feelings, flesh and even life were thought of solely in terms of commercial values. Jesus was thus for the first time face to face with evil in its most hideous form, backed by all the might of Rome. Here the Gentiles were seen at their worst. The Prophets had been understating the sins they denounced so vigorously. Baal was still gloating over his victims.

Walking along the beach, they passed by the chained rows of naked men, themselves dyed purple with the oozy blood of the water snails they trod upon all day long; dyed crimson, too, with the bleeding lacerations of the overseers' whips. Later He passed by the weaving looms wherein the women and children toiled and groaned till they dropped; passed by the glassware factories, the metal furnaces, the ship gangs being marched down to the docks; passed by the slave markets, with their incredible shamelessness. Here, in this proud city, He saw at close quarters the evil that ruled the world; saw the souls of men being seared and shrivelled and destroyed. Peter and the Sons of Thunder, seeing an aged slave unmercifully thrashed and, later, a little child beaten to the ground, looked in wonder on Jesus, silent and inactive. But the lines of His mouth were grim and His lips moved inaudibly and His eyes blazed with fire.

They did not stay long in the city, and Jesus breathed a long breath of freedom and relief when at length they passed out through its gates and were once more moving northward along the coast road. Judas and Simon the Zealot thought that Jesus had decided not to waste His powers upon a lot of evil pagans—dogs, all of them. Was not the Psalmist also tonguetied in the midst of the heathen? *My strength is dried up; my tongue cleaves to my jaws; for dogs have compassed me, and the assembly of evil-doers has enclosed me in.*

Indeed, they went so far as to ask Jesus, "Lord, You would agree, wouldn't You, that it is *not* right to give that which is holy to dogs, any more than one would give, say, pearls to swine. They'd only turn and rend you, wouldn't they?"

But Jesus was silent as He glanced tragically upon them and turned to gaze, long and yearningly, out to sea. But Levi-Matthew, who was a very humble person, having once served the Gentiles as an apostate from Israel and being now ready to be as loyal a Jew as he could, mistook Jesus' silence for consent, and jotted down the sentiment in a papyrus roll, which he carried about with him and in which he had taken down a large part of the Great Sermon Jesus had preached on the mountain in Galilee, besides many of the parables. They all were agreed, as they moved on, that it was a good sentiment, though, underneath, some of them felt a little uneasy as to the real meaning of the look Jesus had given them.

(II) AT SAREPTA

IT was not long before they came to Sarepta. Jesus recalled His own allusion to the place in His sermon in the Synagogue at Nazareth, when He had pointedly mentioned the fact that though there were many widows in Israel in the days of Elijah, when there was so long and grievous a famine over all the land, yet unto none of them was Elijah sent, but only to Sarepta, near to Sidon, to a woman who was a widow there. He had cited this episode in the life of Elijah in order to express His own internationalism, His hatred, speaking in God's name, of the exclusive nationalism of the Jews. For God's universal charity extended to all nations, irrespective of race or religion. His own disciples' lack of loving sympathy where the peoples of other nations were concerned had just been exemplified. How best could He bring them to understand that because God was Father of all, so all men were brothers?

Then it was that a unique opportunity presented itself. Almost as they had entered the town a Syro-Phoenician woman, whose little daughter was suffering from brain trouble, having heard of Him through a friend who had recognized Him, came to the house where He was supping and besought Him that He would cast out the devil from her daughter, crying, "Have mercy on me, O Lord, Thou Son of David! My daughter is grievously vexed by a devil."

This might well be disastrous. He had entered the house of a friend—one of those He had come to know and love among the many Gentiles who had heard Him preach in Galilee—and His requested anonymity here was being carefully guarded. But some other Tyrian convert had also seen Him and had evidently gone off to tell the woman of His presence in the town. Especially He wished to avoid the performance of Miracles in these parts. So He sat there, unanswering, His mind a whirl of seemingly conflicting thought. Then it was that, as usual, His compassionate instincts got the better of His prudence. Also He saw in the woman's importunity an opportunity. He eyed the disciples wryly as the moments passed.

Then, looking at the woman, He asked them, turning away from her as He spoke, *"Now* what am I to do? What do *you* think? Would it be right to offer help to . . . a dog of a Gentile?"

Some of the disciples were not watching Him carefully. "Pack her off," they demanded, "for she'll only worry us all the time if You don't."

Again He turned to the woman. "There! You've heard their verdict. You see, the children of the house must first be served. You must realize that it would never be right to give anything that is sacred to the dogs or to throw your pearls before swine. . . . They'll only turn and trample them under their feet and then turn round and attack you. So, of course, it's perfectly correct that as I've only been sent to the lost sheep of the House of Israel, I really cannot take the children's bread and cast it to the dogs—or, rather to the little puppies in this case!"

There was a twist to His mouth as He gravely uttered this sarcasm. At this the woman rose from the ground—she had knelt before Him in her agonized entreaty—and with a smile that saluted the beacon shining in His eyes, she rejoined, "True, Sir, but, *under* the table, the puppies *do* pick up some of the children's crumbs!"

"Splendid!" cried Jesus. He had forgotten her cunning use of a Messianic title to gain His sympathy. He laughed outright as He relished her wit and her courage in her dire extremity, in so exploiting His irony. "For this witticism—and because of its underlying faith—if you'll now go off home, you'll find your little daughter cured and everything just as you want!"

So off she went, and found the child lying on her bed, sane and happy and quite normal again. Surely, thought Jesus, as He watched the disciples after the departure of the woman, they must have learned their lesson. But He was reckoning on a quickness of uptake that was wanting in most of them; and when, long after, they came to tell the story, they failed to make sense of it. They were men mostly of but simple minds, without much humour. Irony was generally lost on them, and they thought Jesus was very right in all that He had said to the woman. Was it not written in the Scriptures? *You are My sacred men. That which is torn to pieces in the field—fling only that to the dogs!*

As Jesus walked out of Sarepta He was deeply moved. It was proving a very difficult task, training these men.

(III) THE REDEEMER

JESUS refused to stay in Sidon, reputed to be, if anything, even more evil than Tyre. He felt sick at heart with the sin of the world, no longer exasperated, as by the Jews in Galilee, but despondent and all but despairing. The pain of all those blows and scourgings, the aching loneliness of all that exiled slave horde, the degradation and filth of their conditions, gnawed at His soul till He was literally shaking with nausea. The hurt in His eyes was so great that He found Himself continually closing them and holding on to a rock, while the disciples waited for Him wonderingly. As He turned aside from the main Sidon road and moved up into the mighty Lebanon hills, He was, in many ways, seemingly a changed person—even more deeply compassionate than before, if that were possible, more severe and challenging, more claiming and tragically heroic.

Seated there, on a vantage point high up in the hills, He looked back at the fair prospect that hid the monstrous evil of man's cruelty to man and beast. The problem of the delivery of the Message and the implementation of the Mission seemed somehow different, vaster, more cosmically significant, than it did back there in Galilee. It was no longer the mere proclamation of the Glad Tidings and the consequent salvation of His hearers. Something far deeper was at stake: the ingrained and instinctive evil in human nature. Its roots went so deep that it seemed as though no moral ploughshare could upturn them—as if, indeed, they went down into the very heart of earth. He knew now, with a start of realization, how right He had been to concentrate upon the training of the Twelve. How right, too, He had been in His talk with Nicodemus to insist on the necessity for rebirth.

Love alone could give a man Eternal Life, and love alone could awaken love. And love meant love of a person for a person. The disciples' essential loyalty was to Himself rather than to His Teaching. When they had said "Lord, to Whom shall we go? Thou hast the words of Eternal Life," the accent had been on the "Thou" rather than on the "words." He had been on firmer ground when He had seen the light of personal devotion in a man's eyes than when He, by logic or dialectic or even by persuasive Gospel preaching, had defeated an opponent's arguments or opened his eyes to truth. Ethics were seen to be somehow lifeless, powerless to change souls—to alter their whole nature without affecting their basic individuality. It seemed as though it were futile to try to convert the world to a new way of life, to a fresh concept of the Divine; men were too weak, too human, indeed, to respond fully. They needed a greater attractive power than a mere ideal, no matter how true and lofty. The strength of sin was too great, like the pull to earth that dragged everything downward. Men were under the slavery of sin just as surely as those wretched toilers down there by the sea were under the bondage of tyrants. They longed in vain for freedom. Who could pay for their redemption? His heart ached for them and called in silence upon Heaven to redeem them. The answer came in the sudden knowledge that *He* could redeem their souls if only He could prevail over sin and cut through the entail of evil and arouse an answering love that defied the downward drag and soared upward to Heaven—naturally and inevitably. First, the sense of sin must be awakened. Then the hunger for pardon. Then the assurance of that pardon. And lastly the cleansing power of love, at work after the miracle of rebirth, and thereafter inborn as deeply—nay more deeply—than was their former sin.

He thought of the Magdalene—perhaps His most triumphant success so far in life changing. She had been changed because she loved much; and that love had been aroused in her because much had been forgiven her. And this love, purgative, self-abandoning and self-giving to the uttermost, was a love for Himself. He saw that only insofar as He could awaken such a love in every heart could He ever hope to win the world for God by the conquest and redemption of every individual man. Nothing but a gracious personal relationship to Himself, and so to God in Him, could avail to change and purify the evil heart of man. It was borne in upon Him that He now no longer viewed the problem of the world's conversion as from His own sinless standpoint, but from the viewpoint of the sin-stained, weak, despairing average man. There had never been, for Him, any capitulation of "I ought" to "I will"; no surrender of "you must" to "I cannot." He had never known the guilt and stain of sin, its cancerous growth and hold, its wasting, gnawing remorse, its enfeebling and paralyzing effect upon the will and heart. But for some time now He had been increasingly realizing the power of sin; the problem before Him was now seen no longer in the greys of varying discipleship, but in the blacks and whites of tyranny and victimization, of evil and love. And as the thonged and curling lash fell with sickening impact on the quivering flesh of slavedom, He had known suddenly that what the world needed was a Redeemer: One Who would not merely defeat Satan in Himself, but in every man in all the world. Down there in Tyre it would have been but a temporary palliative to exert His voice in denunciation or to interfere actively in defence of a slave. Even to rescue a victim by a miracle, even to startle the whole Tyrian slave-owning class into terrorized requital of injustices, would have been merely to free the bodies of men, not their souls. As in the Wilderness, miracle was seen to be useless for God's supreme purpose. It could never redeem souls. It could never cut out the root of evil in human nature or rectify the basic fault, the seam of sin, that traversed the universe and had its origin in the abuse of free will, itself the essential condition of virtue.

So Jesus stood there above Tyre, the weight of the world's sin—of all the world's ages of sin—heavy upon Him. The disciples utterly failed to realize that those eyes that gazed over the sea coast of Tyre and Sidon were probing a void dark and lonely, in which at last a Cross was slowly shaping itself, as the swirling mists of the future a space unsettled; a Cross whose shaft went deeper into earth than evil at its most deep-sunk and higher into Heaven than wonder could imagine; a Cross whose arms reached out embracingly into all space, entreating the whole universe in a pleading gesture of forgiveness. Down there in Tyre He could do nothing permanently to free the captives, to release the prisoners from the fetters of the soul; but in the greater world of the Spirit, Jesus—so still now—was active beyond all thought to express. He was unravelling—and in one great act was this solution slowly shaping itself—the dual problem that confronted Him: how best to prove to His disciples, and through them to the world, that He loved them to the uttermost in spite of their sins—even in spite of the very worst that sin could do to Him; and how best to prove to them, and through them to the world, that this Friend Who loved them so was indeed God's Messiah, God's Eternal Son, God Himself. Then, and then only, in the Tyres and Sidons of the world, would there no longer be Jew and Gentile, bondsmen and freemen, but all would be one in Him, even in the Christ. The seed, sown indeed by Him in Galilee, and in all the earth by His disciples, would never fully fructify until it had died in that earth. He would then in very truth "sleep and rise," but in how different a way from that originally thought of when first that lovely Parable was spoken!

So was the easy optimism of success gradually exchanged for the tragic, heroic optimism of seeming failure; for He never once relinquished this flaming Faith in eventual success, but carried it aloft as a banner and flourished it in the face of the dark heavens, when, even God Himself having seemingly abandoned Him, He yet could cry triumphantly, "It is finished!" That same Tyrian purple was His robe when Pilate cried, "Behold your King"; but when He went forth to Golgotha His vesture was encrimsoned with His own Blood.

Who is this that cometh from Edom, with dyed garments from Bozrah?—this that is glorious in His apparel, travelling in the greatness of His strength?

I that speak in righteousness, mighty to save.

Wherefore art Thou red in Thine apparel, and Thy garments like unto His that treadeth in the winefat?

I have trodden the winepress alone, and of the peoples there was no man with Me. Yea, the time to redeem Mine own has come. I looked, but there was no one to help. I was amazed that there was none to aid. So Mine own arm shall bring salvation: My passion shall bear Me on. Alone I must tread the winepress; for no one can help. I will redeem you, with outstretched arms!

And there, exalted above physical fatigue, racked and shaken by great storms of the Spirit, Himself the Slave of Heaven, the doomed and devoted Victim suffering for a world's redemption, exultant, tragic, compassionate to all infinity—He stretched out His arms to Tyre and Sidon, to all the oppressed of man and beast on earth, and cried:

"Come unto Me, all ye that labour and are heavy-laden, and *I* will give you rest! Take My yoke upon you, and learn of Me. For I am meek and lowly in heart, and you shall find rest unto your souls. For My yoke is easy, and My burden is light! *Yea, I will ransom you! I will redeem you! I, even I, will come and save you! Your Redeemer is the Holy One of Israel—'the God of the whole earth' shall He be called!'"

And, with a mighty sigh of sorrow mingled with triumph, His arms fell again to His sides and His head was turned once more to the mountains, and He began to move upward again. But the disciples were bewildered, dazed, utterly at a loss to understand Him. One day they dared to ask Him why He had been dumb before all that wickedness in Tyre.

But He only answered, *"I must put a muzzle on My lips, before all those ungodly men. So was I dumb, silent, and ill at ease. But My grief was stirred; My heart was hot within Me: and even as I was thus musing the fire kindled within Me*—a fire that shall one day fall upon the world from above, to burn, to warm, to lighten. He who is near Me is near the fire. But he who is far from Me is far from the King-dom."

He searched their faces for any sign of comprehension, but they were even more mystified when He cried again, *"Dumb, again, shall I be; dumb as a sheep led to the slaughter; despised and rejected of men; a Man of Sorrows and acquainted with grief.* I hear the voices of the slaves of sin crying out:

" *'We took no heed of Him; yet ours was the pain He endured. He was wounded because we had sinned. He was crushed for our iniqui-ties. For our peace was He chastised, and with His stripes we are healed. Like sheep we had gone astray. We had each taken our own ways. And the Lord has laid on Him the iniquity of us all. Yea, He shall see the travail of His soul—and shall be satisfied! 'Twas their guilt He bore. Therefore shall He win the victory! Therefore shall He succeed triumphantly!—because He shed His life blood, bearing the great world's sins, and interposing for sinners.' "*

Thus, as the night clouds descended over Him, the fire of His love waxed ever more glowingly—the whole earth alight in one vast holo-caust, till at last nought else was seen but the one central furnace in a universal void of darkness, and Himself, in the centre, hanging upon a Cross. Thus did Jesus of Galilee wax unto the measure of the stature of the fulness of the Christ. But the disciples were awed and frightened as they followed Him up into these remote and rarefied regions and they found it difficult to breathe.

(IV) RETURN TO THE LAKESIDE

THEY struck across country, travelling by little-known ways and aiming at villages in the hills where a night's lodging could be had. But now that they were in the wilder part of the Lebanon range they were often forced to sleep out in the open under the stars, and the nights were cold and often frosty. Their route, as before, was necessarily circuitous, winding round the peaks or threading a gorge or suddenly dropping to a river ford. Once, when faced by the necessity to pass over a rushing torrent, they sought in vain for any means of crossing till they espied a narrow, high-swung rope bridge spanning the gorge above the swirling waters. They were nervous of attempting the crossing, as the precarious bridge could only hold one at a time.

But Jesus Himself crossed first and called to each of them in turn to follow Him. When they were all safely over, He said, "This world is but a bridge. Pass over it, but don't build your house upon it." Philip thought it was like the river of death the Greeks wrote about. There was but one way over it, and it was a way that each of them had to travel separately. But if one kept one's eye on Jesus, calling from the other side, one was welcomed in safety by the Master.

Not long after this they came suddenly face to face with an even greater barrier to progress: a colossal ravine, dropping away fully fifteen hundred feet below them. Sunset was almost come and in the gloom the depth of the gorge seemed immeasurable, as if it hid the valley of the shadow of death or was even the abyss itself. Great eagles winged their slow way over or poised high in air, their long pinions outspread in the sunlight that was creeping ever higher up the mountain slopes.

Jesus watched their easy flight, their soaring over difficulties. The words came into His mind: *They that wait upon the Lord shall renew their strength. They shall mount up on wings like eagles.* And again: *Yea, I will bear You on eagle's wings, and bring You—to Myself!*— out of it all, away from the misunderstandings and enmities of men. But as He gazed into that bottomless pit that gaped below Him, He knew that its impassability was like that dividing duty from inclination. It was akin to the temptation of the pinnacle of the Temple. There was no way over that gulf.

He turned solemnly to His disciples and, with set face and outstretched arm, His figure lighted to burning beauty by the sundown, flaming and wrathful, He cried, "Do you see yonder gulf? Even so is there a great gulf, fathomless, impassable and dark with death, set forever between right and wrong. There can be no passing to and fro from one side to the other. Either a man is on that side or on this. Either a thing is right or it is wrong. There can be no compromise between good and evil. For these distinctions are eternal, fixed and set in the very heart of the universe—like the gulf separating Heaven from Hell."

Their way southward led them over the River Leontes, with its tremendous gorges and foaming cataracts, and thence by the Hasbany stream, fed from the snows of Hermon and becoming lower down its course the River Jordan. Passing through the magnificent oak glades of Naphtali, they descended once again to the marshes of Lake Huleh and so down to the reaches of the Upper Jordan. Arrived at Bethsaida Julias, Jesus, desiring above all at this juncture to avoid publicity, bypassed the town, but was recognized by a disciple, who besought Him to heal a friend of his who was blind.

Jesus took hold of the blind man by the hand and led him outside the village through which they were passing and, utilizing the alleged therapeutic qualities of saliva, anointed the man's eyes and laying His hands on him asked him, "Tell Me, can you see anything at all now?"

The man gazed about him for a while and then answered: "Yes . . . I just make out people, but they look like trees—only walking!" At this, Jesus laid His hands on the man's eyes once again, and he, staring steadily in front of him, gradually recovered his sight and saw everything distinctly.

Then Jesus sent him off home, with the parting injunction, "Now, not a word to anybody about this. Don't even go into the village."

So, skirting the town (but Peter and Andrew were longing to go back to their many friends there) they made their way southward along the east bank of the river, ignoring the bridge that led across the estuary toward Capernaum and passing instead through the bleak and inhospitable region on the eastward shores of the Lake. Herod Antipas had ordered a search for Jesus to be made throughout his territory, but this side of the Lake was outside his Province. So Jesus wandered, homeless and hunted, along these arid eastern shores; while, just over there, beyond the rippling levels of the Lake, was sunlit Capernaum and their own familiar little creek, under the lee of the rising hills backing the plain. So near and yet so far. That bright vista called to Him and its beckoning beauty made Him doubly home-sick—until He realized anew its hostility and its hardness of heart.

Then it was that He thought of Tyre and Sidon, away over the hills to the far north. Their wickedness, ghastly and unthinkable as it was, was somehow more excusable than was Capernaum's; for Galilee had heard His preaching, had seemed to welcome His Good News, had witnessed His greatest Miracles—signs of His innate authority. The Jews' enmity was inexcusable, merciless and without any extenuation of ignorance. If Tyre and Sidon had had Capernaum's opportunities, they would surely have repented before now. No. He could not cross that narrow sea.

So, instead of going home, He found Himself moving on from one strange city to another, in those cosmopolitan centres of Greek life that formed the confederation of the Ten Cities, spaced about Philip's territory but owing no allegiance to him, among them Geresa, Hippos, Gadara and Scythopolis. His thoughts about Tyre and Sidon encouraged Him to wander here among these pagans—to see for Himself the men of the greater world for whom He was so soon to die. He felt an almost unbearable compassion for them. Over there, beyond those few sea miles, men had seen the light and preferred darkness. Here, in these beautiful cities, in spite of all their superstition and vicious ways, men knew nothing better than the grey half lights. They were indeed sheep without a shepherd.

Then, one day, He ran into His brothers who were going up to Jerusalem for the Feast of Tabernacles.

The brothers were on edge. The tension in the family had grown till they could no longer bear the thought of their Elder Brother's presence in Galilee. They had thought Him gone for good, and now He was back again, albeit on the outskirts of the Province, near the Judaean border. They could not counter their mother's influence to the extent of betraying Jesus to the authorities; but, on the other hand, they could not refrain from doing their best to drive Him into instant departure—and if into renewed danger, well, that would be His own affair. They glanced covertly at His disciples. Sensing their possible disillusionment, the brothers laid their plans with superlative subtlety, as they sat there in a grassy hollow, out of sight of the road, talking with Jesus, the disciples in a group behind Him.

"You see, we are on our way up to the Feast of Tabernacles. By the way, it's a long time since You were present at any feast, isn't it? Why don't You go up to this one? We know why: You're frightened of the Jews—especially of the Jews of Jerusalem. If You're not, prove it by leaving here with us, instead of hiding behind a screen of anonymity. You missed the Passover, if You remember—most reprehensibly, in our opinion. Keep this feast, then, that is, if You dare to show Yourself openly, there or anywhere else. You pretend that You're aiming at public recognition of Your teaching—to say nothing of Your claims, whatever they are. Well, nobody who aims at publicity skulks about furtively in secret. Besides, since we've heard so much about these precious miracles of Yours—not that we've ever seen You perform one—display Your powers openly to all the world, there at the great feast! There'll be people of every nation there. What more could You wish?"

They glanced sidelong at the disciples. "It would be nice, too, for Your disciples to see You openly at work again. . . ."

With a wonderful dignity and patience, though with infinite weariness, Jesus made answer: "Mine hour is not yet come, but one hour is the same as any other so far as you are concerned."

He regarded them with grave irony. "The world can't hate *you*. But it hates Me, because I dare to accuse it of its evil ways. So go on up to this feast, by all means. I'm not going up now. I'll wait My hour!"

With these mysterious hints they had to be content. They rose up and without any further word passing among them they departed along the road and were soon lost to sight. Because they were at heart good men, they would never betray their Brother; but they were vexed and exasperated, making their slow way up to the feast. To their way of thinking, Jesus was obviously mad, with all this talk of "His hour." And what did that mean, anyway?

II

The Feast of Tabernacles

I

BUT He did go up to the feast, nevertheless. The remembrance that He had missed the Passover haunted Him. He felt an urge to worship in the Temple, especially at this feast, since it was not so bloodthirsty as many others, the chief ceremonies being symbolic rather than sacrificial. He thought He might maintain His incognito if every precaution for secrecy were taken. But even so, He hesitated for four days before finally deciding to go up to Jerusalem. But He travelled alone. He sent His disciples home—and they had greatly longed for this—not telling them where He was Himself going but arranging to meet them later in an agreed place, privately.

In Jerusalem there was great excitement. The chief topic of conversation was the possibility of the presence of Jesus at the feast. His absence at the Passover had been attributed to His natural reaction to the Butaiha crisis and the fears of imminent arrest. He had, they thought, been right in refusing to be made a King, for the numbers then with Him had been insufficient for any attempted rising. It was rumoured that He had gone off into the hills somewhere to prepare His plan of campaign and to train His disciples as His chief officers. Besides, there was the added excitement now of knowing that the Jewish authorities were anxious to effect His arrest and had sent out spies to search for Him.

But the days went by and there was no sign of Him. Speculation was rife regarding His place in Israel—His status, His role, His future. Some said, "He is a good man, at any rate." Others held that He was imposing on the people—or would be if ever He reappeared. But no one expressed his views openly, for fear of the Priests. The Beloved Disciple, moving freely among the crowds, noted the expectant ferment in the Pilgrims' minds. He wondered if he would see his Master at the feast. He had missed Him at the Passover, though he fully understood why. Since then he had heard nothing of Him. He seemed to have vanished into thin air. But that Jesus had abandoned His Mission was utterly unthinkable, and John kept a sharp watch for his Lord, searching high and low and especially in the Temple for that beloved Figure. Often he met Nicodemus and talked over with him the problems of conduct and belief presented by the impact of Jesus on their lives. Another Counsellor, Joseph of Arimathea, had begun to interest himself in the new Prophet, having been present when Jesus defied the Temple authorities and cleared the courtyard of traffic and sacrificial beasts. Something within him answered the call, challenging him to re-read the Prophets in the light of this revolutionary teaching. There was little doubt on which side they were.

On the fourth day of the feast John went up into the Temple to search the crowds as usual and, seeing a dense mass of people in one of the courts, edged his way thither and heard to his amazement, the voice—clear, golden-toned and unforgettable—of his Master and saw, in a moment, His tall figure and outstretched arms as He was teaching the people.

Arrived privily in Jerusalem, Jesus had felt the urge to teach so strongly that it was irresistible. As always, love had its way, and here He was teaching the Pilgrims the doctrines of the New Covenant regardless of consequences. As John made his way excitedly toward Jesus, he overheard some of the comments of the crowd. "Isn't this the Man they want to kill? But look! Here He is, preaching openly and nobody says a word to stop Him!"

"Do you think the authorities have found out that He really *is* the Messiah?"

"No. We know perfectly well where this Fellow comes from, whereas the origin of the Messiah will be utterly unknown."

Jesus happened to overhear this exchange, and at once cried out to the disputants, "So you know Me, do you, and where I come from—whereas the origin of the Messiah will be unknown? But don't imagine that I have come on My own initiative. I have been *sent,* sent by Him Who is true. And it's no use your saying you know *Him,* for you don't. But *I* know Him, because I am come from Him, and He sent Me."

There was a glory and a mysticism about Jesus as He uttered these strange and moving words. He was rapt and exalted, far above the world, and His earthly origin seemed a matter of complete indifference. And with that, He ended His preaching.

The Sanhedrin, the Great Council of the Seventy, reacted with swiftness to the reappearance of Jesus in Jerusalem. They tried to arrange for His arrest, but no one actually laid hands on Him. John, who knew from Nicodemus what was toward, marvelled at this, but attributed it to the fact that, as Jesus was so fond of saying, "His hour was not yet come." Besides, he noted that many of the people were so deeply impressed with His words as to join with these Galileans who were already attracted to Him. A general comment was: "When the Messiah does come, do you think He will do any greater deeds than this Man has done?"

This attitude so upset the Pharisees that they connived with the High Priestly party, normally their rivals and even enemies, to effect an immediate arrest, a move which Nicodemus through John made known to Jesus, Who cried to the people, "Only for a little while am I likely to be with you in this world, and then I shall return to Him Who sent Me. You may search for Me *then,* but you won't find Me; and whither I shall have gone, you cannot come."

This sad and solemn truth was lost on His hearers. Their only reaction was to speculate as to His earthly destination. Having discussed the whence? they now wrangled about the whither? But the Spirit has no earthly whence or whither.

"Where on earth is He about to take Himself to, that we shall not only be unable to find Him, but can't even go ourselves? Is He reckoning to fly to the Dispersed Israelites, among the Greeks, to teach them? What *can* He mean by these sayings 'You may search for Me, but you won't find Me,' and 'Where I'm going to, you can't come'? It's impossible to tell what He means."

II

On the last, that is, the greatest day of the feast, John was returning from an overnight visit to his close friends, Lazarus of Bethany and Martha his sister, when, breasting the Mount of Olives, among the innumerable booths set up on the hillside to accommodate the Pilgrims and to fulfil the customs of the feast, he stood in the first glimmerings of dawn to view the world-famous panorama of the Holy City as seen from this spot. He watched Jerusalem change from a black, almost invisible mass, one with the shadows of the valley and the departing night wrack, to a darkly bastioned stronghold, girt about with the sombre rectangularity of her mighty walls, till at length a misty silvered City emerged from the gloom.

As the echoes of the long-held notes at last died away, the slanting rays of the sun gilded with glory the golden dome covering the Holy of Holies, and soon John was moving, with a hundred, a thousand, others, in an ever-swelling concourse, down the hillside toward the Garden of Gethsemane, shady with its innumerable olive trees and surrounding walls. There the Pilgrims would split up into separate streams, some going straight up into the Temple for the Morning Sacrifice; some moving toward Moza to cut down willow branches with which to adorn the altar; the greater part hurrying forward and turning to the left, once they were within the walls of the City, in order to join in the procession which had already started out from the Temple and whose festive music could even now be heard from afar. The ringing shouts and trumpet fanfares, the shrill chanting of children and the deep antiphons of Priests and Levites, echoed out from somewhere in the City; and, there, visible for a moment, till the descent of Olivet shut out the sight, were the white vestments of the Priests and the multitudinous colours of the Pilgrims' robes as they surged by a narrow-headed opening in the maze of streets and houses. The echoes were lost to hearing as John moved down into the valley of the Kedron and thence rose up toward the wall and passed into the cool darkness of the stone gate. Skirting the Temple and crossing the Tyropoean bridge, he and his fellow Pilgrims were at last merged in the concourse of people moving slowly toward the Pool of Siloam for the ceremonial drawing of water for the libation during the great Morning Service in the Temple.

John hurried with those Pilgrims who were intent on joining this procession, running through the streets till, at the end of an alleyway, he caught sight of the stream of people slowly wending its way toward the Pool. It was led by a high official, gorgeously vested, carrying a huge golden ewer; on arrival at the Pool, he descended the steep-cut rock steps that led down to the dark, still water. The depth of the descent seemed all the greater in that the ruins of a newly built tower here adorned the wall close by the Pool. It had lately collapsed and killed some people—Jesus was to refer to the disaster later. The Priest, now hidden in the shadows of the portico, was, as the crowds well knew, dipping his golden ewer into the Pool, till it was nearly full. Then he reappeared, and another Priest joined him, and together they carried the heavy vessel up into the glare of the morning sunlight, while a shout went up from the Pilgrims leaning over the parapets to watch. Then the procession re-formed and marched back with even greater festivity of song and shout and trumpet blasts, toward the Temple, gleaming high up before them on its hill site far above. The procession timed its arrival at the Temple so as to coincide with the offering up of the Morning Sacrifice on the altar. The Priests at the gate marked its arrival to the thousands thronging the Courts by a trumpet blast which was answered from within by a similar fanfare, after which a cry went up: *Therefore with joy shall we draw water out of the wells of Salvation!*

Thereupon the massive bronze doors swung slowly open and the procession entered the Temple. The Priest was met at the entrance to the Court of the Priests by another official bearing the wine for the Drink Offering. Together the three Priests ascended the steps toward the altar, while the crowd stood silent, watching. To the left of the altar were two silver funnels, the wine being first poured out into the easternmost, and then the golden ewer was tipped toward the mouth of the other, the water running out in a clear stream, while the silence accompanying the rite was suddenly rent by a deafening shout from the people as the twin libations were offered to Jehovah. Wine for blood: sacrificial, self-offering; water for cleansing and purifying. "Not water only, but water and blood."

The Beloved Disciple remembered in later years the new significance of this fact; remembered also the water made wine—the enrichment of life into life when offered to God in sacrificial self-oblation.

Then, flooding in upon the moving tide of thought and feeling came the thundering music of the great Hallel, with its dramatic allusions and ever-rising swell of praise.

From the dawn even to dusk the Lord's name is praised! Tremble, O earth, at the presence of the Eternal, Who turned the hard rock into a pool, and the flint stone into a springing well.

Thrilled, John looked at Jesus, standing by him. *The presence of the Eternal . . .* Were those words being even now fulfilled? As for Jesus, in His heart He heard the soul of the world crying: *My soul is athirst for God, yes, even for the living God. . . . When shall I reach . . . God's presence?* Then followed a mighty shout from the assembled Pilgrims: *Save now, O Lord!*

The compulsion of the Divine imperative descended upon Him, and before any sound had broken the silence that ensued He had mounted a plinth of a pillar and His voice was lifted up, echoing all over that vast Court.

"If any man is athirst, let him come unto *Me,* and drink! He who believes in Me, even as the Scripture says: *Deep within him shall well up fountains of Living Water!*"

Every eye was turned toward Jesus, His arms outstretched in an agony of supplication. John was tingling with pride and a burning love for his Master. He beheld a new Jesus, One Who no longer was content only to preach the purest ethics of love, but Who called men to believe in Himself rather than in any ideal—or rather in Himself as the embodiment of all true ideals.

Then, breaking in upon John's spellbound reverie, came turmoil and reaction and multitudinous movement, as people at last turned away from Jesus to discuss this strange appeal. Snatches of talk reached John's ears.

"This is, beyond a shadow of doubt, the Prophet that should come!"

"I tell you, He's the Messiah of God!"

"No, for surely the Messiah will never come from Galilee. Why, doesn't it expressly say in the Scriptures, that the Messiah is to come from the family of David, and from the town of Bethlehem where David himself came from?"

If Jesus heard this wrangle, He let the argument go by default—if ever He knew that He hailed from Bethlehem—preferring to disregard outward origins or fulfilment of prophecy as things of such secondary importance as to merit no pride and substantiate no claim. What He was in Himself—that alone mattered.

There was a violent dissension among the people over Jesus. Some were for arresting Him at once; the Jewish authorities had actually sent Temple Guards to arrest Him, unbeknown to the crowds. The Great Council waited, sullen and brooding, for their return with the Prisoner. The Guards were a long time about this business. Why didn't they come? Could He have escaped or had there been a fight? They grew uneasy and restless as their impatience passed into anger . . . and fear. At last the officer of the guard entered the Council Chamber—without the Prisoner! There was an astounded silence, and then a sharp question: "Why haven't you brought Him?"

Another long silence, and then the amazing words faltered from the lips, trembling and stuttering, of that hard-bitten soldier, "Because . . . no m-man . . . in all the world . . . ever spoke as He does." A mere whisper of awe and wonder, for this soldier has unwittingly stumbled on the truth, to which these crafty Elders were blind and deaf. "No man . . ." Not Socrates or Plato nor even any of the Prophets . . . "No *man* . . ." Only Jesus dared so to speak—to identify Himself with the Source of those Living Waters that give life to the soul.

But the Jewish Leaders were white with rage. "So *you* are deluded, too!" Their spokesman swept an arm over the downcast faces around him. "Have any of us Rulers ever believed on Him?" There was a slight pause as he glanced at Nicodemus. "As for the rabble, with its ignorance of the Law, it is accursed!"

An uncomfortable silence followed, Nicodemus looking troubled. That probing taunt pointed a minatory finger at his disloyalty both to the Sanhedrin and to Jesus. He stirred himself slightly and, plucking up courage, tried to assume an air of studied impartiality.

"But surely," he argued, trying to keep his voice calm and steady, "our Law never allows anyone to be condemned without first hearing what he has to say and ascertaining the real facts—formulating the charge, I mean."

The Rulers had their retort ready for this suspect Ruler. "So you're also from Galilee, are you?" they sneered. "Search as much as you like, and you'll see from the Scriptures that no Prophet ever sprang from Galilee."

Nicodemus left it at that. He had made his protest and salved his conscience; and he noted, with uneasy satisfaction, that no one took the opportunity to ask, "What about that secret visit of yours to Jesus?" so probably his fears on that score were groundless after all. No one, either, bade the Temple Guards go back and fetch in the wanted man. The Leaders uneasily allowed the matter to drop, for the present. A rising was to be avoided at all costs, and there were many Galileans at the feast who might be depended upon to side with any impostor if trouble ensued. But this brawler would have to be laid by the heels sooner or later—sooner by choice.

The Pilgrims had much to talk about during the heat of the day, when Jerusalem rested before returning to the Temple for the last and greatest service of the feast. With most of them it was more the strangeness of the interruption than the meaning of it that occupied their thoughts. But with John deeper issues contended in his mind for mastery. As he reflected on the compulsive quality in Jesus' words that morning—so self-authenticating, so moving—he found his heart in full agreement, though his mind was as yet baffled. One thing emerged clearly. Belief, in Jesus' sense, was in a person—*Jesus* Himself—not in a code or creed or any racial inheritance. What was already for him a gracious personal relationship seemed about to become a cosmic dependence, a universal trust. Even more, it was on the verge of becoming an identification of Godhead with Jesus. Indeed, Jesus' words could mean nothing less than this. Was it, then, the truth that only in Jesus could his soul—could any man's soul— find true rest, slake its thirst and enjoy life to the full? But somehow the truth had seemed to shine from His eyes as that cry had gone out to all the listening crowds—went out to all the listening world. How could religion be centred in a man? Yet love was unintelligible apart from personality . . . and, for him, John, this Person was the very centre and source of love. It radiated out from Him and returned to Him. John thrilled to a new sense of inspiration, of uplift and intoxicating well-being—not unlike a first experience of falling in love— only this was allied to ultimate truth, to ultimate beauty, to ultimate goodness. It were as if a light had suddenly shone around him and revealed the glory of the world, and its reality and happiness. He felt as though he had entered on a new and larger life; was as if born again into a deathless Eternity of love and safety and rest, of joyous energy and self-forgetful service. This was the life that was life indeed, and it came solely from Jesus; for in Him was summed up all space, all time, all virtue, all reality, all joy. To trust Him would be to surrender all, and to find All—enriched and glorified.

As afternoon began to wane, the Pilgrims made their way once more toward the Temple. Excitement and exaltation glowed in every eye, for tonight the great golden candelabra were to be lighted! Nearly everybody carried an unlighted torch, in readiness for the dramatic ceremony of the illumination at sundown. As John entered the Court of the Women he could see, towering up thirty feet high above the marble pavement, the pair of candelabra, which, once they were lighted, would illuminate the other Courts on either side. This ceremony was known as the "Joy of the Feast." It was the supreme occasion of festivity.

The service, alternating in psalm and antiphon and response, mountingly approached its climax as the sun sank slowly behind the western hills. A golden glow, deepening to crimson, suffused the evening sky as the shadows began to darken the Temple Courts and only the topmost towers on the walls yet held the last red gleams of the sunken sun. At a signal from a watcher on one of these, the chief celebrant, a long taper in his hand, came slowly down the fifteen steps that separated the Court of the Women from that of the Priests, through the vast choir of Levites, silent as yet, which was crowding the terraces. Every eye was lifted to the pair of enormous candelabra, beyond which the first pale stars were gleaming high in the September sky. Then a priestly voice rose in the still evening air: *Arise, shine! for thy Light is come!—and the Glory of the Lord is risen upon thee!* And lifting high his taper the ministrant touched first the central lamp of the northernmost candelabrum, proceeding then to light the other six lamps that lay on either side; thence passing on to the southern candelabrum and lighting that in similar fashion.

As the brightening stars were lost to sight in the gloom that enveloped everything beyond the central clusters of artificial light, a great shattering burst of song went up from the massed choirs as the last lamp flared up. *The Lord went before our fathers by day in a pillar of smoke, to lead them in the way; and by night in a pillar of fire—to give them light, that they might go by day and by night. The*

*pillar of smoke by day and the pillar of fire by night departed not
from before the people. Hallelujah!*

Then the Levites, in ordered sequence, lined up in procession, all
of them, as they reached the candelabra, mounting the steps and reaching high their torches, to light them from the great lamps flaring high
above, till the torchlight procession was a flaming column moving
slowly around the Courts. Then came the people's turn, each Pilgrim
lighting his torch and crying "Hallelujah," as the glare increased to
a blinding conflagration and the glorious Temple buildings stood out,
flood-lighted against the impenetrable darkness of the night.

This took a long time to complete; and when at length every torch
was alight, there followed much dancing and waving of torches and
shouting, till, as the night wore on, many of the torches burned themselves out and were cast down upon the marble pavements and extinguished by the trampling crowds. The Courts grew dark again and
soon the first glimmers of early dawn quivered in the east and made
the few torches yet alight and the tall candelabra look suddenly pale
and thin—mere pinpoints of artificial illumination, waging a pathetic,
losing battle with the fast-rising day. As the sun's first horizontal
ray, like a rapier of gold, pierced the trepidant air and burst upon the
Temple towers, the threefold blast of the silver trumpets once more
rang out, as two Priests, themselves holding trumpets, descended the
steps leading down to the great courtyard. At the tenth step they
halted and answered the bright summons with another threefold fanfare; and yet again they blew as they entered the Court. So, still
sounding intermittently their strident challenges, they marched toward
the Beautiful Gate. Arrived there (and by now the sun was mounting
momently, and its rays were beginning to stream out over the City),
they turned themselves about and faced westward toward the Holy
Place, crying, "Our Fathers, who were in this place—they turned
their backs upon the Sanctuary, their faces toward the sun. . . . But
our eyes are turned toward the Lord!"

And there before them, had they but realized it, stood the Lord
Himself—the outworn, shoddy-looking candelabra eclipsed by the
rising sun, lighting not only Israel, but the whole world; the Priests
of the Old Covenant turning toward the Mediator of the New, Himself the Sun and Centre of the whole universe. . . . The full dramatic

significance of this superb moment struck young John so strongly that he could hardly stand, he felt so giddy. . . .

Then it was that the clear voice of his Lord once more rang out over that rapt and startled throng, *"I am the Light—of the world!"*

The simple, amazing words, so few, so unutterably profound, were followed by a silence and a stilling of all movement, as if that vast concourse of people were suddenly caught in a spell, every upturned face being seen as though held a moment in the wonder of an eternal awareness. Here, in Christ, was the reality behind all symbols, behind the beauty of art, behind even the sun's radiance.

The Beloved Disciple, musing upon that strange scene long afterward, saw more deeply than any other its true import. Just as the sun rising lighted not Jerusalem or Israel only, but the whole world, so was Jesus potentially the Light of the world. In Him was life, and the life was the light of men.

The voice of Jesus was heard again. He was thinking of the Pillar of Fire. "He that follows Me shall not walk in darkness, but shall enjoy the light of life!"

And again the Beloved Disciple mused upon these words. They reminded him of Enoch's fine passage: *The righteous shall be ever in the Light of the sun, and in the Light of Eternal Life. They will seek out the Light, and It shall become for them bright as the sun upon earth. For the darkness is past, and the Light shall be unceasing. The righteous shall walk in Eternal Light!* Long after, he recalled another saying that Jesus had uttered on that occasion, and his eyes glowed with joy at the recollection.

"I'll give you the Message Jesus gave us then," he added, "and remember, I am telling you only of the things—nay of the Person—which I myself heard; which these mine eyes have seen; which these very hands handled; the things that I myself can vouch for from personal experience, in order that our united joy might be full—as Jesus Himself wanted. . . . Well, this is the Message Jesus gave us then: *God is Light, and in Him is no darkness at all!* Is that not a very lovely saying?"

But the Priests that day were furious. The implications of Jesus' words were so fantastic, even to the point of profanation and blasphemy, that they could only have been uttered by someone driven mad by excess of egoism. Such claims counted for less than nothing when viewed dispassionately, even pityingly. . . . There was a cold contempt in their rejoinder.

"You are but testifying to Yourself; therefore, Your evidence is invalid."

The reply of Jesus was calm. "Though I do testify to Myself, yet My evidence is completely valid. You were discussing My origins recently, in your search for My credentials. Well, you see, I happen to know where I come from and where I'm going to. I'm not walking blindly. Besides, Mine is not merely a single, uncorroborated testimony; and your own Law makes it perfectly clear that *the evidence of two persons is valid*. I am the One—I testify to Myself, as you say— and My Father is the Other, testifying to Me."

Light's self-witness is always valid, being self-authenticating. But all that the Priests could sense was that this second witness was no-where to be seen. The idea of an absent witness was fit subject only for ridicule. "And *where* is Your 'Father'? Why don't You produce Him?"

But blindness cannot see the Light. It was on account of no inability on the part of *Jesus* to reveal the Father that this "absent" Witness was not recognizable by the Elders.

"As for My Father," answered Jesus, "you know as little about Him as you do about Me. If you had known anything about Me, you would have known also about My Father. He Who sent Me is never an absent Witness. He is ever at My side; for He has not left Me alone, because I do always what pleases Him."

This, He well knew, was the secret of His unity with the Father: the very essence of all Christology. The warrant of truth was stamped on His words. It shone in His eyes and rang in His voice. "As He said this," says the Beloved Disciple, who was there, "many believed in Him." He recalled, too, how Jesus sought out these new disciples and spoke earnestly to them.

"It is the same for you as it is for Me," He told them. "If you abide by My Teaching, that will show whether you really are disciples of Mine; for then you will realize the truth—and the truth shall set you free!"

Jesus never said anything of vaster or more ultimate import than this. Perfect freedom comes alone from perfect obedience to God's will. Freedom is uninterrupted obedience to Law—the highest and most truly natural Law of one's being. But the Leaders caught hold of the word "free" and were incensed at what they thought was an implied denial of their racial freedom.

"Free!" they retorted. "Why, we are Abraham's descendants, and have never known what it is to be slaves to anybody." This was far from being true, but Jesus let it pass. "What do You mean," they asked Him, "by saying 'You will become free'?"

But Jesus was not bothering about their racial history, either way. As always, He was contemplating Eternal Truth. "In most solemn truth, I tell you that everyone who commits sin is a slave. Now, a slave has no permanency of status; only the Son of the House possesses that. If, then, the Son sets you free, you will be free indeed. As for Me, I speak of what I have actually seen with My Father; just as you also have learned from *your* father."

"But *our* father is Abraham, as we told You."

"If you were really Abraham's children, you would do as Abraham would have done. You don't show much likeness to him in wanting to kill Me just because I have dared to tell you the truth. No. You have another father."

This infuriated the Elders. They recalled the tales spread by Jesus' enemies from Galilee—tales of queer happenings in Nazareth, long ago. "*We* were not born of adultery. . . . *We* are no bastards. *We* have one father only—even God."

The veiled reference to His earthly origin roused Jesus to anger. A steely glitter shone in His eyes. "No. Neither Abraham—and certainly not God—begat you. *Your* father is the Devil—and the lusts of the Devil, you, his sons, desire and do: murdering—yes, and lying, the Devil's chief characteristics from the very beginnings of time. Yea, a lie is truth to him, and so it comes about that you don't believe Me, precisely because I speak the truth!"

He looked round on their glaring faces. Was there *no one* present who could see things right way up and recognize Holiness when he saw it?

So Jesus, almost in desperation, flung down the great challenge—

which still remains for all time the charter of His Divinity. "Which of you can convict Me of *sin?*"

Silence followed this unanswerable question. Not only was it not met then; it has never been met, and it can never be met. Peter and Paul, John and the unknown author of the Epistle to the Hebrews, each of them testified to the sinlessness of their Master, and none denied their testimony.

At length His voice was heard again. "Well then, if I speak truth, why don't you believe Me?"

They could not argue. Insult was the only weapon left to them. "You were in reality born in Samaria. . . . In any case, You are obviously mad."

The taunt about being a Samaritan was but cheap invective, wisely ignored by Jesus. "I am not mad," He replied. "In most solemn truth I tell you, whoever holds to what I say, he shall not even notice death—no, not to all Eternity!"

Of course, the Elders thought Jesus was talking in terms of physical existence. "Now we *know* that You're mad," they retorted, "for Abraham died, and so did all the Prophets; and yet You declare that if any one observes Your teaching he shall never die. You evidently think You're greater than our father Abraham and all the Prophets. Who do You think *You* are?"

Jesus remembered their objection to self-testimony. "As the Scripture says: *For men to seek out their own glory is* not *glory.* No. As you said, to commend Myself would count for nothing. . . . It is My Father Who glorifies Me, the Same Whom you call your God. . . . But you don't know Him. *I* it is Who know Him, and were *I* to say 'I don't know Him,' it would be as much a lie as when *you* say 'We know Him.' For I do know Him, and hold fast to His word. And as for your father Abraham—why, he exulted of old that he would eventually see My day. Yea—*and he saw it, and was glad!*"

The face of Jesus was upturned toward that Heaven wherein Abraham was even then looking down and rejoicing. The Priests were awed by that rapt radiance. They made slow reply, looking at Him scrutinizingly. They were ignorant of His earthly origins—of His birthplace and age. They saw in His countenance the signs of aging anxiety.

The bearing of the world's sorrows was deepening the lines of care in His face.

"*You* . . . why, You're not yet fifty years old. How could Abraham have seen *You?*"

But their literalism failed to bring down Jesus from His exalted spiritual stance. There, far above all gulfs, beyond the last boundaries of finite existence, on the topmost summit of experience—apart, as on a lonely peak—cut off from earth by the rolling clouds of misunderstanding, Jesus stood in spiritual isolation, viewing all the world and all the days, and uttered the solemn words:

"Amen, Amen, I say unto you, before Abraham was, I AM."

I AM . . . the self-given name of the Eternal God, repeated to Moses at the burning bush. The echoes died away, and the awful words were at length lost in the silence of stupefaction, as the Priests stared in horror at Him. If this were not true, it were the grossest blasphemy—the ultimate insult to God, deserving of immediate death. If it were true . . . But that was unthinkable. Their own eternal destiny demanded urgent action. The bolder among His enemies quickly stooped to pick up some of the loose stones lying on the ground—the inevitable debris of large-scale building still in progress. Others followed their examples, and a lynching was suddenly threatened. There was a momentary hesitation, however, as no one cared to carry out the execution, since capital punishment was the prerogative of the Roman Governor only. In a flash Jesus was surrounded by some supporters and hustled out of the Temple, and the threatened stones dropped to the ground unhurled. Many of the Jews were relieved by His disappearance. Besides, they were acutely uneasy and frightened. Awe breeds fear, and fear panic. It does not do for mortal beings to stand, even in imagination, upon the topmost peak of exaltation. But what if He were an Immortal Being? What if that Being were soon, in very truth, to stand on that self-same peak, physically then as well as spiritually and to break through into Heaven, His feet still upon earth? What then? Were there any categories for such an One? And could death stop His activities?

III

The Crisis

. . . .

(I) AT CAESAREA PHILIPPI

I

It was night in Capernaum, and a still hush had fallen over the town. The streets were empty and the high road stretched tenantless away into the distance. Only the soft lapping of tiny waves and the rhythmic refluence of water over small shingle broke the silence as with a lullaby. Unless you were especially wakeful and watchful you would never have noticed the tall Figure moving swiftly in the moon's shadows along the street leading to Peter's house, till it silently disappeared into the darkness of the portico and the latch was quietly dropped into place again. If you happened to be about later that night, you might have wondered what figures were those emerging from side streets and moving quickly out of sight along the Bethsaida road; and who comprised that other group that made its secret way toward the little creek and silently sailed away toward the head of the Lake. And next day Peter and Andrew were missed, Matthew too; and no one knew where John and James had gone, either. And of Jesus there had been no word. None had betrayed the fact that the hunted Prophet had returned during the night, and that His disciples had been secretly told to assemble above Bethsaida, and had disappeared with Him in the darkness.

When daylight came at last, the sun looked down on a little group of friends already some miles within Herod Philip's territory, making its way once more alongside the Upper Jordan marshes toward Lake Huleh and its wide flats, bounded by far blue mountains. Away to the northeast, mighty Hermon, crowned with its everlasting snows, lifted its proud summits to the skies, above and beyond its floating girdle of clouds.

Jesus considered the nature of redemption. It was not a salvation from consequences, since all natural law, both material and moral, was remedial in its results—indeed working together for good not only by direct consequence for them that loved God, but also by warning and pressure of circumstance for them that rebelled against Him. To be saved from causes rather than from consequences—that was true salvation.

What, then, availed to change the hearts of men? Nothing but love could effect that. And love was necessarily love for a person. What, then, could arouse such an answering love—for the right kind of person? Only a supreme initiative of love by that person. What could best prove the reality of that love? Only such a deed as revealed love at its uttermost. What conditioned such a deed? The meeting of hatred at its most implacable by love at its most forgiving.

So far the Divine logic was inexorable and unanswerable.

But the argument went further. Not only was this generation of men in need of redemption, but all men since time began till time should end. Unless man knew for a certainty that not only was Jesus of Nazareth filled with this love but that the Eternal God Himself was an identity with Him, Jesus—there could be no pledge or guarantee of redemption to all Eternity and for all men.

Then it was that He realized as never before the role of the Messiah in the counsels of Heaven and in the world of men. He it was Who was to prove what God was like, to reveal God for all time. And this Revelation must necessarily be in terms of the Suffering Servant if God were to be fully revealed.

He knew that He Himself was Messiah—God's Regent upon earth. It followed therefore that He must fulfil this role. His very trials, therefore, by the intercombined logic of spiritual and material facts, provided at once the confirmation of His Messiahship and its uniquely fitting opportunity. The sense of this rightness, this fulfilment, exalted Him to thanksgiving that He would thus be enabled to accept His terrible destiny and make of it the supreme Act of Redemption.

But one thing remained to be effected, if the Master Plan were to be implemented. Unless He were indeed acknowledged as Messiah, the Revelation would inevitably fail in its chief purpose, for it would not prove that *God* was like this. He knew that the world's—and, for that matter, the disciples'—false conception of Messiahship was based on a false idea of God. To reveal the true God—a God Who is Love—the Revealer *must* be accepted as God's Son. One with the Father, not only in this deed, but since God is eternal and changes not, One with Him eternally—of which unity this deed was the supreme sacrament. Love must always be eternally self-giving. Light was an energy, an outgoing, self-giving always. The problem was how to draw all men into the orbit of that light; and He saw the Cross as the very centre and focus of that light. If He were lifted up on that gibbet, He *would* draw all men to Him, into His unity with God, Who was Light.

Thus inner conviction and outward circumstance combined inexorably to lead Him to His destined goal. To Him, in these hours of insight and foresight, was given that ecstatic exultation that comes alone to one in whom a fully integrated personality advances upon inevitable, Divinely appointed lines. From now onward He was colossally, incredibly triumphant. So was the vast and sublime concept of the Abrahamic story—"God providing Himself a Lamb"—become the even vaster and more sublime conception of the Lamb slain before the foundation of the world.

II

They moved along the ascending road toward the foothill town of Caesarea Philippi, the disciples labouring mentally and spiritually so far in His rear as to feel almost cut off from Him. His spirit was climbing out of their sight, ranging and roaming in heights where they could no longer comfortably breathe. As they listened to His rhapsodic dreams, realistic as all idealist visions are—they found themselves lapsing into silence, full of awe and of an eerie, uncanny fear.

So travelling, they at last reached the city newly built by Herod Philip in honour of Caesar Augustus, having passed through some of the most magnificent scenery in the world: vast tracts of rolling grasslands set with gigantic trees, mostly oak, as though the region were a huge natural park, surrounded by densely wooded hills. The snowy mountains that rose high and far beyond made a marvellous backcloth to the riot of autumnal colour in the foreground. Swollen streams, tempestuously swirling between precipitous outcroppings of rock, irrigated this region to a luxuriant fertility. The air grew more keen and bracing with every ascending step. Jesus loved the heights. They invigorated His soul. Striding through the woody, bird-haunted glades, they at length arrived near the base of a great rock mountain, beneath which a fully grown river gushed out, over thirty feet wide, the precipice rising a thousand feet over it. Here there was a temple in honour of the god Pan. Inscriptions abounded on the stones, or were carved in the rock face. "Priest of Pan." "Pan and his nymphs dwell in this place." The cavern from which this river gushed out was prodigiously deep and full of still water. In its darkness, it was regarded as an orifice of the nether world, haunted by evil spirits. It was, in the past, the focus of human sacrifice.

Fifteen hundred feet above stood a gigantic castle erected by the ancient Phoenicians and recently rebuilt by Herod in honour of Augustus. It was garrisoned by Rome's legions—a northern stronghold of great strategic value. Jesus one day took with Him His disciples and climbed up through a medley of orchards—of vines and figs and mulberries—past cascading fountains and many ruins of ancient temples, till they at length emerged on to the top of the rock mountain, and turned to face a breathtaking view of unparalleled magnificence. The whole of the Upper Jordan region was laid out before them, as on a relief map. There, beyond the wide, still waters of Huleh mere and marshes, at the far end of the silver streak that was the Upper Jordan, shone and glistened His own beloved Lake, gleaming blue and golden in the forenoon sunlight. Somewhere in the mist there lay the hills and plains, the cities and villages, where He, the radiant Bridegroom, had lived out the Acceptable Year of the Lord. He felt the menace of fate's far-heard knocking, of the shortening stretch of time before Him and the dread doom waiting inexorably at the end.

But, now, though misunderstanding and enmity remained—heightened and sharpened to strike—frustration had disappeared forever. Instead, fulfilment, splendid and terrible, thrilled His soul. He sur-

veyed His past life and found God's strong hand in it, God's leadership clear.

And the future? That all depended on the answer to the vital question now to be asked of the disciples. If they could be led to acknowledge Him as Messiah, then the Master Plan might be implemented in
full. But nothing could be done unless they were convinced beyond a
shadow of doubt that He was in very truth God's Regent on earth.

Leaving the disciples, He moved away to a near-by boulder and
flung Himself down in an agony of prayer to His Father. The disciples watched Him wonderingly. They loved Him as never before,
but they felt estranged from Him as well. He towered above them,
colossal, apart, like Hermon. At length He rose from His knees and
stood facing them. The urgency within His soul shone in His eyes.
A set tension, as of the moveless stress of equal and opposing forces,
gripped His features. He knew He was about to know where He
stood with this, His little handful of friends, upon whom all depended. The world's future waited on the answer they would make
to the question He was now about to ask them.

He rejoined them, and they rose in His presence. He planned to
make the meaning of His question clear by leading them in thought
toward the one supreme issue.

"Tell Me . . . Whom do people say that I am?"

They looked at one another, a little bewildered, and answers came
haltingly.

"Some say that You are John the Baptist, risen from the dead. . . .
Herod says that, so we hear."

"Others say that You are Elijah returned to earth."

"The general opinion seems to be that You are, at any rate, a
Prophet, or a reincarnation of one of the Prophets. Some suggest
Jeremiah. But no one denies that You are a Prophet."

Jesus waited till the replies were finished. He moved forward to
the supreme question—not what other men thought of Him—but
how these men here, His chosen Apostles, regarded Him.

So, in a tense expectancy, came the vital query, "Yes, but Whom do
you say that I am?"

There was a long silence, as the disciples realized from His manner and look how desperately in earnest He was. Then something snapped in Peter's soul, as, trusting love's impulses and flinging all scruples to the winds, He leaped in one mighty bound from hesitancy and speculation to certainty and faith.

"*I* say, You are the Messiah—the Son of the Living God!"

The tension was at once broken, and the immediate, spontaneous reaction of Jesus was among the most joyous moments in the Gospel Story.

"Blessed are you, Simon, son of Jonah, for flesh and blood hath not revealed this to you! No, it's come to you from My Father Who is in Heaven!" He looked at Peter, now shy with self-consciousness and flushed with pride. But Peter had reached bedrock truth, got through to eternal values, found himself—his very central self—inviolate, secure, and lo! Jesus was enthroned there! Peter never could deceive anybody. He was enduringly honest, even when he tried to be subtle, even when he afterward tried to betray his Master. Not for nothing had Jesus named him "The Rock." And now Peter had uncovered the naked rock of his heart's deep faith, and had taken his stand firmly upon this basic certitude. Here was something as solid and as enduring—and as exalted and bathed in light—as was the vast rock mountain on which they were standing. The love name given by Jesus to Simon in the far fords of Jordan so long ago was now seen to be justified to the full. For the stream of blessing had been traced back to its source, here, beneath this very rock from which the full flood gushed out—and Peter had found that "that Rock was Christ."

Jesus gazed with grave, smiling happiness into the honest eyes of His first full believer, and He added:

"I tell you, further, that today you have richly deserved the name I gave to you because I had faith in you! As I then named you 'Peter, the Rock,' so, on such a rock as this mountain—on faith such as yours—I will build My Church!"

Jesus turned to look at the colossal gateway of the Castle of Caesar frowning on the peak just above them. That fortress was the stronghold of the king of this world. Those bastioned towers, those turrets darkly silhouetted against the noontide blue, those enormous portcullised gates, represented the utmost strength of which those times were capable. The castle was considered impregnable. Its black rectangularity looked as though it grew out of the rock itself, as if formed by nature to command and crown the mountain peak. Rising majestically from its three-sided precipices, its base lost in shadowy depth and its towers aspiring skyward, it defied earth and challenged heaven. Yes, and dominated Hell. For was not the rock fortress raised upon the orifice of the netherworld—that fearful cavern of legendary fathomless depth, aptly named locally "the Gate of Hell"? The everlasting surge and swirl of the fully grown river gushing out so far below had not since creation's hour disturbed the dominance of this rock. . . . Though who would dare to prophesy its eternal duration?

Jesus looked at the castle gates . . . and thought of the floods beneath; thought, too, of their respective significance for finite durance. Caesar's castle symbolized man's dominion over the earth; the floods, nature's challenge to that power. And undermining even that undermining attrition, was the terror of the bottomless pit. So was man's strongest fortress based. Caesar might defy the world. Nature might in the end conquer all Caesars. But Hell waited, yawningly.

But Jesus in vision saw His Church rising on the Rock of Petrine Faith, defiant not only of Caesar's challenge but of time's erosion, nay, even of Hell's terrors. No gates, no matter how forbidding—not even the brazen gates of Hell—could stop the majestic marching of His army. Nor would the floods ever wear it away. The storms of Lebanon might sweep down upon it, the rains descending, the winds blowing, but it would stand foursquare to all assault of man or nature, truly impregnable.

Exultantly He cried to Peter—and through Peter to all the world and to all time's generations—"On the Rock of your faith I will build My Church, and not even the Gates of Hades shall ever prevail against it!"

He saw, too, in vision the Gates of Heaven, and their Keeper admitting or barring the multitudes seeking admission thereto. There was but one condition of entry: faith in Himself and in the truth of His Teaching. Peter's confession was the one sure password of admittance. So once more He turned to Peter and cried, "And to you, Peter, the Rock-like, I will Myself deliver the keys of the gates of the Kingdom of Heaven. It will be for you, My first full believer, to let down or lift up the portcullis of My Kingdom's citadel. No longer shall the Jews claim the keys of the Kingdom, admitting and expelling whom they will. On the Saints, instead, will fall the privilege of judging the souls of men—and Heaven will ratify your judgments!—for God's Spirit shall guide you."

III

But a far harder task awaited Him: that of educating the Twelve—and through them the world—in the new conception of Messiahship that was in itself the heart and kernel of His Message and Mission, now merged into one. So at once, since time was short, He proceeded to tackle this tremendous task. The first precaution must be to safeguard the secrecy of this Messianic acknowledgment, for there must be no risking of tumult and misplaced enthusiasm—not until He chose. And the hour must be fitting, and then He Himself would be the proclaimer both of His Messiahship and of its nature. The risk attendant upon staking everything on the disciples' recognition of His Messiahship had been gloriously vindicated. But unless He could now convert them to His own concept of that office, all would be lost. For if He were killed while they yet believed in a nationalistic Messiah, then their belief in *Him* would be broken, while their faith in the false idea of the Messiah would survive. Therefore the issue before Him now was whether they would cease to believe in Him when they knew of His inflexible decision to challenge death on this very issue of the true nature of Messiahship, as embodied in Himself. If their faith in Him held in spite of the revolution in thought such a concept involved, they would be forced to see in the Messiah—and so in God, Whom He represented—a suffering, loving, forgiving Friend and Redeemer, dying to change their hearts, saving to the utmost those who believed in Him. He well knew the awful risk He ran in thus challenging their basic conceptions of Messiahship. But the redemption of the world demanded that the risk be taken.

So at once He began to teach them the further truth. It could not be taught until they had acknowledged Him as Messiah, but, that past, this next task was immediately taken in hand.

"You mustn't say a word of this—that I am the Messiah—to anyone anywhere. You must keep it strictly secret till I give you leave to publish it."

They found this tantalizing and bewildering. Why shouldn't the world know of their great discovery—that Messiah had come, and was their own Master? They glanced at Him, surprised at His command.

But He was obviously desperately in earnest and continued: "Listen. Now I'm going to tell you a further truth. As Messiah, I must go up to Jerusalem and suffer many things. I shall be rejected by the Elders and the Chief Priests and Scribes . . . and most likely be killed." Then He added, in faith in God's vindication of His plan, "And after these things have happened, I shall be raised to life again!"

He glanced upward toward Heaven, His eyes resting a moment on Hermon's snow-crowned summit. Like that remote peak, He was from henceforth a lonely, isolated Figure, surrounded by clouds of misun· derstanding, which He was to try desperately to clear away, in vain. The Father alone understood and that thought sustained Him. "I am alone . . . and yet I am not alone, for the Father is with Me. I go to the Father." And Heaven beckoned from above. Where Hermon's snows merged with the central blue—up there, in that remote region, He might commune with God and rest upon the Father's bosom for a while, gaining strength and solace before starting out on the long trek southward.

But even as His gaze remained fixed on that glorious summit, Peter, impulsive as ever, was filled with sudden reaction to His Lord's mystic words about His coming suffering and death. Jesus' stark statement, so relentlessly explicit, seemed at this moment so unthinkable—and Peter was also reacting to His Lord's praise of himself—that, awaking to the sudden realization of their import and seeming absurdity, Peter moved swiftly over to where Jesus was standing, and taking hold of Him in his excitement—his great hands clawing at Jesus' shoulders in his efforts to turn Him toward himself—blurted out his indignant protest:

"Don't talk like that, Master! Merciful Heaven, that's the last thing that can ever happen to You! Indeed, it never *shall* happen!"

Jesus turned Himself slowly about, and seemed to become aware again of the disciples' presence. The awful import of Peter's championing words burned itself into His mind. This was the supreme temptation, to evade the issue, to triumph without sacrifice, to find reconciling length of days in a halcyon Galilee appeased with His return as a peace-loving quietist. He stared at Peter in horrified amazement; then once more swung round and turned His back on poor Peter, recoiling even from his touch, while the harsh words stung Peter's soul like a lash.

"Get behind Me, *Satan!* For now you're no longer the mouthpiece of the mind of God, but of man—of earth!"

It was as though some fault, some fissure, had suddenly opened in that Rock, leading downward to that bottomless pit gaping in its heart so far beneath . . . as though Jesus' brave words about His Church were vitiated in a moment by Peter's dread protest. But the lash, as it curled about Peter's shrinking soul, lapped about him also like a lifeline, to lift him up again from that abyss toward which he was sinking. He was all contrition when he saw how greatly though unwittingly he had hurt Jesus. But he found it all but impossible to understand Jesus either way. . . . "The Keeper of the keys of Heaven," and then "Satan!" It was all dreadfully puzzling.

Only Jesus knew how His own cry of triumph was dependent solely upon His following cry of impending doom. And, lest any disciple thought with Peter that sacrifice was needless for redemption, or, indeed, that personal sacrifice was obviated in the future by reason of Christ's own substituted sacrifice, He went on to utter the solemn, terrifying words—this time to all the disciples, "If any man—any one of you here—would come after Me, wishing still to follow Me, he too must be prepared to deny *himself* . . . and take up his own cross . . . and *so* follow Me. . . ."

The silence that ensued seemed endless, so horrified were the disciples. For there, on that high, gaunt precipice, beside Rome's castle they listened, in the very hour in which Rome's dominance was challenged in the name of God and her downfall prophesied, to a foretelling of Rome's earthly victory over each believer of them individually. Were those gates to be triumphant after all? It was as though they had been precipitated down those thousand feet of sheer rock face from the sun-bathed Mount of Vision to the lightless, fathomless caverns below.

The voice was heard again: "For whoever only wants to save his own soul will be sure to lose it. But whoever is willing to run the risk of losing his own soul for My sake and for the sake of My Good News, *he* it is who'll save it!"

Jesus saw in vision men so concerned for others that they were almost indifferent to their own salvation. Thoughts of Heaven and Hell, of reward or punishment, were crowded out by their care for men's needs. This was an echo from the debonair Jesus of the Sermon on the Mount. Because God was Love, nought else but this carelessness of personal salvation, rooted in care for others, could achieve personal salvation. That was the sublime paradox of realism, the most profound utterance in all history, the very heart and core of truth. He *must* make the disciples understand, if they can.

"Why, what profit could anyone get, if he were to gain *the whole universe* . . . if in doing so, he were to forfeit his own soul? Think— what *could* such a man give in exchange, in order to buy back *his soul?* Don't you see, that the whole universe amounts in reality to less than one soul? Yea, for the Kingdom of Heaven is so infinitely precious that it's like a hoard of hidden treasure one day uncovered by the plough, or the one really perfect pearl in all the world, for which a man would gladly realize his every possession! So now you know how you should treasure the Kingdom and make it the first claim on your lives and energies.

"You have this day confessed Me as your Lord Messiah—the King of the Kingdom. One day I shall want you to be ready to confess Me not only before your fellow believers but before the big outside world of men. And I tell you that whoever shall confess his faith in Me before men, him will I, the Son of Man, also confess before My Father which is in Heaven! Yes, before all the Angels of God I'll confess My faith in *him!*" (So was Peter reinstated!) "Equally, whoever shall be ashamed of Me or of My Teaching or deny Me before this sinful and adulterous generation, of him shall I, the Son of Man, also be ashamed when, as shall unfailingly happen, I shall come in Mine own glory and in the glory of the Father and of His Holy Angels! Yea, him will I also deny before My Father which is in Heaven, and before all the Angels of God!" (So was Peter warned.)

"For, as I now tell you truly, I *shall* come again in glory! Did not

Ezra cry, *The men that are received shall see it; and those who have not tasted death from their birth?* So, even now I tell you in solemn truth, that you who are now reborn into the Kingdom—yes, some of you actually standing here—will not even notice death till you have seen the Kingdom of God already come in power! Oh, then you'll know its blessedness, its preciousness, its beauty. . . . "

Standing there in the sunlight, He, the ex-carpenter of Nazareth, the hunted outcast, not only challenged Rome—and Hades—through the might of an as yet almost non-existent "Church," but was actually prophesying, on the token of one man's faith in Him, a complete victory over all the forces of time or Eternity. He went even further: He prophesied His own exaltation to an equal glory with God and the Angels, staking His all on His scale of values because He felt it was inherent in the true conception of God. His flaming faith had never been so incandescent, but the disciples only realized its brightness as they looked back from Calvary to the great hills of the north, seeing them illumined in the afterlight that shone from the Cross.

(II) THE TRANSFIGURATION

A WEEK or more went by, spent in wandering about the foothills of the mighty range looming above them—long autumnal days of leisurely walks and quiet intimate communion, while Jesus tried to teach them the inner meaning of His plan. Long nights, too, of frosty cold and snowy horizons, of a strange nearness of stars and the slow-sailing moon. And over all, the shining summit of Hermon beckoned to Him, called to His soul. Its autumn snows, as evening had drawn on, had flashed golden and crimson; and now it gleamed with an even more startling grandeur against the blackness of the night, its cold clarity and lofty isolation seeming to offer Him the one place on earth where, utterly free from distraction, He might view in their entirety all things, both which were in Heaven and which in earth. There, from that towering stance, was the central viewpoint of His Galilean and Syrian world. Not only did it offer Him an ambient panorama of earth, but it seemed also to offer an all-embracing view of spiritual reality. Far away in the south, He had been the Hero of the multitudes—and having failed with them had escaped hither to avoid them. Here, He was acknowledged only by a handful, but He had never been more optimistic of eventual results. Up there, on Hermon's height, He would be almost alone, but He would, as from afar, see the travail of His soul and would be satisfied, for all men would be included in that vision of the Redeemed. He Who ever loved the hills, was drawn to climb the greatest hill of them all, in company only with His most trusted followers, in order to gain that infinite strengthening which He felt He required before essaying the southward march toward Jerusalem. His spirit had already ascended up into the Heavens; and now His feet would carry thither His earthly body also.

So one day, as afternoon drew on into mellow evening, He climbed with Peter and the brothers James and John, ever higher and higher, past the castle of Caesar, up toward the great hills, where loomed the shining peak of Hermon. The air grew colder with every step as they passed the last lone straggling trees—up and over the green aprons of grass and heather, sweet-scented with the warmth of the now sinking sun; over the lower slopes and shoulders of the hills, where drifts of melting snow made climbing difficult; up, yet farther, into the thick snows glistening white in the chill autumn air.

As they rose ever higher the sunset passed from a golden glory to a fiery holocaust, lighting up the mountains with crowns of flame. They turned for a momentary rest to gaze on the southward scene, as the splendour of the west lighted up the Promised Land, laid out like a gigantic relief map below them. The shadows of the western hills raced over the plains and the far shining waters of Huleh—with the Lake of Galilee a mere glimmer on the horizon—until His home country was at last dark as death, as the great red sun sank suddenly below the dazzling line of the Mediterranean. Its glow—a vivid crimson—shone yet around about them here on these heights some minutes after the distant view was blotted out in impenetrable darkness. To their right hand yawned a terrifying ravine, as they traversed a snow-covered ledge with a precipice dropping sheer away from it. But God would not suffer their feet to slip. The Lord Himself was their Keeper, and their defence upon their right hand. Though they felt strangely sleepy, they knew that He that kept them would never slumber nor sleep. The words of the Psalm haunted their ascent and brought a sense of immunity from dangers to body or soul. The sudden change from that golden glory to this cold white sheen (in which the virgin snow was frosted over as with stardust, as the remote cold moon rose serene and pure over the far Arabian deserts) brought with it no sense of loss, but rather of gain, as the giant peaks loomed even yet more sublimely before the immensity of the starry worlds. Without warning a swirling haze enveloped them as clouds from the sea wreathed about the mountain slopes, cutting off the peaks from sight and chilling the body. Looking down they found that they were also cut off from the world that lay below them. Then the mists cleared as they continued to ascend, until they were well above the clouds.

They had the impression of entry into a secure, supramundane existence, in a world of stellar timelessness. The peaks were clear in the moonlight, shining whitely against the dark spaces of the sky. But somehow they seemed to have but little relation to earth. It was as though that cloudbank separated them from all the ills and unrealities of finite existence—as though the mists of dissolution were passed through and emergence into deathlessness were triumphantly achieved. A sense of invulnerability, of scatheless security, exalted the soul of Jesus, filling His body with a Divine well-being, as the frets and hazards of earth were left far behind. Here, in this high purity, halfway to Heaven, His spirit so took possession of His consciousness that the intoxication of height, this exaltation, this Divine Afflatus, lifted Him in dream far out and up and over the earth, untouched and untouchable of death and decay, secure and serene in the arms of the Father. It was as though He were exultantly inebriate with immortality. Here was perfect freedom and an infinite accession of health and wholeness and holiness, and above all, of power, all matter being instant to His centred thought, wherein the soul escaped from this world's limits to breathe, expand and exult in its native air, the air of Heaven.

They were now nearing the summit, and the world lay far below them, hidden by the mists and shadows of night, a world even more strangely remote now than was Hermon beforehand, a world lying somewhere beneath that billowing sea of moonlit clouds. And the Christ, in orbed and regnant isolation, moved away from His friends, to be utterly alone awhile with God Himself—stars about His head and clouds about His feet.

Peter and the others were very tired, the mountain air having made them already heavy with sleep, as the Christ of God, there on the cold snow, poured out His heart to the Father, reconsecrating Himself to His will, receiving His final strengthening before turning again to take the downward road that led to Jerusalem and to death. It was the Apotheosis (how true a word!) of life lived Divinely, the consummation of perfect obedience. Here was soul-experience at its highest, revealing the full stature of the manhood of Christ, the life that was life indeed, His by inherent desert, showing forth the ultimate potentialities of human experience as God meant them to be. And in Him manhood revealed Godhead, since full circle was complete, Divinity stooping and manhood rising in the merging arcs of earth and Heaven.

Here on Hermon's shining height, Heaven broke through to earth to meet earth breaking through to Heaven. This was the final, the ultimate sacrament, the complete fusion of matter and Spirit, of time and Eternity, of the human and the Divine, of the Incarnate Son with the Transcendent Father. This essential union was effected by the Holy Spirit, the power that ever works in man to raise him into unity with God. No wonder that Spirit suffused and transfigured flesh in that high hour; that Jesus, there above the snow line, against the background of the everlasting stars, shone so brightly that Peter's after narrative to Mark faltered and struggled in its efforts to convey an experience that defied description. For what he was witnessing was not only the suffusion of matter by Spirit, but the actual process of translation from earth to Heaven, the transformation of an earthly body into a Spiritual body, whereby it was leaving time space and rising into timeless Eternity, and achieving by inherent right that which is the last and ultimate development of personality in its ascension to God. It is vastly significant, in this connexion, that there appeared with Jesus the very two figures whose graves were never found, Moses and Elijah. They were the representatives of the Law and Prophecy, both of which were superseded in the New Covenant of Grace and the fulfilment embodied in Christ.

*Who shall rise up in His holy hill? Even He that hath clean hands
and a pure Heart. . . .*

*Behold, in the vision, clouds and a mist beckoned Me. The course
of the stars and the lightning drove and impelled Me, and the winds
gave Me wings and drove Me on. They conducted Me to a mountain,
the point of whose summit reached the sky. They lifted Me up to
Heaven and all the portals stood open before Me. Its floor was of fire,
and above were lightnings; and I saw therein a lofty throne, like as of
hoar frost, and the Great Glory sat thereon, and His raiment shone
more brightly than the snow—yea, whiter than any snow. The Everlasting One was there. And the Lord called Me with His own mouth
and spoke with Me, "Come hither." And He bade Me rise and
approach the door. But I turned My face downwards.*

If death be thought of not so much as a penalty as a natural consequence of an imperfect relation between soul and body, then the
outcome of a perfect obedience would be translation rather than dissolution. So Christ here on Hermon's shining height was offered as
of right the opportunity to break through earth's crust, time's
sequence, space's curved and clamping limits, and in a moment of
transfusing ecstasy would have passed from earth's midnight to
Heaven's high noon, risen on the air and been lost to human sight
behind the thronging company of Heaven till at length the light
faded and the far singing died away—had not Christ, in a decision of
incredible renunciation, shaken Himself free from Heaven's embrace
and turned His back on those shining Hosts and those open portals,
to be found once more by Himself, in the Body of His human flesh,
together with those who could not win through to Heaven with Him
in this way and without whose company Heaven itself would not be
worth the winning. That was why Jesus and His two celestial visitants
spoke together not of Ascension here from Hermon but of Exodus—
that *going out* which was also a *coming in*—which He should accomplish at Jerusalem, far away to the south beyond and below the clouds
that rolled into the moonlit distances. It was Heaven's Eternal will
that He—*the Lamb slain from the foundation of the world*—should,
in this supreme crisis of His Ministry, turn back from the Golden
Gates and tread the path that led to the valley of the shadow of death.

This, then, is literally the turning point of the whole amazing story. It is, furthermore, one of the most incontrovertible evidences of Jesus' Divinity. For had He been merely a man, the creaturely consequences of His perfect obedience could surely never have been rejected. It was indeed a far greater miracle that Jesus was eventually seen alone—"Jesus only"—there in the cold moonlight once again, than would have been His Assumption there and then into Heaven; for only God Himself could thus have superseded His own Laws and turned His back upon Heaven and all its joys. As Luke long afterward wrote: "The time for His Assumption being now due, He yet set His Face steadfastly to go to Jerusalem." Only by appraising something of the exaltation, the dizzy height to which He had climbed here on Hermon, can we gauge the greatness of the sacrificial descent that followed: from Heaven's open doors to the darkness of the rock-hewn tomb; downward even further, into the depths of the abyss. Something of this unimaginable range and sweep may have underlain the words of Paul, struggling to make his converts feel the matchless glory of the Crucified: "What does 'He ascended' mean save that He first descended to the nether regions of earth? He Who descended is He Who ascended above all the Heavens to fill the universe."

No wonder God clove the darkness with the thunder of His acclamation: "This is My Beloved Son! Hear ye Him!" For Christ had won His greatest battle. In the Wilderness He had rejected the sovereignty of earth; here on Hermon's height He rejected the inherently achieved Sovereignty of Heaven; for only so could He be Lord of the Universe. From that exalted stance, amid those peaks and eternal snows, amid those glistening stars, earth's wranglings and trivialities were seen as from an immense distance, sunk and shrunk to remote and almost irrelevant unimportance. Yet Jesus relinquished this high, withdrawn region to immerse Himself once again in men's sordid and petty quarrels. From here it was but a wing's short flight to Heaven. But His feet never left their hold upon earth till they turned again from the Mount of Vision toward the valley of the shadow of death.

So few ever break through the veil of mists and clouds to climb the upper Heaven-facing ridges of the Mount of Vision that perhaps it was merciful for the Nine that they were left behind in the lower levels of earth. For only the greater mystics have ever ascended even as far as the foothills. The peak was for Christ alone; not even Peter and the brothers could share with Christ the glories of the summit. They tried to wait and to watch, but the flesh was frail and they were drowsy in that rarefied atmosphere and fuddled with fullness.

Peter's bewildered reaction to the Heavenly vision was, he afterward felt, foolish and ignorant. "I was only half awake. . . . I began to babble something about making three tabernacles there on the cold sloping snow . . . not really knowing what I was saying."

But he had spoken better than he knew. For his subconscious mind had uttered the very words that lie at the root of all art: the impulse to enshrine and somehow thus to perpetuate the fleeting, ecstatic moments which are for us the sacraments of Heaven. Even as Peter gazed on a Christ Whom the lightning of the Spirit had illumined to His true glory, a great rolling cloud, dark and terrible, swallowed up the peak in its swirling grandeur, and the thundering Voice of God burst about them, the echoes—"Hear ye Him! Hear ye Him!"—rolling and reverberating among the ravines of that terrific region and down the long centuries and out into the infinitudes of space.

Having Himself made the great renunciation, Jesus' talk henceforward was to be centred on this one theme: of the spiritual law that conditions glory through sacrifice. His faith was set on a greater victory than ever He could have achieved by translation; and when at length Heaven should acclaim His "coming in," it would be an infinitely more glorious and triumphant welcome home, for then He would have won redemption for *all* men, and with it the right for them, by virtue of His suffering, to enter with Him into His glory.

ACT FOUR

. . . .

The Christ of the Road

PART FOUR

The Christ of the Road

I

The Descent from Hermon

An end is come. An end is come. It watcheth for Thee—behold it come! For the morning is come nigh unto Thee. The time is come, the day of trouble is near, and not only an echo upon the mountains. . . .

The cold grey morning light seemed pale and flat after the celestial brightness of the night. Gone now the mounting up with wings as eagles. Gone, even, the swift movement of enthusiasms shared and spreading. Only pedestrian descent remained, to walk and not to faint. As the rising sun dispersed the mists, Jesus looked long and intently upon the matchless—and ominous—view spread out before Him to the south. For here in the dawn glory lay the one hundred and twenty miles that separated Him from His goal; a distance marked by the long straight line of the Jordan—the very name meant Descender.

Indeed, Jordan was a visual parable of His Ministry on earth. Beginning with a tumultuous outpouring and onrush from beneath the rock of Caesarea Philippi; moving thence through the loveliness of Galilee, where it opened out into a very sea, warm and deeply blue; dropping after that into a tortuous trench, whose general line was straight as a spear as it clove its way through the narrows and torrid seats toward the bitter, brackish Sea of Death . . . whence it was drawn up again to that Heaven from whence it had first descended.

As they descended the mighty slopes of Hermon, Jesus impressed upon the disciples the urgent necessity for complete secrecy regarding this Divine confirmation of His Messiahship, until they should be able to realize something of its import and Jesus have chosen the hour of its manifestation. So He charged them that they should tell to one what they had seen on the mountain, adding the mysterious words: "Not till the Son of Man shall have risen from the dead . . ." as if to say, "I shall never rise to Heaven as did Elijah or Enoch. I am

259

going to die an ordinary death; but I *shall* rise to Heaven after that."

The disciples were deeply mystified by this saying, questioning one with another what it could possibly mean. But they obeyed their Master and did not even tell the other disciples about their experience on the mountain. Indeed, they obeyed His further behest and did not speak about it till after the Resurrection. But the injunction made their relations with the others and with Him even more tense and strained.

So Jesus and His three friends came down from the heights to the levels once again. The thoughts of them all were often centred about Moses and Elijah, heroes both of them, defiant of kings and zealous for the Lord of Hosts. But the three disciples were perplexed by the fact that Elijah, who was to appear on earth to herald Messiah's reign, had indeed appeared, but only to vanish there on the mount, his restoration of God's Rule unaccomplished. They approached the Master with their problem.

"Elijah?" He answered. "Yes, Elijah has indeed come, but no one seems to have recognized him. So that—" pointing toward the blue haze far away to the south—"they did to him . . . just what they wanted to do. . . . "

They saw then that He was referring to the Baptist, but they were unprepared for His addition: "Even so they will likewise do what they want with the Son of Man."

Arriving in Caesarea Philippi, Jesus and His friends noticed a crowd in the distance, which, as soon as Jesus had been seen, ran forward with cries of salutation to meet Him. Arrived at the centre of the disturbance, Jesus saw the Nine there, clustered about a prostrate boy lying in their midst. They had been having a bad time, struggling vainly to invoke the name of their Master to cure the demoniac, and to deal with the shouted insults of the hangers-on standing on the outskirts of the crowd, and with the sarcastic questions of the Scribes enjoying their discomfiture.

"What is all the trouble about?" asked Jesus.

Thereupon a man ran forward and kneeling before Him said, "Master, I thought to bring my son to You, for he is an epileptic who suffers terribly when the fit takes him, suddenly crying out and being thrown down, foaming at the mouth and grinding his teeth; and it takes a long time before he comes round. He nearly dies each time, and, in any case, is horribly bruised as a result of the fit. I do pray that You will help him. I asked Your disciples to cure him, but they couldn't. . . . "

The contrasts between Heaven's faith in Him and earth's faithlessness—even on His own disciples' part—almost overwhelmed Him. The Scripture came into His mind: *How long will this people provoke Me? How long will it be ere they believe Me, for all the signs which I have shown unto them? How long shall I bear with this evil generation? But your little ones, they shall know . . . what you have rejected.*

So now Jesus cried in His distress of soul, "O unbelieving generation, how much longer shall I be with you? For how long must I have patience with you? Bring the boy to Me."

So they brought him, and when he saw Jesus, at once a fit convulsed him, so that he fell to the ground and rolled about, foaming at the mouth.

Jesus then asked the boy's father, "How long has he been like this?"

"From early childhood," he answered, "and often it has thrown him into the fire, or into rivers or pools, to destroy him. *If* You can do anything for him, have pity on us and help us!"

" '*If* You can'!" echoed Jesus. "Why, everything is possible to him who believes!"

At once the father of the boy cried out, with tears starting from his eyes, "Lord, I do believe! Help Thou mine unbelief!"

Then Jesus, seeing that the crowd was rapidly growing, rebuked the foul spirit, saying, "Come out of him, and never enter into him again!"

And it came out, but not before it had shrieked aloud and convulsed the boy with fit after fit. He looked so much like a corpse that most of the people said, "He is dead." But grasping hold of his hands, Jesus raised him up and he stood on his feet. Then Jesus gave him back to his father, while everyone was astounded at what one of the crowd called the God-like Majesty of Jesus. . . .

When the Master had returned to His lodging—with the woman whom He had cured of the issue of blood in Capernaum, for she lived at Caesarea Philippi—the Nine asked Him in private: "Tell us, Master, *why* couldn't we cure him?"

He looked long and keenly at them. They lacked faith, His sort of faith, the faith that was advancing upon Jerusalem believing it could uproot even the most deeply embedded traditions and remove the mountains of prejudice that stood in His way, and with the help of a few untutored followers conquer the world for God—through the dying of a condemned felon. He *knew* God would give Him the victory, and every tree not planted by His Father would be uprooted at the last.

"Why could you not cast out the evil spirit?" He repeated. "Why, because of your lack of faith. For I tell you truly that if only you had a speck of real faith—say, only the size of a grain of mustard seed—you could say to . . . that sycamore tree over there: 'Be uprooted and be replanted—yonder, in the Great Sea!' and it would obey you. Why, you could even dare to say to yonder mountain—" and He pointed to Hermon—"'Move from here . . . to there!' and move it would! Nothing, I repeat, would be impossible to you.

"However," He added, "this sort of evil spirit can only be driven out by prayer."

The Nine noticed how silent were the Three: strangely silent, thought the Nine, about that journey up the slopes of Hermon. But not only so; they seemed a trifle self-important, as though they shared a secret withheld from the others, almost as if they were expecting great events to happen, in which they themselves would be taking a conspicuous part. The Nine were guessing rightly. For though Jesus was continually and very earnestly ("Let these words sink into your ears!") telling them all that He was going forward to betrayal into the hands of men—so different, this, from the welcome into the arms of the Angels—and the Leaders would kill Him, but that, after He was dead, He would for a certainty be raised up again—yet, though, of course, they were exceedingly sorry to hear Him talk like this, they, the Three, were utterly at sea to know what He could mean, since not only had they proof of His Messiahship in the Acclamation on Hermon, but He Himself was, by this very advance toward Jerusalem, moving to the royal city of David, where all Israel's kings had been crowned.

So—still by night—they came at length to Capernaum, home

again. But it was no longer home to Jesus, but merely a necessary place of call for such brief preparations as had to be made for the great campaign ahead. He had noticed that there was a feeling of strain among the disciples as they approached Capernaum. Sounds of argument had reached His ears from time to time as He found Himself walking ahead of them, and it was an uneasy and sulky group that entered the house of Peter behind Him as the door closed upon the night skies. He asked them directly, "Tell Me, what were you arguing about on the way here?"

Jesus' blunt question found them embarrassed and silent, and rather ashamed; for they had been arguing about who should be the leader of the group when, as they all expected, Jesus entered into His Kingdom. Sitting down, He called round Him the Twelve.

"Whoever among you wants to be leader, he must be ready to be the lowest servant of all." And He took a little child, belonging to Peter's household and set him in the midst of them, and, putting His arms around him, said to them: "Whoever for My sake welcomes one such young child, I tell you he welcomes Me. And, remember, whoever welcomes Me receives not only Myself but Him Who sent Me. Truly I tell you, unless you change your hearts and become as little children . . . you will never enter the Kingdom of Heaven at all. Whoever, therefore, shall humble himself and become as this little child, *he* it is who will be greatest in the Kingdom of Heaven!"

He recalled once again the words of Scripture: *Your little ones, they shall know . . . what you have rejected.* He was banking on the next generation's understanding. Everything depended on the children of today, and therefore upon the responsibility of the disciples for their being brought to love Him. His face hardened. His eyes rested a moment upon the millstone lying there in the courtyard, and raised themselves to glance out through the open lattices to the moonlit waters of the Lake.

"Whoever is a hindrance," He cried, "to one of these little ones who believe in Me, better it were for that man to have a great millstone fastened about his neck, and to be sunk in the depths of the sea! Alas for the world, because of such hindrances! They cannot always be prevented. But woe to anyone by whom they do come!"

Someone, more bold than the rest, dared to question Him regarding this dread saying. "*Better* . . . to be drowned like a dog? Isn't that going rather too far?"

But Jesus was iron-girt for combat. He would not have a vestige of compromise with evil.

"Better, far better, a body destroyed than a soul lost to all Eternity. I tell you, if hand or foot or eye be a moral hindrance to you, get rid of it and throw it away. Better be maimed or crippled or blind, and enter into life, than have a whole body cast into Hell." His thoughts still on the fires of purgation, He continued: "For everyone must be salted with self-discipline and purified and consecrated as by fire, even as a sacrifice is prepared for the altar."

He looked at His disciples. "Salt is an excellent thing, and you are indeed the salt of the earth! But if the salt becomes tasteless and lose its potency, how can you restore its flavour and power? It's no longer good for anything—fit neither for land nor dunghill—but only to be thrown away and trodden underfoot by the passers-by. So," He added in conclusion, "see to it, then, that you have the salt of self-discipline within you . . . and be at peace with one another."

The anger was visibly fading from His face and voice. His eyes turned again to the rather scared little child, still held protectively within His encircling arms. "And see also that none of you ever despises one of these little ones." A note of mystic beauty and ineffable tenderness crept into His now quiet voice: "For I say to you— and I *know*—that their Angels, in Heaven, are continually gazing on the face of My Father," as this child was even then gazing on His own face. Jesus' eyes were soft and tender as He added: "If a man has, say, a hundred sheep and one of the little lambs strays away, will he not leave the ninety-nine out there on the hills and go in search of the one which has strayed? And when he finds it—for he *will* search for it until he does find it—I tell you truly he will rejoice over it more than over the ninety-nine that never went astray. Just so, it is never the will of your Heavenly Father that one of these little ones should ever perish."

They were silent . . . and the child was asleep in the encircling arms of the Good Shepherd. And as the moon sailed up the starry sky the stillness of the night was stirred only by the faint, far breaking of little

waves on the shingly beach. *As His majesty is, so is His mercy. . . .*
And as He moved, doom-ridden, glory-drawn, on that long journey
toward distant Jerusalem, the sense both of His strength and sweetness
was enhanced in the perfect balance of His nature.

They were to notice this tenderness again when, in Peraea soon
after, He blessed many little children and dreamed of a time when
the Heavenly Jerusalem should be called *the city of truth, and all
the open spaces shall be full of boys and girls playing there.*

Before they left Capernaum one absurd and casual little incident
occurred that stayed in Peter's memory. One day there came a knock
at the portal door, and, when Peter went to answer the summons,
there was the local collector of the Temple dues. Peter thought at
once of the Master within, and of the need for shielding Him from
prying eyes.

"This Master of yours," began the collector, "never pays his annual
didrachma to the Temple, does he?"

It looked like a trap, so Peter told the man to call later and he
would see about it. When, a moment after, he came bursting into
the house with his news, Jesus saw he was resentful and suspicious.
"He got nothing out of me, anyway," Peter said.

But Jesus was quietly amused at the situation. The summer lightning of His irony and humour played over the incident. He saw it—
as humour must see everything—in relation to the serious truth of
life, and placed it against the background of cosmic reality; and He
smiled that He, God's own Son, should have to pay for the upkeep of
His Father's House.

He turned quietly to Peter. "What do you say, Simon? From
whom do earthly kings collect customs and taxes? Is it from the
Princes of the Blood Royal or from others?" (For even Caesar
exempted from taxation certain folk who possessed the *jus Italicum.*)

Peter answered: "From the others, of course."

"Then the sons are free?"

No answer being forthcoming, Jesus nodded in assumed surprise
and continued: "Nevertheless, we don't want to vex the Priests need-
lessly, do we? So we'll pay the tax. Anyone got a didrachma?"

There was a searching of girdles, but the required coin was not
available. "Never mind; we'll manage it somehow. Simon, you slip

out and go down to the beach, get out your handnet, and see if you can catch a nice big fish—you know, the sort that has a double didrachma in its mouth!—and that will pay the tax, not only for Me, but for you as well!"

There was a general laugh at this—and a bigger when Simon came back having caught a large fish and sold it on his way home. And Jesus gravely sent Judas, their treasurer, to the collector's office with the huge coin, saying, "Tell the collector we found it—in a fish's mouth!"

But Mark's readers, long after, misunderstood the story, for they had never seen the disarming smile of Jesus; though Peter often thought in afteryears how wonderful it was that Jesus could so relax after all He had gone through—and in the face of what He knew He had yet to endure.

II

Farewell to Galilee

NOCTURNE

HAVING rested for a short while, Jesus decided to go forward once again toward Jerusalem. No one had discovered the secret of His return to the Lakeside though many people wondered why Peter was home again without the Master. It was late autumn now, and Mary His mother was terribly anxious as to His whereabouts. She had heard, too, of the strange words He had used at the Feast of Tabernacles, and of the fury of the Chief Priests in the capital. His name was never mentioned in the Nazarene home.

As for the Magdalene, when Jesus had disappeared, it seemed as if all the spring had suddenly gone from her step. She became flaccid, inert, dreamy. She could never go back to Magdala, with its shameful associations. So one day she took a long journey southward and turned up again at her old home in Bethany; and Martha and Lazarus, in their greatness of heart, welcomed her back. But it was an utterly different Mary they embraced from the one who had flung herself out of the house so many years before. This one was quiet, preoccupied, becalmed like a deep sea. . . .

Jesus, as He stepped out for the last time from Peter's door, knew that He was leaving Capernaum forever. Galilee had failed Him. The very province that had witnessed His most sublime and most sustained eloquence, His greatest Miracles, His constant presence, had become indifferent to His Teaching, His power, His person. If, they had argued, He would not lead them against Rome and Herod, He might clear out and stay out; let Samaria or Peraea have Him, if they so wanted. Very well, then. Through Samaria He would go, and He would give its people, instead, the fullest opportunities of both knowing Him and His Message. Indeed, He planned to organize this Samaritan—and Peraean—campaign on the widest and most intensive scale. He would gather to Himself all those followers who had remained loyal to Him. Such a gathering would show, too, how many hearts had survived the Butaihan crisis and His long absence; and He would then go up to Jerusalem with an ever-increasing following. Once out of Galilee, there was to be no more seclusion and furtive movements. The Samaritan fields, seen once as "white to harvest," would at long last be fully reaped and garnered. So a secret rendezvous was arranged on the lonely hill where He had preached the Great Sermon, and thither one night He moved forward, together with the Twelve. It was the place from which the southbound traveller enjoyed his last view of the Lake before the great mountains of Samaria shut off the Galilean scene from sight.

Here some seventy-odd followers had assembled and were awaiting their beloved Master's arrival. It was so long a time since most of them had last set eyes on Him. Their memories centred most often on that immortal day when, at the sun's rising, they had assembled to hear Him preach. In imagination they heard again Jesus saying, as He watched the young sun rising through a distant grey blur of down-sagging streaks, blotting out the fields and casting a slow-sweeping shadow over the Lakeside towns: "Look! See how God makes His sun to rise on the good and evil alike, and sends His blessed rain on the unjust as well as on the just." They saw again Jesus, seated on a mossy stone, the silences in His speech broken only by the purling of a clear mountain stream, His hand tenderly fingering the petals of a wild crimson cyclamen, and saying, "Consider the lilies of the field"; or, lifting up His eyes to Heaven and watching the birds wheeling singly or flying in great coveys, or, near by, darting joyously from bush to bush or drinking out of some little pellucid pool in the shallows of a stream: "Behold the birds of Heaven."

But now it was sundown, not dawn, and the once carefree Master could envy the birds their freedom and their security. Having greeted the Seventy, He at once told them of His plan. Everyone was deeply thrilled when they learned that they were to act as His heralds in a great missionary campaign, preparing each village in turn for His coming, going in pairs as had the Apostles before. Jesus proceeded to give them their final instructions.

There was a biting irony in His opening words: "Well, go your ways. But remember, I am sending you out—as lambs among the wolves!" This refreshing reversal of the familiar figure of speech eased the tension a moment—until they saw how grimly serious He was. "Be then as wise as serpents, and as guileless as doves. Whoever receives you receives Me; and whoever rejects you rejects Me—and Him Who sent Me. For whoever accepts you because he thinks Me a Prophet will receive the reward due to a Prophet. Indeed, whoever receives you merely because he thinks I am a 'good man' will receive a good man's reward. I would go further. Anybody who only gives some little child a drink of cold water in My name—why, I solemnly tell you, he will not lose his reward.

"As before, carry no purse, no wallet, no change of sandals even. And don't stop to salute anyone on the road. There's no time to be lost. Into whatever house you enter, first say, 'Peace be to this house!' Then, if there be a peace-loving person there—whether he be Jew or Gentile—your peace will rest upon him. If not, it'll return to you again. Stay at the first house that receives you, eating and drinking whatever they put before you. Heal the sick in that town and tell everybody, 'The Kingdom of God is now even at your very door!' But wherever you are not welcomed on entering a town, go out into the streets and cry, 'The very dust of your town that clings to our feet—see, we now wipe it off as a protest against you. Nevertheless, you can be sure of this: The reign of God *is* very near.' I tell you, it'll be more tolerable even for Sodom, when the great day comes, than for that town! If they should persecute you in any town, don't stop to argue—hurry to the next! And don't imagine that you'll receive any easier treatment than that meted out to Me." There was a curious hint of irony in His observation: "After all, a scholar is not *above* his Teacher, is he? Nor a slave *above* his Master. Enough for the scholar to be, shall we say, on a *level* with his Teacher, and the slave as great as his Lord. For if men have called the Master of the house 'Beelze-bub,' how much more will they not revile His household servants!" That supreme insult still deeply perturbed Him.

For a time He fell silent, as His eyes turned to survey the land of lost content, His own beloved Galilee: the shining Lake and its shores and towns, in their setting of rolling hills lighted to gold by the late evening sun. His heart nearly broke as He looked—as He knew, for the very last time in this life—upon the vista spread before Him. He

Who had ascended this self-same hill but a year and a half ago, turning His back upon the Old Covenant and the gaunt Judaean hills and viewing the land of promise before Him, looking then so bright and lovely in the spring sunshine, was now taking His last leave of His home country. The glad onrush of that northward journey, its infinite optimism and leaping joyousness, were now exchanged for the march back toward the place of a skull.

Here, in retrospect and prospect, Jesus could view His life work, and see it whole. Just over yonder rise lay Nazareth's hilltop, on which He had so often dreamed as a Boy. Along that white road that spanned the Great Plain He had stridden southward in eager enthusiasm to join the Baptist. And, sweetest prospect of all, there, shining blue and clear in the late evening sunlight, lay the heart-shaped Lake whose waters lapped the scenes of those long days of teaching and healing and ever-clamorous crowds. Happy, happy days, now past forever.

Why? Into His gazing eyes welled up tears of sorrow and infinite sadness, as He tried anew to trace out the causes of this searing grief, the genesis of this most tragic Exodus. As the many interrelated reasons piled up one upon another, like some colossal storm massing from all horizons to encircle and engulf His soul, a deep and passionate disappointment rose within Him and at last overflowed into agonizing condemnation.

"Better for Sodom than for that city" which rejected His disciples? Why, there before Him, to the left, was Chorazin, on the western hills by the head of the Lake. To the right, where the Upper Jordan flowed into the Lake, stood Bethsaida. And, nearer, lay Capernaum, His own city, which He had loved so dearly: and all three had rejected *Him,* the Master. . . . He had imagined His Message to be so shiningly clear—like Safed, high up and far away, the "city set on a hill" that just could not be hidden. But, instead, it had been largely lost and forgotten, like a candle hidden under a bushel basket or a bedstead. And as the huge red sun sank to the far sea, shortly to be extinguished like a funeral torch, the words of Jeremiah echoed in His soul, as though crying to Galilee:

Listen! Be not too proud to hearken, ere the darkness falls, ere your footsteps stumble on the twilit hills; lest, while you are still de-

*bating about the light, it turn into the shadow of death, even into
pitch darkness. If you will not hearken, then must I weep in secret.
Yea, Mine eyes must stream with tears for the loss of My beautiful
flock.* Job's words also rang in His ears: *Yea, they rebelled against
the light. Their sun is gone down while it was yet day for them.
Never again shall they behold the eyelids of the morning!*

Then Jesus' thoughts broke into agonizing speech: "Woe unto you,
Chorazin! Woe unto you, Bethsaida!" And then His eyes ranged
over and beyond those growing shadows to the distant heights of
Lebanon, still lighted to glory, beyond which lay the teeming cities
of the Great Sea with which He had never pleaded in vain. "For if
the mighty works which were performed in you had been performed
far yonder, even in Tyre and Sidon, I tell you they would long ere
now have repented, sitting in dust and ashes. Therefore I say unto
you, Chorazin and Bethsaida, it shall be more tolerable for Tyre and
Sidon in the Day of Judgment, than for you."

Then His eyes rested on Capernaum, over which rose distant Hermon, the *Throne of the Most High,* where He Himself had communed
with God. And Isaiah's startlingly apposite words came into His
mind, and He cried: "And as for you, Capernaum, I know what you
said in your heart: *I will ascend into Heaven! I will exalt my throne
above the stars of God! I will scale the sky, rising up above the heights
of the clouds. I will sit upon the hill of the gods, there, there in the
far north. I, even I, will be with the Most High!* But God answered
you, saying: *Nay, but thou shalt be cast down to Hell—even to the
uttermost depths of the abyss!* For if the mighty works performed in
you had been performed even in Sodom, it would have survived to
this very day. Yea, I tell you, it will be more tolerable even for
Sodom in the Day of Judgment than for you!"

And as the shadows swept over the Lake waters till the last red
streak was lost and darkness slowly flooded and overwhelmed the
earth, so Capernaum . . . Bethsaida . . . Chorazin . . . one by one, were
being blotted out in impenetrable gloom. For the Bridegroom was
shutting-to the doors, and the lightless were left in the outer darkness. Once again, *Darkness covered the earth, and gross darkness
the peoples. . . . It is night down there. There is no vision. It is dark
for them, so that they cannot see.* In the Seer of Patmos' words:

The light shall shine no more at all in thee, and the voice of the Bride-groom shall be heard no more at all in thee. . . . Ichabod! The glory is departed!

He knew the false values of men; their dependence upon outward "signs" rather than upon inward worth. They were essentially unspiritual in that they expected spiritual results from material causes and judged spiritual values by material "proofs." He cried, "This is indeed an evil and disloyal generation forever craving for 'signs.' But no sign shall be given it, save only the Sign of Jonah—a straight call to repentance. For just as Jonah was a sign to the Ninevites of old, so is the Son of Man to this generation. I tell you, the men of Nineveh, when in the Resurrection they rise up together with the men of this generation, will condemn it. For *they* repented when Jonah preached to them; and One greater than Jonah is here with you today. The Queen of the South will rise up together with the men of this generation and will also condemn it. For she came from the ends of the earth to listen to the wisdom of Solomon, and lo! One greater than Solomon is here."

As He gazed upon that vast panorama of sunset and eclipse—and its attendant vista of history—He cried to His disciples, "Would that each one of you could realize how blessed are your eyes, to be seeing what you now see, and your ears, to be hearing what you now hear. For I tell you that countless Prophets and Kings have longed to see the things that you see, but they never saw them; and to hear the words that you hear, but they never heard them."

Having so vividly scanned the infinite ages of the past and seen their dim gropings and intense longings for the Messianic era, His mind ranged out over the vistas of the future, seeing His Mission against the dark background of time. It was as if the present were lighted to sudden glory in the converging beams streaming out from the past and future, whence respectively the seers and remembrancers look forward and back respectively to a golden age, separated from them by an impassable gulf of space time.

Looking with passionate love upon His disciples, He said, "There will come a time when you also will long for these days, to be able to live over again just one of the days of the Son of Man; but, like them of old, you will long in vain. *Then,* if anyone should say to you, 'Look! Here is the Messiah!' or 'See! There He is!' don't believe it, nor start off in pursuit. For there are sure to be many false 'Messiahs' and 'Prophets' and they may even show some of their precious 'signs' and 'wonders,' even possibly misleading the very elect. So remember: I have told you beforehand. If, therefore, they should say to you, 'See! Here He is in the Wilderness!' don't go out to see. If they say 'Here He is, in this very room!' don't believe it.''

His eyes gazed on the rugged outline of the Lebanon mountains, seen against the last glow of the sundown; and even as He gazed, it was lighted for a blinding moment by a terrific flash of forked lightning.

"For when I do return, there'll be no mistaking that! For as the lightning flashes from one side of Heaven to the other, so shall be the coming of the Son of Man, when He returns in His most glorious day!"

His mind dwelt once again upon those ill-starred ages of the past, and of the piled-up need for the trials He must now undergo.

"But first He must endure great suffering and be rejected by this generation. For just as it was in the days of Noah—that is, before the Flood, so will it be in that great day: eating, drinking, marrying, being married; each and all equally oblivious of the coming doom, right up till the very moment when Noah entered into the ark and the deluge descended and drowned them all. It was just the same when Lot lived. They ate, they drank, they bought, they sold, they planted, they built—right up to the day when Lot left Sodom, when God suddenly rained down fire and lava from the sky and destroyed them all. So will it be on the day when the Son of Man will be revealed to all the world."

He scanned in the dim light of the rising moon the just discernible houses of a village in the valley below them.

"Can you make out a man on yonder rooftop? I tell you, on that day he will not have time even to run down and save his goods. That other man, over there in yonder field, will find he has no time in which to 'turn back' and get his coat. (Do you remember Lot's wife?) Even so, he who elects to follow Me must never return home; for there's no going back in the journey I must take."

The thought of that "day" has, in this darkness, given place to that "night."

"I tell you, in that night there shall be two such men as you see yonder, out in the open fields. But, the morning after, only one will be found. The other will have been . . . taken away. Two men will be asleep in one bed. One will be taken, the other left. Listen . . . from far away, I can hear two women grinding with a double-handed millstone. In *that* night one will be taken and the other left." The words of Isaiah were in His mind: *At eventide, behold, terror . . . and in the morning they are not.*

There followed a bewildered silence. Then some puzzled disciple, far out of his depth, asked in low tones, "Left? Where, Lord?"

"Where?" answered Jesus. "Why, down there . . . anywhere in all the world where, the morning after, the bodies of those that are 'left' lie huddled together in death. There will the vultures be gathered together."

The disciples shuddered. This was a new Christ. The terrible sternness of His words appalled them. He continued: "So, remember, what I have now told you here in the darkness, that speak out in the daylight! What you have heard here whispered in your ears, that proclaim from the housetops of the world! I tell you, My friends, have no fear of those who, like Herod and Caesar, can only kill the body . . . and after that can do no more to you. No. But I will show you Whom you should fear. Fear Him Who, after He has killed, has power to cast you into Hell. Yea, I tell you, fear Him!"

The disciples blanched and quailed before this terrible prospect. Then, with the sublime irrelevance of genius, He asked them: "What's the price of sparrows? Two for a farthing, isn't it? And five for a halfpenny?" The disciples were utterly bewildered. "Yet not one of them is forgotten by God. Not one falls to the ground without your Heavenly Father being there with it. Why, the numbers of the very hairs of your heads are all known to God! Are you not worth far more to Him than sparrows? Don't look so frightened, My little flock! For your Father finds a pleasure in giving you the Kingdom!"

And there in the misty moonlight they all fell silent awhile; and, after a brief space, Jesus lay down to sleep. But there was no slumber for the disciples. Image after image raced through their brains and disturbed their rest, and often they shook with fear.

It was not long before the Seventy mustered again, this time near to the Samaritan border. Their mission had been accomplished with urgent haste, and now they were returning to give their Master an account of their stewardship. They were exultant with their new-found power.

"Lord," they cried, "even the very demons obey us in Thy name." Jesus thought of the passage from Isaiah in which the *Shining sun of the dawn* fell from the zenith to the pit in a moment of illimitable descent.

"I watched Satan fall from Heaven—like lightning!" Still using the language of poetry, He continued: "I have indeed given you power to tread serpents and scorpions underfoot, and to trample on all the powers of the enemy. Nothing shall harm you!" (But He was thinking of their souls.) "Nevertheless, do not rejoice merely because the demons obey you. Remember how in the book of Enoch it is written: *I swear unto you, that in Heaven the Angels are mindful of you for your good before the glory of the Great One; for your names are written before Him!* Rejoice then, rather, in that your names are enrolled in Heaven!"

The elation of Jesus was awe-inspiring to watch. He thrilled with joy as, lifting His eyes to Heaven, He cried: "I thank Thee, O Father, Lord of Heaven and earth, in that Thou hast chosen to reveal these things, not to the wise and prudent, but to these simple-hearted folk! Even so, Amen, O Father; for such was Thy chosen purpose."

In this He saw Heaven's confirmation of His own judgment of men. But He knew that not only this choice, but *all* judgment was His to wield. Was it not written? *The sum of judgment was committed unto Him, even unto the Son of Man. He rules over all.*

In this elation of Spirit He cried, "But now . . . *all* choice, all decision and all power has been delegated to Me by My Father; and just as no one knows fully Who the Son is, save only the Father, so no one can know the Father save he to whom the Son chooses to reveal Him!"

Lonely, hunted outlaw—Arbiter of all destiny. That was the measure of His faith.

III

Rejection in Samaria

HAD it not been for a rich Greek, one Theophilus, commissioning the Beloved Physician, Luke, to search for any who remembered Jesus, not only in Judaea and Galilee, but in out-of-the-way places, such as Samaria and Peraea, the full story of the road might never have been told. One day Luke arrived at a hill town on the main Jerusalem road which runs through Samaria, and, having found an aged man whose eyes lighted and then fell tragically when Jesus' name was mentioned, asked him his story. He was seated on a wayside stone beneath the shade of a tree, gazing steadfastly on the southward road where it curved west in the distance and climbed over the shoulder of a great hill on its way to the capital. His speech was slow and full of pauses.

"Remember? Yes, I remember. Never could I forget, for He called me to follow Him . . . and I stayed here. And He went on, out of sight, along that road there. I never saw Him again. It was late autumn, getting toward winter, when I was a youngish man—though it seems but yesterday—when a number of Galileans came from the north, hurrying through our village. But two stayed with us; their names, they said, were James and John, sons of one Zebedee, of Bethsaida of Galilee. They explained to the headman of the village that they were the Apostles of Jesus of Nazareth, the great Prophet. We had heard a good deal about this new Prophet—queer tales, too, some of them, about His power to heal the sick and to cast out demons. It was even rumoured—and in more than one quarter—that He had raised the dead. Not that we took overmuch notice of these tales, especially when they rose from hot-headed Galilee. Indeed, they were forever hailing some new 'Messiah,' until Rome put an end to all such talk.

"These two followers of the Prophet told our headman that Jesus would very shortly be visiting Samaria and would be coming to our

276

village. Could it be arranged that the people should be assembled in the market place on the evening He appeared? It was evident that these two disciples of the new Prophet were very excited about Him, though they forbore to say whether or not He were the Messiah. But anyone could see what they themselves thought. It was all rather high-pitched and queer, and they seemed ready for any revolutionary enterprise, talking a great deal about the 'Kingdom' of their Master, Who, they said, was the greatest Leader that had ever appeared on earth.

"That evening we all talked with them about the chief pride of our village—its connexion with Elijah. 'Here it was,' we told them, 'that the Prophet called down fire from Heaven upon the troops of Ahaziah!' They seemed deeply moved at this, and there was a good deal of nodding between them at the mention of Elijah. They went on early the next morning to visit some of the other villages in the neighbourhood. When they had gone, the villagers were divided in their views. Some were for giving the new Prophet a great welcome, especially as One who had defied the High Priests in Jerusalem. Others said, 'He is a Jew, at best. The less we have to do with the accursed race the better.'

"The day of the Prophet's coming duly arrived. The whole village had assembled in the market place. The headman was there, fussy and pompous as always, and full of his own self-importance. Then we saw them; with James and John leading the way, one on either side of their Master, Who certainly looked very royal and kingly. We were ready to greet Him all the more cordially in that He had healed a number of lepers just outside a near-by village. We were, I remember, very proud that the only one of them that had had the grace to return thanks to the Prophet for his healing was a Samaritan! So that when the Prophet did arrive—it was late evening—He was greeted with much ceremony by the headman, who made a long speech of welcome, evidently prepared with much care.

"What he said I cannot remember, for I was not listening. I was watching Jesus. He just stood motionless, gazing up along this very road, His eyes never once wavering—not so much as a flicker of an eyelid, as He stared at the horizon that hid the Judaean hills. There was a tension in His very immobility that suggested terrific power held in reserve. An iron cast about His jaw signified unalterable resolution, and His lips were set in a thin straight line. The words came into my mind at that moment: *I have set my face fast as a flint, and I know that I shall not be ashamed. For He is near that justifieth me. . . . As an adamant harder than flint have I made my forehead.* I noticed, too, that His hands were tightly clenched.

"Realizing suddenly that He was not hearing a word of the flowery harangue, I turned to watch the possible reactions of the headman. And it was only a moment or two after that the speaker took his eyes off his tablet for a space and glanced at the Prophet. There was a sudden silence, as the headman looked intently to see what Jesus was staring at. It was like the sultry silence between the flash and the thunder one knows must follow. Then the storm burst—but it was not thunder after all, only the crackling of thorns under a pot. The little man raved in his fury. He was grossly insulted, he said. The 'Prophet' was a Jew dog, thinking only about Jerusalem. 'Go up to Jerusalem, then—*now,* for not a manjack of your party shall find a bed in my village!' There was a shout of approval at this from some of the more hot-headed Nationalists among us; but the others held off, feeling deeply uncomfortable. All Jesus did was at last to turn His beautiful head away from the road toward the raving lunatic before Him . . . and there was pity in His eyes.

"But the brothers James and John were blind with anger. They thought of Elijah and turned to their Master. 'Will You let us call down fire from Heaven, as did Elijah, to consume this rabble?' they cried. (I could see now what they meant when they told us on their previous visit that Jesus had nicknamed them the 'Sons of Thunder'.)

"But Jesus slowly shook His head. 'You do not realize,' He said, 'what kind of fire is needed here, what sort of fire you are baptized with: the fire of the Holy Spirit of Love. The Son of Man has not come to *destroy* men's lives but to *save* them. Come, let us move on.'

"At once He turned away and began to walk along that very road, amid the stupefaction of the crowd. James and John were the last to move. It was, I could see, only with the greatest self-control that they obeyed His command. Some of the villagers started jeering and cat-calling after Him; though the greater part went off home shame-facedly.

"But I stayed where I was, watching that forlorn little group trudging dejectedly to the next village—a long way, as I well knew, and night fast falling. Jesus had looked so tired, and His unexpected reaction to His rejection had pierced my soul as with a sword, making my heart bleed for Him. After a long time of indecision I found myself edging away toward the southward exit of the market place, and there, in the fast-falling dusk I ran . . . and ran . . . trying to catch up with Jesus, Whom the distance and the darkness had swallowed up. At last, on yonder rise, breathless and spent, I caught up with Him and His friends. Hearing my footsteps, He turned round and gazed questioningly at me. He looked so wan and pale in the eerie half-light and so tall. . . .

" 'Lord,' I burst out, falling on my knees in an impulsive outrushing of love and loyalty (though why I did it I could never reason out; it was something deeper than reason impelled me), 'O Lord, I will follow You wherever You go, even to the end of the world!'

"I think I meant it; I hope I did. Jesus came toward me and looked down on me, stretched at His feet before Him. From far away in the silence came the distant barking of a fox, and, nearer, the whirr of birds returning home to roost.

"Jesus turned His head to listen, then He said, 'The foxes have their holes, and the wild birds their nests . . . but the Son of Man has nowhere to lay His head.' All the loneliness of all the world was in His voice.

" 'Come back to our house,' I implored Him.

" 'Nay,' He returned, in severer tones. 'I go not back but forward. Follow thou Me.' And once more He moved on, inexorably and with measured tread, with not one backward glance.

"I stood rooted to the spot, struck into sudden immobility as if a chill blast had frozen my blood. There, in that grey-glimmering road, miles away from home, I felt lost and terribly frightened. Then I thought of my dear parents and of how I should bring down their grey hairs with sorrow to the grave if I let my impulse master me. To follow Jesus was like following the very spectre of death, whereas life and comfort were behind me. Duty, prudence and common sense all pulled one way. And the other? What could I call it? Intuition, impulse, love? All I know is that when I saw Jesus moving away from me again, I raced after Him and caught hold of His arm. 'Master, I *will* follow You! But *please* just let me first return home and explain, and say good-bye to my father and mother.' After all, Elijah had let Elisha say farewell to his family. . . .

"I had counted on His understanding and sympathy, but once again He surprised me. Drawing Himself up to His full commanding height, He answered in a hard, almost rebuking voice: 'No man, who once puts his hand to the plough and then looks back, is of any use to the Kingdom of God.' Evidently, He too was thinking of Elisha, who had been ploughing when Elijah called Him. But here was One sterner even than the great Prophet. . . .

"And He once more strode on, leaving me this time crushed and beaten, and in a few moments the night had swallowed Him up and even the far sound of their footsteps was lost.

"How I got home that night I never knew. Slowly and staggeringly, almost like a drunken man or a scourged, I stumbled back along yonder road, downward into Hell, it seemed to me; through the moonlit market place, looking pale and deathly, as though from it also the soul had fled; creeping forlornly into my bed and crying my heart out in utter unrelieved agony and anguish. My people never knew of it. They never even guessed, though I sometimes caught my mother looking narrowly at me during the days that followed; days in which a nerveless stupor of soul was screened by a furtive and aimless activity of body—mostly a gravitating toward the road that stretches there far away to the south.

"I heard afterward that Jesus had been crucified . . . and my heart nearly broke. I had failed the one Master in the world worth following, even if it were to death. And now I sit here, gazing at the road along which He trusted me to follow Him . . . and I let Him go. . . . I let Him go. . . ."

So it was that, never looking back, Jesus listened for any sign of the Samaritan's obedience to His command. But only silence closed in behind Him . . . and the man was far away by now, lost to the cause, safe in his home. . . . Jesus and His disciples trudged along in little groups, on their way toward Dothan. But that town would be night-bound and shuttered now and it was clear that they would be forced to sleep out in the open, under the lee of some strawrick, perhaps. When at length Jesus spoke His thoughts aloud, His voice took on an even deeper note of tragic rumination. He was thinking not only of that lost follower, and of what would have happened had he followed Him, but also of His own home back there in Nazareth. . . .

"Think not that My coming will suddenly bring peace to the world. No. It is not peace that My coming brings . . . but a sword—a sword to pierce, to destroy, to cut, to liberate! It serves, the Prophet foretold, to *set a man against his father;* yes, and a father against his son; a *daughter against her mother,* and a mother against her daughter; a *daughter-in-law against her mother-in-law,* and a mother-in-law against her daughter-in-law; and *a man's worst enemies are those of his own household.* Men shall be divided about Me—all five persons in one house split up into different sides, three against two and two against three. Whoever, then, loves his father or his mother more than Me, is not worthy of Me. And likewise anyone who loves his son or daughter more than Me, is unworthy of Me." There was a short silence; then He spoke again. "Yes, a man must be ready to *hate* his own father or mother if need be—and his wife and brothers and sisters, too—*and even his own soul* . . . else he can never truly be My disciple. As I said before to you, whoever is prepared to *lose his own soul* for My sake and the Gospel's, *he* it is who is worthy of Me! Whoever, therefore, is not ready to take up his own cross and to follow wherever I lead, is unworthy of Me; He cannot be My disciple. I would, therefore, that every would-be disciple should sit down calmly to weigh and reckon up the cost of discipleship."

He spoke of a rich man's "folly"—a great tower never more than half built, which was the butt of much mockery and jeering, everybody crying: "This fellow started to build, but he couldn't finish!"

His mind veered to another folly—Herod's war with Aretas of Petra. "Or to take another instance, what king, setting out to fight against another king, does not first sit down to calculate whether he can, with but ten thousand men, successfully encounter the enemy who is about to attack him with twenty thousand men? If he feels he cannot, then, if he be wise, he will, while the other is still a great way off, send an embassage to sue for peace. So it must be with each of you. Whoever is not able to tear himself away from *every* tie and every possession, he just cannot be My disciple."

He looked long at James and John. "And as for your wishing to call down fire from Heaven upon that village, I tell you I *am* come to call down fire from Heaven—but not merely to burn up a village, but to set fire to the whole earth! Would to God it were already alight! Did not the Baptist prophesy that I should baptize with the Holy Spirit—even with the fire from Heaven? *That* is the Baptism of Fire the earth needs."

From where they now stood, high on a hill, could be just descried, in the unearthly light of the moon, the far vale wherein Jordan ran, constricted between her steep banks, till she reached the Sea of Death. Somewhere down there He had been baptized. . . . But now He knew that He "came, not by water only, but by water—*and blood. . . .*" The shuddering urgency of the world's need and His part in it overmastered Him: "Yea, I have yet another baptism to undergo! And, oh, how pent up and constricted I am till it is all over!"

IV

The Paraean Ministry

. . . .

(I) JESUS ON DIVORCE

REJECTED in Samaria, Jesus crossed the Jordan and entered Peraea. Here He was in no danger from the authorities in Jerusalem. The best protection for Him—since He was determined to challenge the High Priests in Jerusalem and therefore safety in reaching there was of paramount importance—lay in attracting to Himself as large crowds as possible. Besides, such a course would furthermore serve to open His campaign, to be consummated in the Holy City when He would publicly claim the Messiahship and then reveal its true nature in His own sufferings. So, now that He was quit of Galilee and rejected in Samaria, He openly challenged attention.

The Pharisees were awaiting this, and at once countered with a campaign to undermine His popularity with the crowds. If, they reasoned, they could only think of some question to ask him which would necessarily, in the answering, alienate either the orthodox Jews or the people, then they would have won the first round. If, at the same time, they could, further, succeed in enraging Herod with Jesus on some personal issue, then indeed they would have triumphed signally.

With the most precise exactitude, they managed to combine all these dangers in one question. From this valley of the Jordan could be just seen, away to the southeast, the great fortress of Machaerus, perched high on its rock more than three thousand feet above the steely shimmer that marked the Dead Sea and its everlasting vapours. It was the eastward bastion of Herod's territory against the threatened invasion of King Aretas, who was preparing for war because his daughter had been divorced by Herod when he had incestuously "married" his brother Philip's wife, Herodias. There in the dark dungeons of Machaerus, had been silenced the one voice that had dared openly to arraign the royal sinners for their joint unfaithfulness to their respective marriage vows. Furthermore, the superstitious Herod was convinced, and would not be persuaded to the contrary, that the new Prophet was an avenging reincarnation of "John, whom I beheaded." Thus the stage was dramatically set for this crucial question of the Pharisees: "Tell us . . . do You think it is legal for a man to divorce his wife, or not?"

Of course they knew perfectly well that it was "legal." Jesus reminded them of this, throwing back their hypocrisy at them.

"What did Moses enact for you?" He asked.

They had no option but to reply, "Moses ruled that a man could divorce his wife by merely serving her with a written separation notice."

In other words the Law of Moses entirely exonerated even royal adulterers, providing they divorced their respective mates before marrying again.

Jesus could easily have left it at that. His enemies would have been trebly confounded, in failing to entrap Jesus, in having their question exposed as superfluous and hypocritical, and in being left—the very guardians of the Law—as the unpopular champions of the hated tyrant and his false Queen. But truth was at stake, and the courage of Jesus was challenged. To reveal truth was more important than routing enemies, even if such a revelation played straight into their hands.

"But it was only because of the hardness of your hearts that Moses allowed you that provision," He continued. "It was not so ordained in the primal purpose of God. For from the beginning of creation, God made the sexes for each other. Is it not so written in the Law? *Male and female created He them. Hence a man shall leave his father and mother and shall cling instead to his wife, and they twain shall be one flesh.* So, you see, they are thenceforward no longer separate entities but one in a unity of being. What therefore *God* has joined together, let not man put asunder!"

The disciples were puzzled by this further instance of what seemed a supersession of the Law. So when they reached their lodging they asked Him further of the matter. He made His meaning still more clear, if that were possible. "No matter *who* he is, if anyone divorces his wife and marries another, he commits adultery. *And* she also who divorces her husband and marries another equally commits adultery."

And so both Herod and Herodias were indicted of sin and found guilty. There was no mistaking the purpose of the twin clauses in His judgment. Jesus had nailed His colours to the mast for all to see. The disciples, however, were inclined to argue the point. "If that's the case with regard to a man and his wife, well, it's better not to marry."

"Maybe . . . for some," He replied. "This great truth may not be practicable for everyone. It is only for those who are big enough to accept it."

Small wonder that, shortly after, some Pharisees came up and pretended to warn Him, saying, "You'd better clear out of here, for Herod is sure to try to kill You, especially after what You said the other day."

Jesus saw through the "warning" which was, in fact, a lure to get Him out of Peraea into Judaea. But He was magnificently indifferent to both warning and lure. He would neither be delayed nor yet hurried.

"Go, now, and take a personal message from Me to that . . . *vixen!*" (For well He knew whose subtle brain was behind this "warning.") "Tell her, I shall continue to perform My public healings both today and tomorrow, and to preach openly as before. Did not the Prophet cry: *After two days will He revive Me, and on the third day He will raise Me up, and I shall live before Him; for My going forth is as sure as the morning!* So, you see, I shall continue My work, not only today but tomorrow as well. Then, the day after, My work will be completed and My journey ended. For of course it would never do— would it?—for any Prophet to perish anywhere but in Jerusalem!"

(II) RENUNCIATION

ONE day Jesus was in the middle of a discourse, and was saying, "If your brother sins, rebuke him——" when a man out of the crowd suddenly shouted out, "Well, then, what about my brother here? Tell him to divide our joint inheritance fairly with me and not to grab the lot himself!"

Jesus immediately remembered that Moses had once found himself in a similar situation. When *he* had interfered in a fight between two men, all he received in reply was: *Who made* you *an umpire or judge over us?*

So Jesus answered the complainant, "Man, who made *Me* a judge or arbiter over your affairs?" There was the implied question: "For what reason do you appeal to *Me?*" Did they really accept Him as judge or not? As no answer was forthcoming, Jesus continued: "If your brother really has sinned against you, go and show him his fault, as between you and him alone. If he listens to you, you will have won your brother over. Then, of course, you must forgive him. And even if he sins against you seven times in one day and all seven times turns again to you, saying, 'I'm sorry,' you must forgive him each time."

Peter was always argumentative. "Lord, do you mean *only* up to seven times and no more?"

Jesus, smiling, answered, "Seven times, did I say? Why, I mean seventy times seventy! For you cannot expect God to forgive you unless you are ready yourselves to forgive. Let Me tell you a story. It will show you the underlying principles of God's Reign.

"There was once a king who decided to have a settling of accounts from his servants. But as soon as he began the settlement, one debtor was brought in who owed him a fortune. As he couldn't pay up, his master ordered him to be sold as a slave, along with his wife and children and all that he had, the whole amount to go toward the repayment. So the servant fell down at his feet and entreated him, saying, 'Only give me time, and I will pay in full!' Whereupon his master took pity on him and with infinite graciousness, cancelled the debt.

"But no sooner had that servant gone out than he happened to meet one of his fellow servants who owed him some twenty pounds. And seizing him by the throat and nearly strangling him, he cried, 'Pay me what you owe me!' His fellow servant thereupon fell down at *his* feet and implored him, also saying, 'Only give me time, and I'll pay in full!' But he refused to give way and had him thrown into prison till such time as he should pay the debt.

"Then his fellow servants, who knew all the facts, were exceedingly angry and went in a body to the king and told him all about it. He immediately summoned the servant and said to him, 'You scoundrel! I cancelled that colossal debt because I was sorry for you. Oughtn't you to have had pity on your fellow servant, just as I had pity on you?' And in hot anger his master handed him over to the torturers till he should have paid all the original debt. In the same way My Heavenly Father will deal with you, unless you all forgive one another from your hearts whenever anyone sins against you. God's forgiveness of each one of you depends solely upon your forgiveness of your fellow men.

"Now for the root cause of all such quarrels as that over this inheritance—and take special notice of what I'm going to say—guard yourselves against covetousness in its every shape and form, for the true life of man has no connection with mere superabundance of possessions.

"A certain man's estate yielded him very heavy crops. So he debated within himself, saying, 'What *am* I to do? For I haven't room enough in which to store all my crops.' Suddenly he said to himself, 'I know what I'll do! I'll pull down my granaries and build larger ones, wherein there'll be plenty of room for all my crops and produce. Then I'll be in a position to say to myself, 'You've got nothing to worry about any more. You've ample stores laid up for many years to come. Take it easy, man! Eat, drink and be merry!' But God said to him, 'You foolish fellow! This very night your life will be demanded from you, and who then will reap the benefit of all your fine arrangements?' So fares the man who lays up treasure for himself, instead of gaining—and storing up—the riches of God. So do not aim at hoarding up treasures for yourselves on earth, where moths destroy and rust corrodes and thieves break in and steal. But rather aim at storing up treasure for yourselves in Heaven, where neither moth nor rust can destroy nor thieves ever break in and steal. Rather than hoard upon earth, sell everything that you possess. Then give all the money away in charity, and so provide for yourselves granaries that can never go to ruin, purses which can never wear out, a treasure in Heaven which can never fail you. For wherever your most treasured possessions are, there will inevitably your souls be also."

During the delivery of this discourse there had been listening to

Jesus a rich young aristocrat, who did indeed possess a huge estate which yielded him very heavy crops. He had heard the strange counsel of perfection just uttered by Jesus, advocating the complete renunciation of all worldly possessions, and was pricked by conscience: in turn attracted and repelled by this cutting-free from all worldly cares. Was this the one indispensable condition of gaining Eternal Life, of securing the eternal safety of one's soul? He saw Jesus proceeding along the street, and, like the Samaritan, found himself running breathlessly after Him and kneeling prostrate at His feet and saying, "Good Master—what good thing can *I* do to obtain this treasure in Heaven, this Eternal Life?"

Jesus looked down upon him with eyes of infinite love; for He, the Lord of Grace, was quick to see the lovely grace shining in this lowly suppliance. But, as always, Jesus was not satisfied with glib phrases. He would probe to the depths into this heart which had been pricked by His words.

"Now, *why* do you call Me 'good'? And, again, you asked Me what 'good' thing you could do to obtain Eternal Life. What exactly do you mean by this word 'good'? For if by 'good' you mean the best possible, that is an attribute of *Divinity*. Did you mean to attribute this to *Me*? Or perhaps you mean by 'goodness' the keeping of the Commandments—not killing, not committing adultery, not stealing, not lying, not cheating, honouring your parents, etc."

The question was a crucial one, if the young man were to be led to take the one decisive step that would match his gracious suppliance with a deed truly worthy of it, and so gain at a leap the life that was life indeed. Was his a conventional aim in life or that Divine perfection demanded of God—and by God?

But the young Ruler was obviously out of his depth. He answered hesitantly: "Well, as for the Commandments, I've tried to keep them ever since I can remember. What I want to know is what *more* is wanted?"

Jesus saw deep down into his heart, knew how moved he had been by the admonition to sell up and give all away. Peter, who was watching Jesus and not the young man, noticed the intensely tender look the Master bestowed upon the kneeling figure before Him. Jesus

oved this young man so greatly that He felt that nothing less than the
very best was good enough for him, and that he was capable of attain-
ng it. He had everything that could make life radiant and joyful:
grace, beauty, riches, youth. "Only *one* thing you lack," said Jesus.
'If you want to be the *best* you can be, go and do as I counselled a
moment ago. Sell everything you possess and distribute the proceeds
among all these poor folk, and then you'll have that treasure in Heaven
of which I spoke. And then come and follow Me!"

The hands of Christ, Who, for love's sake, had renounced even
Heaven itself, were stretched out in loving entreaty and welcome.
Peter's eyes turned, as did everyone else's to the young Ruler, as the
silent seconds ebbed away and the decisive battle for a soul was being
fought out. And what Peter saw nearly broke Jesus' heart; for the
countenance of the young man fell at the saying, and slowly the
kneeling figure rose, eyes downcast in an agony of shame, and turned
away and departed, bowed and broken. "For he had great possessions," as Peter long afterward told Mark.

As the young Ruler was at last hidden by the crowds, the arms of
Jesus fell in despair and His eyes were lowered in grey disillusionment. The smile faded, the brow contracted, the jaw closed; and Peter
noticed how intently Jesus glanced round about Him, searching the
hearts of that embarrassed crowd. Memories of His mother's teaching
surged up into the consciousness of Jesus. Because love could not rise
to "fill the hungry with good things," avarice had "sent the rich
empty away."

"How terribly hard it is," He cried, "for anyone who is rich to
enter into God's Kingdom! Why, it's easier for yonder camel to get
through a needle's eye . . . than for a rich man to get into the Kingdom
of God!"

The disciples were amazed at these words of His. But Jesus went
further, and insisted: "I tell you truly, My children, it's terribly hard
for *anyone* to enter God's Kingdom."

Hearing this, they were simply astounded and asked one another,
"Whoever, then, *can* be saved?"

Jesus, gazing upon them, said, "I agree. For men, as men, it is
impossible to be perfect: to take this colossal step that bridges the

Great Gulf, stepping out into the void with eyes on Heaven and your life in God's hands. But with God as your help—why, all things are possible!"

Peter meanwhile had been busy thinking, and at last he spoke. "Lord, *we* have left our homes, given up our livelihoods, everything, in fact. How do *we* stand?"

Jesus knew that Peter was not just arguing; his question was desperately sincere. Jesus also knew that they were waiting upon His own answer to it to learn their future to all Eternity. Seeing the anxious care in their eyes, He answered plainly, simply and splendidly, "I tell you, in most solemn truth, that in that New World, when the Son of Man shall sit on His glorious throne, you that have followed Me *and loved My holy name* shall, as Enoch says, sit, each of you *clad in shining light, upon the throne of his honour*—yes, even upon twelve thrones, governing the twelve tribes of Israel!"

The Sons of Thunder pricked up their ears at this. Might it be possible for them to be the two chief viziers in the Kingdom? And what did Judas think? For this high destiny *was* intended for him as well as for the others, had not sin made shipwreck of his life's voyage

Jesus continued: "And I'm not thinking of you only. There's no a single soul who has given up his house or his brothers or sisters o mother—" as He Himself had and the Samaritan had not—"or hi lands or possessions, for My sake and for the sake of My Good News who does not receive in return a hundred times as much—yes, here i this present life, even if it be with persecutions thrown in!—and i the world to come, Eternal Life! For earth's values are there reverse First things are last there, and last things first."

And so the story came full circle, and the rich young Ruler's quer was answered, and what he lacked also revealed. And Peter was als answered—astoundingly, gloriously.

The Master and His disciples were once more going forward upc their journey. Long years afterward Peter recalled the scene. "W were on the road, going up to Jerusalem—and Jesus was ahead of . . . and we were amazed . . . and as we followed we were afraid. . . That was all. But Peter's soul, as it had been at that momen was stripped naked before his listeners, who felt his fear and share

n that inexpressible sense of doom, of iron circumstance, of love's
nexorable logic. Every detail of the picture stood out in stereoscopic
clarity within his memory.

There was Jesus, tormented by a sense of urgency, wrapped in
onely thought, striding ahead, oblivious of the distance separating
Him from His disciples. And Peter remembered how at times Jesus
awoke from His dreams to find Himself so far outdistancing the
others that He had to wait for them to catch up with Him, He look-
ng dejected and forlorn the while. His own repeated words about
His coming sufferings, though they were discounted by the disciples'
incurable optimism regarding the coming Kingdom and their part
n it, were having their effect in unconscious realms of the mind.
Mixed with their dreams of a conquering Christ—dreams reinforced
by His recent words about thrones—were fears of the coming impact
with Rome; fears, too, of an even more terrifying nature—of cosmic
doom and apocalyptic signs—till, as they followed, they became more
and more the victims of an awed and intimidating amazement.

Peter remembered the long road, narrowing to a mere thread; the
very skies seemed held in the clutch of timeless immobility; the far
distances were overclear; a lurid light struggled with approaching
darkness. Peter—as Mark long afterward gazed wide-eyed at him—
found himself looking with a dread clarity at "one of the days of the
Son of Man": at the white, high forehead of Jesus, set like an adamant, harder than flint, at His eyes, staring, fixed upon those dark
horizons where the mountains of Judaea fronted the twilight. And
as Peter gazed upon the scene, retained thus in the galleries of memory, he shuddered and was silent.

When the Twelve had again caught up with Jesus, He began once
more to tell them of the things that were destined to happen to Him
upon the journey's end. Pointing along the road, He cried, "Behold,
we are going up to Jerusalem, and the Son of Man shall be delivered
to the High Priests and the Scribes. They will sentence Him to death
and will hand Him over to the Romans, who will mock Him, spit
upon Him, scourge Him and then kill Him. But on the third day He
will rise to life again!" And His eyes lighted up with exaltation and
the sound of triumphing trumpets thrilled in His voice. But the
Twelve were still bemused with a strange mixture of fear, ambition

and inherited traditions of the Messianic age. The awful, detailed
precision with which Jesus had just forecast His doom had not prevented them from indulging in dreams of their own approaching
glory. The Sons of Thunder recalled that Jesus had said, "Ask, and
you will receive"; and how on one occasion He had bidden His disciples "ask for great things, and then you'll find that the little things
will be yours as well." But they forgot that He had continued: "Ask
for Heavenly things, and the earthly shall be added unto you." They
were, instead, filled with apocalyptic imagery interpreted in terms of
this life. The old jealousy regarding precedence in the Apostolic
band had reared its head again.

The brothers approached Jesus and said, "Master, we want You to
do anything we ask!"

"Well, what is it you want Me to do for you?"

"To promise that when You enter into Your glory You will give
us the two seats on either side of You!"

Jesus searched their faces for any sign as to whether they were
thinking in terms of spiritual or material blessings. Either way, they
did not know the import of their tremendous request. He glanced
down at the Jordan River, in which the late evening twilight shone
softly, where He Himself had been baptized. And now He was moving forward toward the place of that further baptism in His own
blood. Unless they could share in that second baptism, how could
they share in His glory? So, as in Peter's case, He took this question
in perfect seriousness, going straight to the basic qualifications of
glory.

"You do not realize what it is you are asking," He answered. "Can
you both drink the cup I have to drink, and undergo the baptism I
have to undergo?"

"We can!" they replied. The die was cast; not that they understood
yet the implications of their tremendous affirmation, but that He saw
that they were sincere in laying their all at the feet of their Master.

Jesus was proud of them. "I believe you," He answered them. He
saw further into the future, too, saw the persecutions and martyrdom
awaiting their discipleship. "You shall indeed drink of My cup and
undergo My baptism. . . . But it is not even for Me to grant seats a

My right or left hand. They belong as of right to those who shall deserve them, for that shall be their glorious destiny."

The Ten were angry with the brothers as soon as they learned of this presumptuous request. They felt that they had an equal right with the Two to whatever honours were going in the earthly Kingdom to which they looked forward.

"You know well enough," Jesus told them, "how the great ones among the Romans and Greeks enjoy lording it over their 'inferiors'; and how also the members of their ruling caste command authority, not by inherent right of worthiness, but by extrinsic circumstances, loving to be called *'Euergetoe,'* 'Benefactors'! But it must never be so with you. Whoever among you wants to be called *'Magnus,'* 'Great,' must qualify for it by being your servant. And whoever hankers after the title *'Maximus,'* 'Lord of all,' must be slave of all! The elder must be prepared to act as the younger, the leader as the follower. And ask yourselves who is generally considered the more important, he that sits down to a meal, or the servant who waits on him? Wouldn't you answer 'He that sits down to eat'? I am sure you would. But you would be wrong, nevertheless, in Heaven's view. For I am here in the midst of men—as a Slave. Even so the Son of Man has not come to be served, but to serve: even to give His life as a ransom for many."

In afteryears the disciples realized that Jesus had not meant this merely in a compensatory sense—service in this world to be rewarded by lordship in the next—but rather in an inherently true sense, eternally, both here and now as well as there and then; service being the condition, rather than the precondition, of exaltation, the very basis and intrinsic nature of Heavenly honour; Heaven being not so much a reward—that is, a reversal of fortune awaiting the suffering soul—but rather the state of blessedness wherein a soul exemplifies the true nature both of honour and of service; God's own Son, even in Heaven ever serving most of all and so holding His rank eternally.

V

The Pharisee and the Publican

. . . .

(I) THE PHARISEE

THE next day was the Sabbath, and Jesus was teaching in a Synagogue in the Jordan Valley when He noticed a woman present who was terribly bowed over with chronic arthritis, being quite unable to raise herself. Pitying her, Jesus called out, "You are released from your infirmity." Going over to where she sat, He laid His hands upon her, and at once she stood upright and began to give glory to God.

But the Ruler of the Synagogue, indignant that Jesus had dared to heal on the Sabbath, said to the people (not daring himself to attack Jesus directly), "There are six days in which work can be done. In future, therefore, be careful to come on one of the weekdays to get healed, leaving the one day of the Sabbath sacred to God!"

The obliqueness of this censure was not lost on the Master, Who replied directly to him, "You hypocrite! Doesn't each one of you untie his ox or ass from his stall on the Sabbath and lead him away to drink?"

Jesus looked at the poor woman, now released and being given the water of life. "Well then, what about this woman, tied up by Satan for—how long was it? What, eighteen years?—wasn't it right, I say, and *fitting* too that she should be loosed from *her* chain on the Sabbath?"

Everyone present felt a straightening of his moral sense in this new found freedom to work God's works on God's own day.

As Jesus approached Jericho, followed by His disciples and a considerable crowd, it chanced that a blind man was sitting by the roadside, begging, and, hearing the noise of the crowd approaching, he asked some of the passers-by what it all meant.

"Jesus of Nazareth is coming along!" they told him.

Then, at the top of his voice, he shouted out, "Jesus, Thou Son of David, take pity on me!"

Those in front rebuked him and told him to be quiet, but he shouted out all the more, crying, "Thou Son of David, take pity on me!"

When Jesus had arrived at the place, He stood still and listened, and ordered that the man should be brought to Him. And they went to the beggar, saying, "Bartimaeus, the Prophet wants you!" and he, throwing away his upper garment, leaped up and was led to Jesus.

Then Jesus asked him, "Well, what do you want Me to do for you?"

"Lord, give me back my sight!"

And Jesus, being visibly moved with compassion, touched his eyes, saying, "Receive your sight! It was your insistent faith that cured you."

No sooner were his words spoken than the man found himself able to see; and he followed Jesus, glorifying God. And everyone who saw the miracle gave praise to God.

The same day Jesus was invited by one of the chief Pharisees in Jericho to dine with him after the morning service. All the food having been prepared and cooked the previous day, there was no limit to the luxury in which hosts vied with one another in these Sabbath banquets. This particular dinner had been arranged as a trap by which to catch Jesus off His guard. They had heard of His Sabbath healing in a neighbouring Synagogue and were anxious to bring Him to book before a representative company of rich and influential Jewish Leaders. As He was about to enter the courtyard of the Pharisee who had invited Him He noticed that an invalid had been purposely placed directly in His path; and, looking round, He observed how the guests had left a lane before Him, so that He could not miss the sufferer, and how they were all keenly watching Him.

Seeing the sufferer, He asked the company a direct question, "Tell Me, are you going to allow Me to heal this sufferer or not?"

They realized that He saw through their plot, and took refuge in a trained silence, signing to one another not to speak.

Nothing incensed Jesus more than this despicable parading of human suffering as a trap for the merciful. He turned to the invalid—

who was suffering from dropsy—crying, "Be healed!" clasping him in a warm and protective embrace. "Now go," He said, and the man departed.

Then He turned to the assembled guests. "I fully expect you have heard of My Sabbath healing in the Synagogue, and of My plea for the suffering woman there. I repeat it here. Which of you, if you had a child, or even a beast, that had fallen into a well this morning, wouldn't have pulled it out, Sabbath or no Sabbath?" Once again He was met by a stony silence.

Then the banquet began, and there was a glint in His eyes as He noticed the undignified scramble for the places nearest the host, and how He Himself had been left to take the end place at the horseshoe *reclinium*—the humblest position of all; and the words of Solomon came into His mind: *Put not thyself forward, and stand not in the place of great men. For better is it that it be said unto thee, "Come up hither," than that thou shouldest be put lower.*

A gravely ironic comment fell from His lips; addressing Himself primarily to those who had gained the "best" places, He said, "My friends, when next anyone invites you to a meal—let us say, to a marriage banquet—never recline in the place of honour, lest a more distinguished guest than you be invited too, and the host has perforce to tell you, 'Do you mind moving, please? Your place is for *this* guest,' and then you'll be obliged to move down, perhaps even to the lowest place. Oh, no. When next you are invited, go and recline in the humblest place, and then, when the host comes along, he will—doubtless—say to you, 'Friend, go up higher!' and then you'll be honoured before all your fellow guests!"

There was a tense embarrassment as this shaft sank in and the host in spite of it, did *not* ask Jesus to move up higher. The Master had a good look round upon His fellow guests: probably relatives, certainly personal friends, of the host, and all of them obviously from the same social caste, rich and able to repay such hospitality as lavishly as it was now offered.

Once again He spoke His mind; turning to His host, He said "My friend, when next you give a dinner party or a supper, be careful not to invite your relatives or your special friends or your rich neighbours. You see, they might possibly one day invite you back in return and so you would get repaid for all your hospitality. So, when next you give a banquet invite the poor and the maimed and the blind."

They were there to be seen, crowding in at the portals and some even watching the feast in the courtyard. "Then, indeed, you will be blessed. For, you see as *they* cannot possibly repay you, well, you'll just *have* to be repaid at the Resurrection of the just!"

At the mention of the blessed consummation awaiting the just, a fat, complacent, well-fed ecclesiastic, sententious, pious, exclusive, made a vapid platitudinous remark to fill in an awkward gap.

"Yes, indeed," he purred; "blessed is he who will one day dine in the Kingdom of God."

Jesus glanced swiftly at him—self-satisfied, smug. What did he know of the true meaning of the Kingdom? Or of its only conditions of entry?

"Ah! I've got a story for you, too."

The fat Jew started in surprise that his so harmless remark should somehow have raised this queer Prophet's ire. His little eyes, set deeply in his puffy cheeks, dilated as Jesus told His story.

"There was once a king who decided to give a banquet, in honour of his son." The telling way in which Jesus took up this chance remark—so connecting *this* banquet, supposedly given in honour of Himself, in which He had been so signally ignored, with the banquet given by God at the Resurrection of the truly just, truly given in honour of Him, His Son—was masterly in its power of swift and devastating irony.

"He invited a large number of guests; and when the hour of the banquet arrived, sent out his servant to announce to the guests: 'Come now, for everything is ready.' But what do you think happened? They all alike proceeded to decline the invitation, each having some excuse ready. The first to be visited said, 'I have bought a farm, and I am obliged to go and inspect it. Pray have me excused.' The second said, 'I have just purchased five yoke of oxen and I must needs try them out; so pray excuse me.' Another said, 'I have just married, so it is obvious I cannot come!' Thereupon the king sent out other servants, saying, 'Go, make it clear to all my guests that my banquet is prepared, my oxen and fat cattle are killed, and everything is now ready. Come to the marriage!' But they made light of it. Then he said to his servants, 'The banquet is indeed ready, but those who were invited have proved themselves unworthy to be present.' And being enraged he said to his servants, 'Go out into the streets and alleyways of the town and invite anyone you meet to attend the banquet. Bring in the poor, the maimed, the blind and the lame!' " Jesus remembered, with a thrill, Levi-Matthew's great feast, and continued: "But after a while the steward announced, 'Sir, your orders have been carried out, but there are still some empty places.' So his master cried out to him, 'Go out again, further afield this time—along the highroads, out into the open country, even comb out the hedgerows. *Make* people come back with you—for I *will* have my banquet fully attended! Though I tell you, not a single one of those who were originally asked shall have a taste of my feast!' "

This was a complete answer to the last speaker's complacent assumption of Israel's exclusive right to the Kingdom's plenty and seemingly a stark contradiction of the doctrine that only few should be saved.

Someone voiced the objection, "But . . . I always thought that the few, not the many, would be saved?" The crowds by this time were to be seen thronging the courtyard portal, and at a sign from the host, the servants forcibly closed the door, and cries of protest were heard from without.

Jesus then answered His objector: "All the more reason that you should strive to get in through the narrow portal, else you'll be among the many who—too late—will try to push their way in but won't succeed. For when the Master of the House has once risen and closed the door, you will find yourselves standing forlornly outside. How you will batter on the door, crying 'Lord, Lord, open to us!' But all you'll hear will be the voice of the Master from within, answering, 'I don't know you, or where you come from.' Then you will cry clamorously, 'But, Lord, You know us well! *Have we not eaten and drunk in Your Presence?* And You have taught in our streets.'

"But He will answer, 'I tell you, I do not know you, nor do I care wherever you come from. Clear off, all of you, you evil-doers!' And then, outside, you will wail and gnash your teeth, to see Abraham and Isaac and Jacob, and all the Prophets, inside the Realm of God, and you yourselves shut out. Yes—and there *shall* be 'many' within, for they shall not only come from the streets and alleyways and from the more distant highroads and hedgerows, but from the whole wide world—from east and west, from north and south—to sit down at their places at the great banquet in the Kingdom of God. For the lowest *here* shall be the highest *there;* and the highest *here* shall be the lowest *there*."

The Jews recoiled in horror from Him at this uncompromising rejection of Israel's "few" in favour of the wide world's "many," and at the pointed allusions to *this* banquet and its moral—and eternal—significance. But He had not finished with them yet.

"There was, once, a rich man, who was habitually arrayed—" He looked His host up and down—"in purple and fine linen, and fared sumptuously *every* day. Outside his outer door there lay a beggar—let us call him . . . Lazarus or 'God is *his* help.' He was nothing but a mass of festering ulcers, and was so hungry that he longed to get what would have been a full meal for him from what was thrown away as waste from the rich man's table. Though men had but scant pity for him, the dogs came and licked his sores. Well, in course of time this poor beggar died, and was carried by the Angels into 'Abraham's Bosom.' The rich man also died, and *he* was . . . buried. And there in Hades, being in torment, he raised his eyes and saw Abraham, far away, with Lazarus reclining there in his bosom. So he called out, 'Father Abraham, take pity on me and send Lazarus, if but to dip the tip of his finger in water, to cool my tongue; for I am tormented in these flames.' But Abraham answered, 'Remember, my son, that you had all your good things in your lifetime on earth, whereas Lazarus only received the evil things of life. So now, here, the position is reversed; he is in comfort and you are in agony.' "

Jesus recalled the great ravines that yawned so terrifyingly wide in Lebanon, and extended such a gulf in His imagination not only beyond the bounds of the cosmic chasm that yawned between earth and the stars, but even to the spiritual separation between good and evil—impassable, fixed for all Eternity, bottomless, the abyss indeed. He went on: "Abraham then said, 'But, quite apart from all that, between us and you there yawns a great gulf, set there in order that there shall be no passing over from one side to the other: no confusion between the eternal distinctions of right and wrong.' The rich man then said, 'I entreat you, then, O Father, to send Lazarus to my father's house, for I have five brothers. Let him bear testimony to them, warning them, lest they also come to this place of torment.' But Abraham answered, 'They have Moses and the Prophets. Let them hear them.' But he retorted, 'That would be no good, Father Abraham! But if only someone from among the dead would appear to them, I'm sure they would repent!' But Abraham answered, 'If they will not listen to Moses or the Prophets, no repentance of theirs would be convincing which only resulted from the appearance of a ghost to them.' "

Moral value must be its own guarantee and spiritual worth its own authority. And these are evidenced respectively by good deeds and a loving heart. There was no more to be said, and never can be, on that score.

(II) THE PUBLICAN

THE next day, as Jesus was passing along through Jericho, a man named Zacchaeus, the head surveyor of taxes for that region, was trying hard to see what Jesus was like, but could not, on account of the crowd, for he was very short. No one helped him out of his difficulty, which was only to be expected, since taxgatherers were not popular folk and a chief taxgatherer least of all. This one in particular was known to have amassed a considerable fortune by his cheating ways and general falsifying of accounts, and some of his victims were on the point of accusing him to Caesar. The crowd, therefore, saw Zacchaeus' efforts to crane his tubby neck and see over, or rather through, the throngs of people, only as a source of potential amusement.

They were not ill rewarded, for almost immediately they were witnesses of a really extraordinary scene. Zacchaeus, having tried darting hither and thither, pushing, edging, nudging—and all to no purpose—suddenly ran as best he could forward along the road that Jesus would have to traverse, and managed somehow, with innumerable slippings and heavings—amid the laughs and jeers of the crowds—to haul himself up on to a lower branch of a fig tree. It is noteworthy that the Greek word for "sycophant" meant, literally, "fig revealers," and had come to mean a betrayer by false accusation.

The crowd roared when some wit hurled this epithet against the tax-gatherer, as, owing to his strugglings, some figs fell to the ground, to be crushed beneath the feet of the crowd, as the bough bent and all but snapped beneath his weight.

Altogether ridiculous. Altogether enthusiastic, thought Jesus, as, passing along a few moments later, He caught sight of the fat little man, clinging in comic desperation to his perch. The people about Jesus, following His gaze, broke out in derisive laughter. Jesus was faced with a sudden crisis. He had intended leaving Jericho and push-ing on to Jerusalem; but now He did a lovely thing and decided to stay yet another day in the town after all. For He saw through the humour of the situation—though not forbearing Himself a huge dis-arming smile—to the abandon of love and its superb indifference to consequence.

The Master stopped dead in His tracks, and the crowd wondered what was going to happen. All the elements of high tragedy were present. It would have been so fatally easy to make a false move and alienate forever the embarrassed figure of the little taxgatherer. But Jesus saw in the very humour a glorious opportunity. Plucking Matthew's sleeve, He asked, "What's his name?"

"Zacchaeus, Master—a cheat and likely to be in a tight corner before long."

But Jesus lifted His head and pointed His hand to the figure in the tree, while the crowd relished in anticipation the expected ironic witticism. But a tremendous surprise awaited them. "Zacchaeus!" rang out the strong clear voice of Jesus. "Make haste and come down quickly—for today *you're* going to be My host!"

So the Master, banking on the man's enthusiasm and disregard of ridicule, made clear to everybody His preference for the Publican above the Pharisee; and as the people had heard of the Pharisees' dis-comfiture by Jesus on the day before, they fell in with His merry mood and, though they were still laughing, there was no sting in their mer-riment as they watched the fat little figure slithering and sliding to the ground in his effort to "make haste." At length he was safely on the road again, and there along the crowded highway went the tall Son of God with the podgy little Publican trying to keep in step with Him and failing lamentably.

The party of respectability soon heard that Jesus had gone in to dine with the taxgatherer, and was deeply scandalized. Jesus persuaded Zacchaeus to send a special invitation to the Pharisees to join in the merrymaking, but they indignantly refused. Nevertheless, Jesus was supremely happy. But He had a further aim in view. He was out not only to make a friend of a sinner, but a convert: a restorer of broken relationships. He saw the man Zacchaeus might yet become if love could only break in.

Talking obliquely, Jesus told a story which helped Zacchaeus to make his great decision. Seeing into his mind, He exposed Zacchaeus' own farsighted plans to tide over possible indictment and dismissal. Speaking as if to His disciples, He said, "There was once a rich man who had a steward; and this same steward was suspected of misapplying his master's possessions. And one day he was found out; and he was summoned by his master, who said to him, 'What's all this that I hear about you? You'd better hand in your accounts, for it's obvious that you cannot remain my steward.' Then the steward said within himself: 'What *am* I to do? For I can see I shall be deprived of the stewardship. I can't dig' "—a glance here at Zacchaeus' portly figure—" 'and I should be too ashamed to beg. *I* know what I'll do so that when I've lost my job I may still have *some* friends to go to!'

"So he decided to make voluntary restitution to any whom he had cheated." (According to the Law of Moses, providing no legal conviction had modified its voluntary nature, this would imply an addition of twenty per cent over the amount in question, to be regarded as a fine.) "So he summoned all his master's debtors to him and asked the first one, 'How much did I say you owed my master?' For, you see, he couldn't exactly remember. 'A hundred measures of oil,' the man answered. 'Well . . . I find that was inaccurate. Get out your bill quickly, and change the figure to fifty.' Then he asked another, 'And how much do *you* owe?' and he replied 'A hundred quarters of wheat.' 'Fetch your account,' said the steward, 'and alter it to eighty instead.'

"Now all this time the master had been fully aware of what was going on, and, do you know, he actually laughed about it, and *commended* the dishonest steward for his longheadedness! For he *had* been dishonest, you know. . . . But, at least, he had done very wisely in thus *trying* to put things right before it was too late, or, at any rate, in so doing, winning for himself some good friends against the bad time coming to him."

He looked long at Zacchaeus—seeing into his soul. Then He applied the moral significance of His parable to His disciples. "You know the worldly wise are often far shrewder in relation to the things of this life than are the sons of light in relation to the things of Eternity. So what *I* say is: Use Mammon—never mind how dishonestly it's gained—to win friends for yourselves! Then, when your plan fails—as fail it will, make no mistake about that—there'll be *some* there to welcome you to the Eternal abodes. . . ."

Suddenly His intensely ironic tone changed to one of an equally intense seriousness. "Believe Me, whoever is honest over a trifling matter will also be completely trustworthy in a larger one. Conversely, whoever is dishonest over small matters will be equally dishonest in great ones. If, therefore, you have not proved yourselves scrupulously honest in regard to this world's tainted wealth, who will ever trust you with the True Riches?" His eyes were now on Zacchaeus all the time. "And if you cannot be trusted with what belongs of right to another, how can you be entrusted with what is intended shall be your very own? I tell you, there is not the remotest possibility of compromise over this vital matter. No steward can serve *two* masters. Either he will hate the first and love the second, or else he will decide to cleave to the first and reject the second. One thing is clear. No one can serve *both* God and Mammon!"

Some Pharisees, in the outskirts of the crowd hanging about the courtyard, on hearing these words, sneered disdainfully at Him, being annoyed all the more in that they were great lovers of money themselves. So Jesus turned to them and said, "You are the sort of people who manage to get a reputation for being good, but God knows what you are really like. For what seems good in men's sight is often loathsome in the eyes of God."

All this while Zacchaeus had been listening intently. He was now in the grip of a great emotion, wrestling with destiny and overcoming. At last he stood up and braved it out. Facing Jesus, with an arm stretched out to the crowds, he cried, "Master, I wish to make a public announcement. You have told us of . . . the steward . . . who tried to make voluntary restitution of any dishonestly gained wealth. But I am willing to go much further. Here and now, in the sight of all these people, I promise first of all to give half of all my fortune to the poor; and whatever I have dishonestly exacted in taxes, I pledge myself not only to repay it with the usual extra percentage in voluntary restitution, but to repay *four* times the amount!"

This was magnificent. For according to the Book of Exodus where a cheat had been convicted, and *compulsory* restitution had to be made, *double* the amount had in general to be restored. Thus Zacchaeus was indicting himself as though he were a convicted swindler, *doubly* guilty: convicted by Christ and twofold more a sinner than any this indictment averred. The people cheered on hearing this noble confession and promise of restitution.

The eyes of the Master were radiant with joy as He put His arm around Zacchaeus' shoulders, and cried, "Here and now has salvation come to this house! For Zacchaeus has proved himself a true son of Abraham! For I, the Son of Man, have come for this very purpose—of seeking out and saving the lost!"

Thus the two banquets were contrasted, and the Archisynagogos and the Architelores, the Pharisee and the Publican, set in antithesis, to the glory of the latter and the shame of the former. And now Jesus rounded off the whole double episode with yet another story, especially designed for those who were sure of their own goodness and looked down on everybody else.

"I can see, in My mind's eye, two men soon to be in the Temple, whither they will have gone up to pray: the one a taxgatherer and the other a Pharisee. The Pharisee I see posing very stiff and straight, praying like this—*to himself!* 'O God, I thank Thee that I am so unlike the rest of men—thieves, rogues, vicious, or like yonder taxgatherer over there. *I* fast twice a week, and on all my income I always pay a whole tenth to Thee!'

"But the taxgatherer stands away in a dark corner, and will not so much as lift up his eyes to Heaven, but beats upon his breast in contrition, saying only, 'O God, have mercy on me, a sinner.'

"I tell you," thundered Jesus, *"this* man, rather than the other, is the one who will go back to his house *justified!"*

VI

Between Jericho and Jerusalem

. . . .

(I) STEWARDSHIP AND SERVICE

As Jesus moved forward once again on the last twenty miles separating Him from the capital, He thought anew of the joys inherent in the seeking out and saving of sinners, explaining to His disciples that there were three ways in which a person's soul might become lost. Chance and circumstance sometimes seemed to have a disproportionate part to play in the determination of a soul's destiny. That was not unlike the chance loss of a little coin off a necklet worn by some poor woman. It would roll away and be hidden in some dark corner where there was but little hope that it would be found. But the woman would search for it until she found it, nevertheless. And then when she had found it, what rejoicings there would be, all the neighbours being called in to share in her joy—for the neighbours whom Jesus knew as a Child could not afford to lose even the tiniest coin.

Then there was the soul that became lost through a combination of circumstance and bewildered carelessness. That could be represented by a lost sheep, straying away from the flock till it lost its way in strange and unknown country. But there again the shepherd sought *until* he found!

But there was a third way, the saddest of all and the most difficult to retrace: the way of purposive sin, of wilful selfishness and perverted taste. But this could only be portrayed by a story of a human person.

Then it was that Jesus told them the imperishable story of the Prodigal Son—the Gospel in miniature: that superb allegory of the lost soul at last welcomed home by a father who ran to meet him! Here was the final picture of Jesus' own conception of God—Who is Love.

As they rose above the plain and could look back and see Jericho—its ancient and modern parts clearly distinguishable—Jesus drew attention to the towers of the splendid palace rebuilt not long before by Herod Archelaus, after the former one erected by his father, Herod the Great, had been gutted by fire. He reminded His disciples of the manner in which Archelaus had first come to be called a "King." Under the will of Herod the Great, Judaea had been bequeathed to this, the elder of his two sons by Malthrace of Samaria. Archelaus would not assume his sovereignty, however, till he had received it in person from the Emperor at Rome; a prudent measure, since, in order to quell a revolt, he had just previously slaughtered three thousand people within the sacred precincts of the Temple, and Caesars were apt to frown upon such tumults and disorders. So he went all the way to Rome to get his Kingship confirmed; whereupon (in spite of an opposing embassage from his prospective subjects) he, being successful, had rewarded all those notables who had supported his claims with governorships of cities, and punished all opponents with wholesale slaughter.

Jesus had noticed, with infinite sorrow of heart, that He had not even by now managed to persuade His disciples of the spiritual nature of His Kingdom. They still thought of it as an imminent nationalistic victory, or, at best, as a catastrophic intervention by God to be expected in the very near future. Jesus had learned by bitter experience that the end was not yet; and that between the fulfilment of His plan and its final consummation lay an unspecified gap of time. This interval widened in His mind as the sands of His earthly life ran out. "The Bridegroom tarried. . . . " "My Lord delayeth His coming." "After a long time the Master returned." With these thoughts in mind, Jesus dwelled upon the colossal responsibility devolving upon the disciples following His own death—and their equally tremendous opportunities—providing they were honest in small things as in great. So, with those towers of Archelaus there in view, Jesus told them the story of the talents, with its message: "Occupy till I come!" It should be remembered that the nobleman in the story was not God but Archelaus—indeed a hard man, reaping where he had not sown, fierce, revengeful and merciless.

Jesus at last turned His face away from Herod Archelaus' palace, with its memories of a vindictively cruel tyrant, and summed up the lesson of His parable: "For to everyone who has virtues, shall more be added—yes, and in abundance. But whoever allows his talents to atrophy shall in the end find them taken away from him." And having said this, He went forward again on His way up to Jerusalem.

Soon they arrived at a parting of the ways—each with its tollgate. To the right ran a broad, downhill road that led to Galilee, to Greece and Rome, to escape and comfort, perhaps even to mastery in an appreciative sphere. There, to the left ran a narrow, tortuous road through a precipitous ravine, leading the uphill way to agony and to death. To the right lay possible world sovereignty—at once; not deferred or indefinitely relegated to apocalyptic cataclysms. To the left, life cut short, misunderstanding, failure. *Look, He is standing at the parting of the ways, where the two roads meet. See, He is divining His decision.*

Looking first to the right, and then to the left, He cried, "The entrance into glory is by the narrow gate. For, see, broad is the gate and wide the road that leads to spiritual ruin. And narrow is the gate and confined the road that leads to life!" Then His eyes fell, as He added, "But few there are who find it."

The disciples were bewildered. "Do You really mean," they asked in awed tones, "that only a few will in the end be saved?"

But He only answered, "Try hard to enter in by the narrow gate; for, I tell you, many shall strive to enter in, but shall not be able to." And to the left He turned and strode onward.

Peter looked a little sulky that salvation should have come so quickly to Zacchaeus—himself so late a disciple. But love cannot weigh and calculate. All the labourers in God's vineyard should enjoy the same reward. "I will give unto this last even as unto thee." God's salvation was not so much a reward, as if it were a matter of timekeeping and wage sheets, as of grace. Willingness to serve was all, since to serve at all was such an infinite privilege.

"I am here on earth to serve—for service is the essence of Divinity. So you must serve, too, if you would follow Me. Service implies a sense of responsibility. Some are raised by it, others are ruined. Many are lazy and incompetent; only a few are devoted and zealous. The real test of a servant comes when he is left alone . . . as you will be when I am taken away from you. Only a few days yet remain while I, your Master, am present with you. After that, the Bridegroom will be far away . . . for how long, not even He knows. Then will come your testing time. For good stewardship implies continual watching for the Bridegroom's return. (For I *shall* return again!) You can never tell when He may arrive. If you do not keep watch, thieves may break in, and you will be held responsible. For if a steward, left in charge during his lord's absence, could know when his lord were returning, he would keep watch and not allow his lord's house to be broken into. So be ready always; for your Lord's return may well come when you least expect it."

Peter asked, "Lord, is this talk of stewardship for us Apostles only or for any believer?" He gloried in the responsibility in proportion to its exclusiveness.

Jesus answered, "Well, Peter, what would *you* do if you were the returning lord? Whom would you set as the chief steward over your household, to feed and care for your own folk? Wouldn't you select the most wise and faithful servant, *whoever* he was? I tell you, such a servant will be deeply blessed on that great day! For what I tell you is true: He will set *him* over all his Lord's household!"

Peter was left wondering . . . and great resolves and expectations surged up in his heart as he remembered Jesus' words to him on the Rock above Caesarea Philippi. But Jesus was watching him. He knew his weaknesses, and the warning followed at once: "But if that servant should say in his heart, "My lord is delaying his return. . . .' and should begin to ill treat his fellow servants, and, instead of caring for those under his charge, should feed himself and be drunken, then the lord of that servant will return in a day when he least expects him, and shall cut him asunder from his flock and appoint him his portion with the unfaithful. Remember that those who are most intimate with their lord's will are the ones from whom most will be expected; whereas comparative ignorance necessarily lessens responsibility. So keep your girdles taut and your lamps burning. During what may well be the long night of waiting, be forever on the watch for your Lord's return, so that when at last you hear His knocks on the door, you may hasten to open to Him! And do not behave like foolish girls who thought the time of waiting would be short, and forgot to get in a reserve of oil for their lamps, and were badly caught out when suddenly the cry arose in the darkness: 'The Bridegroom is coming!' and panicked and begged in vain of the more prudent for some of their oil; and then rushed out to the merchants and returned only to find the Bridegroom arrived and the door barred and bolted against them. And all they got for their battering and crying out was: 'Go away! I don't know you.' No. Be like wise virgins who laid in a good stock of oil for their lamps, and were thus able (even if for a while they *had* slumbered and slept!) to rise and take their lighted lamps and go forth to meet the Bridegroom and lead Him in with joy! And what d'you think He will do to those whom He actually finds *awake?* Why, I tell you, He will be so delighted—and surprised—that, in contrast with your ordinary sort of master who says, 'Gird yourselves and serve me till I have finished my meal, and then you can go and get something to eat for yourselves,' He will actually make His servants recline at His own table and, girding Himself with a towel, will come and serve them! Watch, therefore," He summed up, "for you won't know when the Bridegroom will return: whether at eventide, or at midnight, or at cockcrowing, or in the morning; lest, coming suddenly, He find you sleeping. And what I say to you, Peter, I say to you all: Watch!"

And at midnight, poor Peter tried so hard to watch and fell asleep with sheer fatigue; and again at cockcrowing, and denied his Master; and in the morning and believed not the reports of the women. But in the evening of his life, he was found faithful and died with his eyes on Heaven, looking for his Lord's return.

After a time they caught up with another group also going up to the feast. Among these were some Scribes, or official interpreters of the Law. They had been present when Jesus had encountered the rich young Ruler, and had been specially interested in the discussion that had then ensued upon the Commandments and their relation to the winning of Eternal Life. Two of them had been having a heated argument before they had been overtaken by Jesus (Who had, as we know, stayed behind for an extra day in Jericho) about the Master's apparent supersession of the Commandments by a higher Law in His advice to the young Ruler. One of the Scribes had secretly agreed with Jesus, that the mere keeping of the Commandments was not enough. The other argued that the Law could never be superseded; there was no "higher Law." So, when Jesus and His disciples caught up with them, they decided to put the question to the test—the one sincerely, the other with intent to entrap Jesus.

"Master," said the first, "what, of all the commands in the Law, would You regard as the most important?"

Jesus, in inspired intuition, answered, "The first is: *Hear O Israel, the Lord our God, even the Lord, is One; and thou shalt love the Lord thy God with all thy heart, and with all thy soul, and with all thy strength*—yes, *and with all thy mind, too,*" added Jesus significantly. "The second most important command is: *Thou shalt love thy neighbour as thyself.* There are no commands more important than these two."

The Scribe was deeply impressed, and answered, "Of a truth, Master, You have well said. The acknowledgment that there is only One God in all the world is indeed the most important consideration; and to love Him with all one's heart and strength—and understanding—and to love one's neighbour as one's self, these things matter much more, as Samuel said, than all the *burnt offerings and sacrifices.*"

Jesus looked on the Scribe lovingly and said: "*You* are not far from the Kingdom of God!" But the other Scribe was even more dissatisfied after this praise of his colleague. He fastened on to the word "neighbour," in Jesus' quotation from *Leviticus,* and at length approached Jesus with the identical question originally asked by the rich young Ruler. "Master, what must *I* do to gain Eternal Life?"

Jesus countered, "Well, you're the expert; you ought to know. What do you read in the Law?"

The Scribe was ready for this question; indeed, he had been hoping precisely for it. So he replied in the same way as Jesus had done to the first Scribe; to which Jesus answered, "That's excellent! Live up to that, and you shall certainly gain your 'Eternal Life'!"

The Scribe was now prepared to shoot his barbed arrow. "Tell me," he urged, "who exactly is my 'neighbour'?" He remembered that the passage quoted by Jesus expressly stated to whom the command referred. It ran: *Thou shalt not hate thy fellow countryman. Thou shalt bear no grudge against thy fellow citizen, but love thy neighbour as thyself."* That was clear enough. Jesus had wrested the words quoted by Him out of their context. So He could not possibly answer this question without laying himself open to easy attack.

Jesus eyed the Scribe, saw through his trap and decided to answer him, as so often was His way, in story form. They were at that moment passing the very defile where so often passing travellers were brutally assaulted by robbers. Jesus did not bother about defining the word "neighbour," but, instead, Himself answered the question: "To whom can I be a neighbour?" by telling the lovely story of the Good Samaritan, stressing the invidious parts played by the Priest and the Levite in "passing by on the other side." At its conclusion, He asked the Scribe: "Now, tell Me, which, do you think, of these three, the Priest, the Levite or the Samaritan, was 'neighbour' to the man who fell among the thieves?"

The Scribe would not use the hated word "Samaritan," but grudgingly murmured, "The one, I suppose, who took pity on the man."

"Very well," answered Jesus, "so now you know not only who is to be regarded as your 'neighbour,' but also—a far more important lesson to learn—how to be a 'neighbour.' So, copy the Samaritan, and be a good neighbour to everyone in need of your help, whatever his nationality."

(II) MARTHA AND MARY

MARY of Bethany—once Mary of Magdala—was seated in a corner of her garden, from where she could see the road leading to their house. She was shaking with excitement, her eyes never for a moment straying from the far corner where the road vanished from sight in the distance. News had reached her that her Master was coming this way, that He had been to Jericho and was even now moving up to the feast at Jerusalem. He would be passing by this very house. Would He think of her—or, even better, turn aside for a few moments to renew their friendship? Or would He hear that Lazarus, their brother, was absent from home just now and postpone His visit to another time? Or perhaps forget altogether about her and pass by unheeding? It had been such a long time since she had last seen Him.

She had found life unbearable by the Lakeside, with all its sordid

associations and its perpetual gossip, and had fled homeward to
Bethany. She well recalled the moment when she had first arrived at
the door and confronted her sister. How Martha had started and
shrunk back, before she had pulled her quickly within! How well,
too, Martha had been able to master her tears, even when Mary's were
pouring down her cheeks in a paroxysm of hysterical weeping. In
spite of Martha's suspicions, Mary herself had been her own best
recommendation. The petulant, spoiled beauty who had run away
from home so long before, was now a dreamy, still creature, beautiful
as ever—even more beautiful. The wavering, purposeless activities of
her younger days, alternating with idle, sulky tempers—reminding
Martha of the shallows of the seashore, ruffled by winds or stagnant
in the pools—were now exchanged for the stillness of the central
deeps. Her eyes were oceans of experience, as though they held
memories of storms now quieted to a great calm. What was it Martha
had found one day scrawled with a stylus upon Mary's tablets? *I have
behaved . . . and quieted myself. . . . I refrain my soul, and keep it
low. . . . I was in His eyes . . . as one who had found peace.*

And Jesus came—and found Mary there in the garden. He felt a
sense of relief, of blessed comfort of body and soul, in being at last in
a home again, with one so receptive and spiritually aware. She loved
much, and knew the abandonment of love. Yet she had disciplined
herself to purity—a lily now, rather than the flaunting scarlet flower
she had once been. Here was beauty rather than mere goodness, the
numinous rather than the merely moral. And as she listened, all
Heaven listened too, while the evening sun slanted through the bower-
ing trees and the quiet plashing of the courtyard fountain and the far
fluting of some songbird made even more restful the twilit peace.

But if Mary stood for beauty and holiness (now), Martha was
definitely goodness and morality. Mysticism meant nothing to her;
action in a good cause was her strength. And as she bent once more
to peep through the lattice, a pang of unreasoning jealousy smote her.
There was Mary, sitting absorbed and spellbound, filled with dreams
of her Hero, the Prophet, while all this time the hard work of preparing the supper fell to her, Martha. At last she could stand it no
longer. She went out into the garden, to have it out with Mary and

her Friend. If He were a true Prophet He would at least see justice done.

"Rabbi," she complained, "don't You care that my sister has left me to do all the work of preparing the supper alone? Come, tell her to lend me a hand!"

But Jesus gently chided her. "Martha, Martha, I can see you are worried tonight, over your splendid meal and its many courses. One only is quite enough for Me. And as for Mary—why, she has already chosen the best dish, and she shall *not* be dragged away from it!"

But though He smiled in turn at both the sisters, the spell was broken, and with a laugh Mary rose and taking her sister's arm led the way into the house, saying she could not keep the best dish all to herself—and wasn't He very hungry after all His long walk from Jericho?

VII

The Man Born Blind

THE day after, something happened that altered the timing of Jesus' plans. He had been intending to challenge the authorities in Jerusalem at this forthcoming Feast of Dedication, when some people approached Him as He was journeying toward the Mount of Olives to tell Him of a terrible massacre of Galilean Pilgrims by Pilate which had just occurred. This feast was primarily the great nationalist festival, for it was not founded on any event related in the Canon of Scripture, but had been instituted by Judas Maccabaeus nearly two centuries before, to commemorate the rededication of the Temple after its desecration by Antiochus Epiphanes. Accordingly, it was the great festival of the Zealot movement, in that it celebrated a Restoration of Israel and the overthrow of a hated oppressor. As soon, therefore, as Jesus had heard the news of this new tumult and its terrible sequel, He realized that any action on His part at this festival would, in view of Pilate's savagery and its repercussions on the people, be out of the question. Not only would it almost certainly be made an occasion of another nationalistic uprising, but it would, on this account, utterly vitiate the whole purpose of His own revelation, as the Suffering Messiah. So He made up His mind to postpone His revelation as Messiah till the Passover. Nevertheless, He used the news—and the way in which it was told to Him—as vehicles of some of his highest Teaching.

The Jews had come to Him there upon the Bethany-Jerusalem road, and said, "Rabbi, have You heard that some Galilean Pilgrims have just been slaughtered in the Temple—their blood actually mingled with that of their sacrifices?"

This was almost certainly a lie. Pilate would never have sent his soldiers into the Temple precincts. But it was near enough to the truth. "Tell us," they went on: "how would *You* regard these slaughtered Galileans? As specially wicked sinners because they dared to protest against Rome's tyranny and extortion? *You* would say, wouldn't You, that they ought to have submitted tamely to Rome, 'resisting not evil . . . turning the other cheek,' eh? 'Going a second mile'—at the bidding of a Roman, too?''

This was a vastly clever attempt to discredit Jesus with the inflamed populace. He knew, however, that once again their question was based on that hideous doctrine that equated suffering with personal sin. Rejecting this, He suddenly saw His way out.

"Sinners?" He replied. "Special sinners, just because they were martyred by Pilate? Justly punished by God? I tell you, no! Unless you yourselves repent, you will all come to an equally bad end."

He forestalled the implied charge, and dealt with it faithfully.

"I can see what you're thinking, that if rebels do not deserve death then it follows that traitors do. Maybe you are thinking of those eighteen workmen who were engaged on the building of Pilate's aqueduct from the Pool of Siloam and were killed when the great tower on the wall suddenly collapsed on them, owing to its being undermined by the tunnelling. You all hated that aqueduct, didn't you? So those building it deserved to be killed, eh? But I can see through your trap easily enough. You want Me to blame either the Galilean martyrs—as a good Quietist—or else the Jewish workmen—as a good patriot! Yes, I know all about Pilate's seizing of the Temple money offerings, which were 'Korban,' dedicated to God, with which he paid these workpeople. I've got no illusions about either Pilate or Zealots—or you, either. And I'm falling into no trap. For if those Galilean martyrs were not sinners above all else, well, neither were those Jewish workmen. On neither count will I blame anybody; for the whole lot of you will ultimately perish unless you repent."

And so He escaped all their snares; for there never was a brain to compare with His for sheer power of dialectic.

The more Jesus thought upon His encounter with those who had told Him of Pilate's massacre, the more glad was He that He had dealt with their traps in connexion with the falsity of their doctrine regarding sin and suffering. For it was becoming increasingly plain that He would never be able to convince the world that His revelation of a Suffering Messiah was valid unless this ghastly connexion between sin and suffering were completely and finally severed. In a way, He knew that it would be His own Cross which would—provided He were acknowledged as the Messiah—finally complete the severance. But the way would have to be prepared for this revelation by the repeated denial that suffering was a punishment for personal sin. Only so could His disciples be rid of their inbred obsession with this doctrine.

Arriving in the city a day or two before the actual commencement of the feast, He was passing along through the streets on the Sabbath when He saw a youth who, as young John pointed out to Jesus, had been blind from his birth. Jesus' repudiation of the doctrine above referred to, in His reply to the report of Pilate's massacre, had deeply troubled the disciples, in spite of His previous denials of its authenticity.

So they asked Jesus, "Tell us, Master, for whose sins—his own or his parents'—was this boy born blind?"

Jesus replied, "Neither for his own sin, nor yet for his parents', was this poor boy born blind. What matters about this lad is not that he, as you evidently think, illustrates a theory of Divine Justice; nor even, which is a fact, that he contradicts it; but rather that he provides an opportunity for a manifestation of God's will. Here is someone who has never seen the light and beauty of the world. That is a challenge to the light—especially to us who know what daylight is . . . while it is yet daylight. . . . For the night is coming when no man can work, and *the Sun knoweth His going down.* . . . But so long as I am in the world, I will be its sunlight."

Then He proceeded to carry out His Divine intention, to work the works of God. He spat on the ground (spittle being regarded as of great therapeutic value), and making clay anointed the boy's eyes with it, saying to him, "Now go and wash off the clay in the Pool of Siloam," and the boy went away and obeyed, and came up from the pool seeing!

He then went straight home, where his arrival caused a great stir, several of his neighbours saying, "Can this be the very self-same boy who used to sit and beg?"

Some were sure of it, but others said, "No. It's like him, I grant you, but it's not he." The difference in his whole expression was so great owing to his eyes being opened that their doubt was quite natural.

The boy himself, however, put an end to the argument by bluntly declaring, "I *am* the fellow."

The neighbours were avidly curious. "How on earth did you get your sight?" they asked him. Now the boy had, of course, never so far seen Jesus. He had only heard Him speak, and sharp of hearing as all blind persons are, had heard His name spoken by young John. "A Man called Jesus made some clay," he answered his questioners, "and smeared my eyes with it, and told me to wash in the Pool of Siloam. I obeyed—and I see!"

"Where is He now?"

"How can I tell?"

But some of the more busybodying neighbours, savouring trouble, dragged off the young man to the Pharisees. "This boy's sight was restored on the Sabbath," they complained, "by a Fellow of the name of Jesus," they added.

"How was it done?"

"By making clay and smearing his eyes with it."

This was clearly a violation of the Law, since the making of clay was specifically forbidden on the Sabbath. The Pharisees asked the boy to tell his own story, after which they concluded, "This proves that Jesus is quite definitely *not* from God, since He breaks the Sabbath Laws."

"But how could a sinner perform such signs?" cried someone.

Another suggested that the whole story might turn out to be pure invention. "I don't believe this fellow was ever born blind at all."

"Better summon his parents and ask them," suggested another.

So after a while the parents arrived, terrified, before the Pharisees. "Is this your son?" they were asked, "and was he born blind?"

"Yes, this is our son," they faltered, "and he was born blind. But as to how he can see today, or who it was that opened his eyes, we can't tell. Ask him—he is of age to answer for himself."

They were too afraid to tell the truth, since the Jewish authorities had already given out that anyone who confessed that Jesus was the Messiah would be excommunicated. So the boy was summoned a

second time and told, "Now, tell the truth, as before God. We happen
to *know* that this Man, Jesus, is a sinner. . . ."

The youth was bold enough to interrupt. "Whether He be a sinner
or not, I don't know. But one thing I do know: that whereas I was
blind, I can now see!" His grasp of fact was splendid, inescapable.

Again they asked, feebly, "What exactly did He do to you? *How* did
He open your eyes?"

"I've told you once, only evidently you didn't listen. Why do you
want to hear it all over again? Do *you* want to be His disciples?"

This is youth at its most independent and impudent. After all,
unlike his parents, he had nothing to lose. But the Pharisees stormed
at him. "It's obviously *you* who are His disciple! *We* are disciples of
Moses, for we *know* God spoke to Moses; but as for this Fellow's
authority, no one knows whence it derives."

"Well, isn't that just too marvellous! You don't know where this
Man gets his power from, and yet He has opened my eyes! Even *I*
know that God doesn't listen to sinners, but to those who are devout
and obey His will. It is a thing unheard of since the world began that
anyone should open the eyes of someone born blind; so, if this Man's
power were not from God, He could do nothing!"

The logic was inexorable, and they were livid with rage. *"You?"*
they shouted. *"You* teaching *us!* You, wholly begotten and born in
sin!"—as, for them, was proved by his former affliction. So they
solemnly excommunicated him from all worship, whether in Temple
or Synagogue, perhaps not such a very terrible deprivation for him,
but a stigma and a terrible handicap in life and almost a complete
bar to gainful employment.

As soon as Jesus heard that they had expelled him, He sought him
out and, on finding him, asked him, "Is it really true that you believe
in the Messiah?" putting this in the third person, not only because the
boy's sturdy defence of Jesus was the ground of his expulsion from
worship, but because the youth had not been able, of course, to recognize Him as his Healer, since he had never before seen Him.

But the boy knew that his Healer must be Messiah, and he wanted
to find Him and thank Him. *"Who* is He, sir? Do tell me, so that I
may believe on Him!"

Jesus answered, "Well, now you can see Him for yourself! For He is even now speaking to you!"

Falling down on his knees before Jesus, the boy cried, "Lord, I do believe!"

Jesus turned to John and said: "My coming into the world is in itself a judgment of men; for, as they either receive or else reject Me, so is inevitably revealed their capability of *seeing truth*. Those who confess their blindness find their sight restored, whereas those who claim to see are shown up for the blind guides that they are."

Some Pharisees standing by who overheard this remark asked, "I suppose You class *us* among the blind?"

"*Blind?*" Jesus retorted ironically. "Of course not! If you really were blind you might have some excuse for your actions, but as you boast of your good sight, well . . . your sin remains."

It was quite useless for the Jews to sneer, "He's mad!" for, as one of their own number said, such a master of dialectic could hardly be out of his mind. Besides, could a madman open the eyes of a boy born blind? And so, as always, they were back again at the starting point of the argument: the inescapable fact of Christ's power.

Then came the commencement of the feast. It being winter, Jesus was walking up and down in the covered portico called Solomon's Porch, to warm Himself before settling down to teach there. The Rulers were gathering round Him, and at last they asked Him outright, "How long are You going to keep us in suspense? If You really are the Messiah, tell us so plainly."

But, owing to the massacre of the Galileans, this was precisely what He would not do at present, since His whole plan relied upon this revelation synchronizing with His Passion, so that His self-identification with the Suffering Servant might be unmistakable as a showing forth of God's eternal nature. So He evaded the direct question.

"I have told you—but you do not believe Me. The deeds I do in My Father's name testify to Me, but you do not believe because you do not belong to My flock."

His wrath was rising, for had not these shepherds of Israel just cast out a young sheep from the flock of which they had the care?

Jesus contrasted His own flock and theirs, and the words of Ezekiel echoed in His mind:

Behold, I am against the shepherds, and will demand My flock back from them. For, behold, I, even I, will both search for My sheep and seek them out, on a day of clouds and darkness. Yea, I will look for the lost, and I will recover those who have been driven away; and I, the Lord, will be their God, and I will make their folds a blessing, and they shall dwell safely.

So Jesus, Who had just recovered one who had been driven away, went on: "My sheep listen to My voice and understand, and I know them and they follow Me, and I give them Eternal Life. They shall never perish." His voice rose: "And no one shall be able to wrest them out of *My* hand!"

See the mounting anger of the Son of God, all you Leaders cowering there! "My Father Who gave them to Me is greater than all! Therefore I say again: no one can ever wrest anything out of My Father's hand!"

There, just before Him as He was speaking, was the Beautiful Gate of the Temple, sometimes called the Golden Gate, made of superbly wrought Corinthian brass; so large that it took twenty-two men each morning and evening to open and shut it. Its twin doors were seventy feet high and the arch in which they were hung was some seventeen feet higher still. There it was, in front of Jesus—shut. Again, the words of Ezekiel came into His mind:

And the Angel brought me to the gate that faced eastward, and it was shut. Then said the Lord to me, "This gate shall be shut. No man shall enter in by it. Because the Lord, the God of Israel has entered in by it. It is for the Prince—the Prince! He shall enter in by that gate!"

So Jesus, with this gate in view all the time, cried: "In most solemn truth I tell you, he who does not enter the sheepfold by the gate, but climbs up some other way, is a thief and a robber. He Who enters by the gate is the Shepherd—'*It is for the Prince*'—and for those whom the Prince shall bring with Him. And to Him the gatekeeper opens the gate, and the sheep listen to His voice—" and there were the disciples listening to Him "—and He calls His sheep each by its name, and leads them out."

(Out . . . because a sheep had been cast out of Israel, and Jesus knew that *that* fold, *that* Temple, was not of God; so, suddenly reversing Ezekiel's imagery, He was leading His sheep *out* of the cramping exclusiveness of Israel's fold, out into the Shepherd's own pastures.)

"And when He has brought all His sheep outside, He goes in front of them, and the sheep follow Him because they know His voice. But a stranger will they not follow, but will run from him, because they know not a stranger's voice."

Still looking at this vast and magnificent Beautiful Gate, and then thinking of the true fold of God's flock, Jesus, developing His thought, saw Himself as the true Gate of Heaven; in very truth the door of the sheep, since the shepherds so often lay down over the threshold of the fold in order to frighten off any stray beasts and to protect with their own bodies the sheep committed to their care—and often to die in so doing.

So He cried, "I, the Shepherd, the Beautiful One, am also the Gate of the Fold. Whoever enters in by Me will be safe, going in or out freely and finding pasture. For I know My sheep and My sheep know Me; just as the Father knows Me and I know the Father; and I lay down My life for the sheep. And other sheep I have, which are not of this fold. Them also I must bring, and they, too, shall listen to My voice, and there shall in the end be one flock and one Shepherd."

He had been carried away in His rapture of self-revelation, and the result was exactly what prudence might have feared. The Rulers were enraged beyond all bearing, and immediately began to pick up the loose-lying chippings left there by the stonemasons who were still at work on the Temple, in order to stone Him to death for blasphemy. But Pilate's prerogative stayed them in their hot-headed impulse, while Jesus, with magnificent courage, cried out: "Many works I have shown you from the Father—beautiful works, all of them! For which of them do you mean to stone Me? Is it because I claimed God as My Father? But have you not read in the Scripture that God Himself says: *You are gods, and all of you sons of the Most High?* If then, the Scripture attributes sonship of God to all who heard and obeyed God's will in the days of old—and according to *you,* the Scripture cannot be gainsaid—why do you accuse Me, sent as I am into the world and consecrated to God's service, of blasphemy just because I call Myself a Son of God? However, if I am *not* doing the kind of works that the Father would do, don't believe Me. But if I *am,* then admit, at any rate, that the deeds themselves are Divine even if you still refuse to believe in *Me*. Then, perhaps, you may eventually learn and understand that the Father *is* in Me and I in the Father."

The Elders felt baffled. That royal mien, those steady, clear-shining eyes, made stoning difficult. Besides, the crowds were largely on Jesus' side. They tried to arrange an arrest that very night, but Jesus had disappeared from the city when the Temple officers sought for Him. The Shepherd, the Beautiful One, had led His sheep out of the hands of the thieves and robbers, who would steal and kill, that He might lead His own a while beside the still waters.

VIII

The Raising of Lazarus

By still waters . . . Jesus had led His disciples out from Jerusalem, down the Jericho road and across the Jordan, toward the place where first He had seen John baptizing; and there He stayed for a season.

Here Jesus was visited by many residents of the Jordan Valley, who inevitably, in this region, compared Him with the Baptist, saying, "John indeed did no sign, but everything that John spoke about this Man was true," and several believed on Him there.

One day Peter, Andrew and Philip approached Him as He was rising up from prayer, with the request: "Lord, teach us to pray. For we remember how John used to teach us, when we were with him, to pray to God. But we want to be able to pray as *You* do. . . . "

They knew He was possessed of a power that, on His own admission, was due to prayer. So Jesus taught them His own prayer: the lovely prayer we still call the "Lord's Prayer."

The first thing was to project one's self into the presence of God, and to think of Him as a father: the Father of all men. Prayer should not be for one's self only, but for all one's brethren as well. God was in Heaven, so men must imagine themselves in Heaven, bowed down before God. To be in tune with God, one must try to realize anew His holiness, beside which men's sinfulness will be all the more real. The next thing to realize was that we have no right, since it is impossible of fulfilment, to ask that God may do *our* will. *He* cannot change, it is only man that changes. And unless, therefore, we ask something which be according to God's will, we know our petitions *cannot* be granted. So, in order that God's will may be done—and so the very best happen to us—we must try to lose our wills in His. Our whole attitude must be an intense longing to see God's reign as an accomplished fact, not only ideally and ultimately in Heaven, but here and now upon earth. Then—and then only—can we offer up our petitions to God for the daily needs of life: for the pardoning of all past

323

sins, for the avoidance of all temptation if possible, and for its conquest if it come, so that we may be delivered from all the power of evil. So alone can we rest in the Eternal Omnipotence of the Father.

So it was that He taught them, clause by clause, the "Lord's Prayer," they repeating them after Him till they had the prayer by heart. Following this He took the opportunity to teach His disciples to persevere in prayer. Some reminiscences of childhood knocked at the doors of His memory; and He told them the story of the friend who came one midnight to the door of their house at Nazareth. Joseph was so embarrassed to find he had nothing in the larder that he had to run out and try to borrow some loaves, and he only got them in the end because of his perseverance in knocking up the gruff neighbour who was in bed with his children. And the story also of His mother, then a widow, who was forced to worry a lazy magistrate by continually pestering him before she was able to secure justice from an opponent who was trying to swindle her. He remembered that the enemy was a Pharisee, intent on devouring even a widow's livelihood. He laughed as He told His disciples what the magistrate said to excuse himself in giving way to Mary. "Though I care not for God nor man, still, as this widow plagues me, perhaps I had better get the matter settled . . . if only to stop her forever coming and pestering me."

"Take heed," said Jesus, "to what the lazy magistrate said! For if a bad man, for a bad reason, will so react to persistence that 'caring neither for God nor man,' he gives way—to a poor widow—how much more will God see justice done to His elect who cry day and night to Him? I tell you, *He* will not delay before He executes justice for His elect!"

But a saddening thought clouded His mind. Upon how many of His professed disciples could He count for such persistence in prayer and faith? So He added wistfully, "And yet . . . when the Reign of God does come, *shall* the Son of Man find faith on the earth, even then? . . . "

During this enforced wait by the fords of Jordan, Jesus often thought lovingly of the household at Bethany. He had become increasingly intimate with all of the family during the Feast of Dedication, going out to this welcoming home whenever possible. It was, therefore, with deep sorrow that Jesus heard from young John of Jerusalem, who had hastened to the Jordan Valley as the messenger of the sisters, that Lazarus had been suddenly struck down with sickness. John had travelled on horseback, together with a confidential servant of his, and it had taken two days for them to find Jesus. It was like John, who was himself affectionately known as "the disciple whom Jesus loved" to refer to Lazarus as "He whom You love." There was another reason for this. It was essential that this message should be kept as secret as possible, in view of the great dangers inherent in Jesus' entering Judaea again, should He decide to visit Bethany. Nevertheless, Jesus told the other disciples that Lazarus was ill.

This news put Jesus in a dilemma. To return to Judaea would be to court death, prematurely. His arrest and almost certain execution would be all the more easily accomplished by the Jews and Romans in the absence of the Pilgrims; and these latter were, besides, an essential factor in His plan. But even as He was silently listening to John's account of Lazarus' sudden illness and to his own hazardous journey of some twenty-five miles in search of Jesus, a strange conviction—nay, an overwhelming certainty—was borne in upon Jesus that His friend was already dead. There was no need now to move into danger, as He Himself could do nothing to help the sisters. Unless . . . But that was out of the question. It would mean the jettisoning of all His carefully laid plans. Besides, the really important truth for the sisters to grasp was that Eternal Life is something experienced here and now; that physical resuscitation merely to *this* life is no guarantee of Immortality; that death does not matter to the soul which is in unity with God in Christ. And yet love's impulse bade Him help the sisters. . . .

But even as He mused upon these Eternal verities and their relation to this earthly urgency, an idea was stirring in His mind. What if He could find a way in which to use this very tragedy not only as the occasion of the revelation of His deepest Teaching on life and death, but also of a supreme offering of love to the sisters—and, above all, as an incontrovertible proof of His own Messianic status? The Passover was now not far away. If only, after raising Lazarus to life again, He Himself could successfully disappear into hiding till the time of the feast, this very death might prove to be the linchpin of all His master plan. That Lazarus was indeed dead would be an incontrovertible fact. If he were to lie in his tomb, say, for four days—the time required in popular belief for the spirit finally to leave the body—then this miracle would attest the Messianic claims of Jesus beyond all possibility of disproof. Lazarus was well known and many would be present at his funeral to witness his interment. If Jesus raised him secretly, Lazarus would thereafter be alive for all to see—raised by Jesus, on the word of the sisters and of Lazarus himself. The mighty cogency of this plan stirred Jesus to the depths. So He sent John's servant back to Bethany with a somewhat cryptic message: "Not death but the glory of God is the end of this sickness, that the Son of Man may be glorified thereby!"

John, who was expecting to accompany Jesus back to Bethany, stayed with his Master for the moment. He was greatly concerned to find that Jesus did not at once follow up His message in person, but stayed on for two whole days there by the fords of Jordan. Of one thing, however, he was sure. Whatever Jesus did was out of the love that He bore to Martha and her sister and Lazarus. But it was all very puzzling. How could he know that the raising must not take place till Lazarus had been four days dead?

So, two days after first receiving the message from Martha, Jesus suddenly said to His disciples, "Let's go back again into Judaea!"

They were astounded. "Into Judaea?" they echoed. "Why, Master, only the other day the Rulers were trying to stone You—and yet You are going back there?"

But Jesus was thinking of the glory that would be given to God through this miracle. If only He obeyed love's impulse, all would be well with Him, for the light would shine about His path, whatever befell. A passage from Jeremiah called to Him. *Give glory to God . . . before it grow dark, and before your feet stumble upon the mountains of twilight; lest, while you look for light, He turn it unto the shadow of death and make it deep darkness.* He was in a haze of ecstatic thought, ranging on a plane utterly out of reach of the disciples. As if from high up and far away came His answer: "Are there not 'twelve hours' of daylight? If a man walks in the daylight, He will not stumble, for He will still see the light of the world. But if he walks in the night, He will stumble, for the light within him will have gone out."

A rapt silence followed this mystic saying; then Jesus in a quiet voice added, "Lazarus, our friend, has fallen asleep. So I am going to awaken him out of sleep."

They took Him literally, as so often. "Asleep?" they echoed. "Why, if he's fallen asleep, he will probably recover."

Jesus was forced to speak plainly, although He ever disliked using the word "dead" of an immortal being. "Lazarus is dead," He told them. The shock of this stunned them for a while; then, after a silence Jesus added, "I am now glad that I was not there when he died, so that you may learn to trust Me to the uttermost. Come now, let us go to him."

Thomas the Twin spoke for all of them when he cried, "Yes, let us go with Him—that we may die with Him!" Loyalty and love, fatalism and fear, all were intercombined in that despairing cry. But Jesus trusted to the light within Him, never shining more brightly than now. He moved forward resolutely . . . and the disciples followed, but they were very frightened.

So, by a devious route, since Jesus knew the Wilderness so well, they at length reached Bethany, and John was despatched to tell Martha, the elder sister, that Jesus was even then waiting in a fold of the hills, not far from the garden of their house. She at once went out to meet Him, Mary meanwhile, all unsuspecting, remaining at home, passive and still. One thought had continually hammered at the sisters' minds: if only Jesus had come in time! Then the message itself—how it had hurt them!—mocking, as it did, the still white face of their brother, lying on his bier. "This sickness will not end in death!" And now there was the dead man, rotting in his grave.

On seeing Jesus, Martha blurted out the burden of her thoughts. "Had You been here, Master, my brother would never have died. . . ." But, as she gazed piteously into His eyes, her faith in Him again flamed out, unquenched and strong, as she added the amazing words: "Yet . . . even now, I *know* that whatever *You* ask of God, God will give You!" He alone was worthy of the magnificent confidence of God, as heard by the Prophet of old: *Ask of Me; concerning the work of Mine hands*—command Thou Me!

Jesus meanwhile was wondering how far her faith in Eternal Life went.

"Your brother will rise again," He told her.

"Yes, of course," she answered. "I know he will rise again . . . sometime . . . at the Resurrection on the Last Day." *Last Day!*—cold comfort, this. What she wanted was Lazarus himself, in the flesh, by her side again, here and now, not somewhere, somewhen, in a remote future.

Jesus, sensing the desultory drift of her thoughts, realized anew the necessity of teaching her that life, not mere resuscitation or survival, was the chief end of man. He knew that life and immortality were but the twin aspects of this Teaching: the Ultimate-Eternal and the eventual-climactic aspects of the one great Reality whose infinite projection upward and forward embraced all space and time in one continuum of being. Life *was* indeed here and now, if only she could realize this supreme truth. And this life—the only valid guarantee of any Resurrection—was bound up in Himself, apart from Him, having no existence.

So, to Martha in her grief, Jesus uttered the great words that have comforted mourners ever since: the very soul and essence of Christianity. "*I* am the Resurrection and the Life! He that believes on Me—though he were 'dead,' yet shall he live! For whosoever *lives,* believing on Me, shall never die! Do you believe that?"

Martha was out of her depth, but one thing she had grasped. "Yes, Lord," she answered, "I do believe You are the Messiah, the Son of God, the One Who was to come into the world!"

Jesus glanced keenly at her, then suddenly said, "Where is Mary?" at which Martha at once went, in swift movement reacting to unaccustomed confession, to tell her sister—though secretly, for fear of the Elders who were even then present to condole with them—that the Master had come and was calling for her. Mary listened spellbound to her sister's breathless message, and, impulsive, ardent and emotional as ever, was rushing out of the house in such an ecstasy of excitement that all Martha's caution was thrown to the winds, for the Elders saw her and followed to see what it was had so excited her. Arrived at the place where Jesus was, she—so different from the controlled Martha—fell down at His feet, sobbing out the very self-same reproach that was uttered by Martha, and then burst into a flood of uncontrollable tears. The Jewish Leaders, coming up at this moment, seeing her weeping, covered their faces and did their best to show their sympathy in like manner. The sight and sound of Mary's tears caused Jesus, in spite of all His efforts to restrain Himself, to utter groans of inarticulate, choking sobs. The people were by this time deeply moved. "Look," they whispered to one another, "how greatly He loved Lazarus!"

Jesus, seeing the Jews, realized that His desired privacy was not to be granted Him, and that, consequently, the miracle would have to be performed publicly. But the light still shone about Him. Moving toward the house, He asked Martha, "Where have you laid him?"

"Lord, come and see," she answered.

John, following alongside some of the mourners, overheard one of them say, "Could not this Man, Who so recently opened the eyes of the blind boy, have done something to prevent this tragedy?" re-echoing the sisters' plaint.

So they came to the tomb, a cavity cut out of the rocky hillside.

"Roll away the boulder," ordered Jesus. He straightened Himself, getting a grip on His emotions. There was a terrifying majesty in His mien.

Martha, practical as ever, came forward officiously with a remonstrance. "But, Lord, he will be rotting by this time. Remember, he's been dead four days now."

Jesus turned to her and in a more severe voice reminded her: "Did I not send you a message saying that you should see the glory of God—that is, if only you can believe?"

Martha was silent.

So they rolled away the stone; and Jesus lifted up His eyes and cried, "Father, I thank Thee that Thou art listening!" John, close by Him, heard Him whisper an afterthought in His intimate communion with God: "Indeed, I know that Thou *always* hearest Me. It was only for the crowd's sake that I said this—that they may believe that Thou hast sent Me." Then, with a loud voice, He cried: "Lazarus, come forth!"

The echoes of that mighty shout rolled away into the darkness of the vault and were lost within the reverberant hills; and went echoing on into the farthest spaces of the universe, till, sounding even in Hades, they called forth a soul by name. Then, breaking the breathless silence there in Bethany, there came a macabre scuffling sound from within the darkness of the tomb, and presently a terrifying apparition appeared, amid the screams and shouts of the onlookers, as the corpse, bound hand and foot with swathing bands, only his face open to view—framed by the napkin still swathed about his head—shuffled slowly out inch by inch from the tomb, returning from another world.

"Untie him," cried Jesus, "and let him move!"

Some of the people were stimulated into full belief in Jesus. Others at once withdrew stealthily to carry the news to the authorities in the city. Immediately Caiaphas summoned an emergency meeting of the Sanhedrin.

"Whatever is to be done?" they asked one another. "The Fellow is getting past all bearing, performing sign after sign like this. If we let Him alone, why, everybody will believe in Him, and then there'll be a tumult, and when the Romans get to hear of it, very likely it'll be the end of our country and nation." All of which was sound common sense, *seeing they could not deny the fact of the miracle.*

But they had not reckoned with Caiaphas. Nor for nothing had he been chosen by the Romans to be High Priest. Strong-featured, masterful, menacing and utterly unscrupulous, representing evil in all its strength, he was a fitting opponent of the Son of God. But evil in its subtlety was better shown in that far older man seated on the right hand of Caiaphas, withered, agelessly aged, heartless: Annas, the father of the Temple family, once High Priest himself and now fabulously rich and the scheming brain behind his son-in-law, Caiaphas. Over there is Nicodemus, troubled, vacillating, as if some inner conflict were still ruffling the deep waters of his soul. That other patrician-featured notable next to him is Joseph of Arimathea, owner of an estate on the outskirts of the city. He is deeply attracted by the new Prophet, and yet a loyalty to Israel bids him realize the cogency of the Priest's words.

Caiaphas waited patiently, scornfully indifferent to their excited comments; till at last he cut in swiftly with the decisive conclusion, expressed with the urgent finality of a scimitar stroke. His harsh rasping voice suddenly silenced everyone present.

"You know just nothing at all about it," he shouted. "You don't realize it is in your own interests that one man should die for the people rather than that the whole nation should be destroyed."

This was sentence of death, uttered by the High Priest, agreed upon tacitly in the ensuing silence, as Caiaphas rose and terminated the meeting. Long afterward Nicodemus and John recalled this strange, prescient utterance and thought how true a prophecy it was: that Jesus should die, not only for the nation, but for all the scattered children of God.

Jesus was from henceforward a doomed Man. He heard of it all from John, secretly and urgently; and it became more than ever necessary for Him temporarily to disappear, together with His disciples. So that night He set out from Bethany and going up into the loneliness of the hills moved secretly toward a wild region known as Ephraim, in the wilderness of Beth-Aven by the boundaries of Samaria. The authorities sent their guards at once to Bethany, but they found their prey flown. Frustrated here, they sent their spies out. The highways were patrolled, the bazaars searched, the villages visited in turn. But no one knew whither Jesus had gone.

ACT FIVE

. . . .

The Christ of Calvary

I

The Second Anointing

THE Passover was now very near. Jesus, from His vantage height on the hills of Ephraim, saw the swelling streams of Pilgrims swarming along the Peraean road far below. The hour was almost come for which He had waited so long; that culmination which, like the last climax of a giant fugue, had been deferred and interrupted to the increasing tension and strength of the coming full-close, now at last unhinderedly in sight. Those Pilgrims were to be His chosen witnesses—the spectators of the central act in the history of the universe. The chief characters in the cosmic drama were even now assembling. Pilate had already moved into residence in Jerusalem, taking up his quarters in the Herodian palace. Herod was moving up toward the city, to be lodged, much to his disgust, in the old Maccabaean palace, damp and cold and draughty. Annas and Caiaphas had by now laid their plans carefully; their spies were everywhere, searching the caravans at the cross roads, mingling with the Pilgrims in the camps. The altar only awaited its victim.

Jesus at length came out of His retreat in the lonely hills and, travelling by a secret route, arrived in Bethany the night before the Sabbath day preceding the Passover. Making His way after dark to the home of the sisters, He had there been welcomed, not only as the Messiah, but as the Raiser of their brother from the dead. Young John was at once sent for, and when he arrived Jesus told him and the sisters of His plans for the revealing of His Messianic mission: the public entry in state, fulfilling a well-known Messianic prophecy, and then the final revelation of the Suffering Messiah. Mary and John were inexpressibly moved. He explained to them that this time He was courting the crowds. The more there were to witness His triumphal entry the better. He was arranging secretly for a white ass to be available—the sign of a conqueror's peaceable entry into His kingdom. He told Mary that the raising of her brother had played a vital part in this plan by helping to provide the necessary throngs of people—though He was deeply distressed that the Leaders, foiled in their attempt to arrest Himself, were already searching for the subject of the miracle. But Lazarus was not far away.

Mary had suddenly risen, and signalling to Martha they together left the room, leaving John to stay with his Lord and tell Him all the gossip of the arriving Pilgrims. Their one question, he said, was whether Jesus would come up to the feast; for everybody knew that the authorities had given orders that anyone discovering the whereabouts of Jesus was to acquaint them immediately so that His arrest might be arranged. Then, bursting into their conversation, had come the sisters, bringing with them—Lazarus! Martha was even now planning a private supper party this very night in celebration of the occasion. Lazarus listened, and then did a very brave thing. He proposed that the supper party should be a big public affair, in the largest house in the village—Simon's for choice. Let the whole village know of Jesus' return and of this celebration! If Jesus needed witnesses, let the Pilgrims who were everywhere camping out on the hillside share in the rejoicing. Then, shyly and diffidently, Lazarus added, "May I be there too? If they saw me actually there, maybe it would help You. . . ."

They all stared at him incredulously. The danger was immense, not only to Jesus and, of course, to Lazarus, but to the whole community. But the Galilean Pilgrims would be all around, to guard against premature arrest. The plan increasingly approved itself to them all. Mary was the most enthusiastic. There was a faraway look in her eyes, and a secret smile hovered over her lips. Martha sped away to see Simon, the father of Jesus' disciple Judas, who lived in the biggest house in the village. John went to tell the villagers, and Jesus was left to thank Lazarus for his magnificent offer. But Mary disappeared to her room.

The village rose to its full height of courage and generosity. The news that Jesus and Lazarus were to be there together at the supper blazed through the district and soon a vast concourse of people was crowding round Simon's house, to which Jesus and Lazarus were triumphantly led. Martha was in her element, improvising an important banquet in a hurry and seeing that everyone did his share in making it a success.

But Mary, alone in her room, was holding an alabaster vase, half filled with ointment. Her mind had gone back to that day—it seemed so long ago—when that same cruse was first used and its aromatic perfume, the reward of sin—she shuddered as she recalled it—was poured out over the feet of her Saviour. She had kept it ever since, stoppered and wrapped up in a secret place, a precious memento of the day on which her soul had been cleansed. She was even now fingering it lovingly. Itself originally a token gift of sin, it was now a token of the gift of her very soul to Jesus. She was His forever. Love's abandonment had saved her—and she had sinned no more, even as He had bidden her.

And now Jesus was going to His death . . . and His lovely body would soon be cold and still and would slowly rot away in the darkness of a tomb. Tears welled up into her beautiful eyes. Could no unguents, no balsams, preserve that dear flesh? Would no mourners be there to render those last rites over His dead body? For if He died as a criminal, as was almost certain now, His body would be hastily interred in a felon's grave, and no one would be allowed access to it beforehand. This ointment in her hands—could it instead be used on His *living* flesh? And could this be its last use, its final consecration?

Then, with a rush of mounting colour suffusing her cheeks, she realized that such an action would but serve to remind Jesus of that earlier banquet and so of her sins, so great, so horrible. A shudder shook her as she remembered. But she braced herself. She could endure that. Nay, she could wish it. It was but right that all of her— her past as well as her present—should be laid open to her Lord's mind on this, possibly the very last, opportunity she might have of being with Him in this life. Her penitence and her gratitude should be renewed before Him in this most touching way, as if to plead: "Here I am. You know what I was, how I was saved and when. I am still Yours more than ever before. I do this to anoint Your body for its burial. You will remember—and understand." The coursing torrent of her self-oblation raced on to its full Niagara. Not only would she anoint Him once again from this, the very self-same cruse, but she would endeavour to reproduce in utmost detail the former anointing. She planned to loosen for the last time her wonderful tresses, in token of her former profession, and in her utter abandonment to expose herself before all her fellow villagers, that they too might remember her shame and that her soul might rest in the totality of confession and abasement. And, lastly, this phial, so precious and so dear and so soon to be doubly consecrated to her love for Jesus, should by no other human hand be forever touched. All the ointment should be poured out on those beloved feet, and then this pale-veined marble loveliness should be shattered to a thousand pieces.

She carried out her plan in minute detail. Everyone was astounded and mystified . . . save Jesus. He understood and read her thoughts and blessed her for her lovely act of self-immolation. But Judas, whose father had supplied the room for the banquet, being deeply incensed at this shameful profanation of this celebration, complained about her act, hating its theatricality, its waste.

He was the treasurer of the Apostolic band and thought that Mary should have had other and better uses for such costly ointment.

"What a waste!" he muttered. "And all to no purpose! If she wanted to do Jesus honour, why on earth didn't she sell the wretched stuff and . . . well, give the money to the poor? Jesus would have much preferred that. It would have sold for . . . a hundred dollars, I shouldn't be surprised, or we could have had the money for the Master's use. . . ."

Jesus swung round on him. He was very angry.

"Let her alone!" He cried. "She has done a very lovely thing. I tell you, you can always help the poor, and whenever you want to you can do them good. But you won't always have Me with you. She has done all she could, in thus anointing My body beforehand, to prepare Me for My burial. . . ."

The words of a well-known Rabbi, often quoted, came into His mind: *Oil spreads its fragrance from the chamber to the hall, even as a good name reaches out from one end of the world to the other.*

He cried, "Wherever My Good News shall be preached throughout the whole world, this act of Mary's shall also be spoken of as a memorial of her love!"

But Judas was furious. To be thus insulted, and in his own father's house, so freely lent for the occasion, just because he was trying to be careful, as a good steward should, of their frugal resources! For, as he remarked, he hadn't even suggested that the proceeds of the sale of the ointment *should* be used for them. He had expressly said *"for the poor."* Wasn't that what Jesus was always teaching? The whole thing was unpardonable. Jesus was a queer sort of Messiah, in any case. All that talk of "suffering servants" and dying. . . . What good would *that* do Israel? Maybe the Priests were right about Him after all.

II

The Triumphant Entry

JERUSALEM was tingling with excitement. Everywhere the Pilgrims were discussing the strange news about Lazarus of Bethany. Four days dead and now alive again, raised by Jesus, the Prophet from Nazareth. There was, so people said, a price on the head of the Prophet. That, at any rate, proved that the story was true. Jesus had disappeared, however—a good thing. A Prophet like that must not be lost to Israel. But He would be safe among the Pilgrims; "especially among us Galileans," shouted someone, and there was a roar of assent at this. "Do you think He will come up to the feast? What do you think about Him, anyway?" And then there were noddings and whisperings. Some, however, were inclined to doubt the story about Lazarus.

They soon had their answer, for the sisters' plan had succeeded beyond all expectation. The news of the presence together at this public feast in Bethany of Jesus and His friend Lazarus—alive and well, and in the very place where he could most surely be identified—flashed like lightning over those million Pilgrims camping out on those rocky hills. The next morning the village was packed with curious, excited crowds. They met the residents of the village. "Yes, of course it's all true! We saw them together. Yes, and we had seen Lazarus buried, too."

As the day wore on there was a mass exodus from the city. It was the very thing the Jewish Leaders most feared. They had ordered that Lazarus should be arrested, and, knowing him now to be in Bethany, they sent to take him. They meant to kill him. But he had disappeared again, though Jesus was still there, so people said. And the sisters' house was surrounded by thronging crowds.

Yes, Jesus was there, and about to put His plan into operation. He had made most careful preparations, carrying them out in secret, largely to avoid incriminating any friends who were co-operating with

Him. The Beloved Disciple had acted as His agent in these preparations. In the late afternoon of the Sabbath Jesus commissioned two
of His other disciples to "go to the village over yonder" (the other
side of the valley) "and as you enter it—by that road you can see over
there—you will find a white ass tied. It is an unbroken one, but it
will be all right with Me. Loose it and bring it here to Me. Almost
certainly someone will try to stop you, saying: 'What are you doing
with the ass?' And—listen, this is very important—you are to make
answer in the following words: *The Lord has need of it.*' And at once
they'll let you take it. Have you got that clear?"

Everything happened just as Jesus had said, and soon the white
ass was brought to the garden entrance of the sisters' house. Jesus
was about to fulfil—literally and unmistakably—the great and well-
known Messianic Prophecy of Zechariah: *Rejoice and shout aloud, O
daughter of Zion! For here comes your King, triumphant and vic-
torious, riding humbly on an ass—even on an unbroken foal!* The
crowds were trebly excited as they realized the full significance of this
entry into the Holy City. It meant that Jesus was openly claiming—
at last—to be the Messiah of God. The disciples were thrilled. And
Judas nearly forgave Him for the insult. This would atone for everything. It would surely mean the end of the hated Romans' usurpation
of power and the restoration of Israel. He found himself shouting as
loudly as any of the others as the procession wound its way up the
hillside and over the shoulder of Olivet. The crowds from Bethany
were met by even huger throngs surging out from Jerusalem. And led
by the Galileans and worked up to frenzy by the Zealots in the press,
the people shouted themselves hoarse, plucking down branches from
the palm trees lining the road, taking off their cloaks, too, and spreading them on the ground before Jesus. "Hosanna! Hosanna to the Son
of David. Blessed is the King that comes in the Name of the Lord!
Blessed is the Kingdom that now comes, even the Kingdom of our
father David! Hosanna in the highest!"

Caiaphas and his friends were dumbfounded and powerless. From
the Temple walls they could see the head of the procession breasting
the horizon on Olivet. "You see? And nothing can be done about it.
Look, the whole world has gone crazy about Him!"

Then, as Jesus turned a corner of the hill, there suddenly burst into view the Holy City, fair beyond all words to express, chosen once of God, now the most unholy place upon the earth, rejected of Heaven. He saw behind this gleaming, golden beauty—so lovely as to catch the heart—to the depths of its black soul.

Some Pharisees in the crowd about Him were deeply shocked. Approaching Him, they cried, "Rabbi, rebuke Your disciples!"

But Jesus would not disclaim His Messiahship, and answered, "I tell you, if these should hold their peace, why, the very stones would cry out!" Was it not written? *Woe to them that build a city with bloodshed!—for the very stones would cry out against them.*

There, over the dark bastions of the turreted walls, rose Herod's palace, the Roman Fortress of Antonia, the High Priest's residence, the flashing, breath-taking grandeur of the Temple. And all were ranged against Him: enemies of the truth, all of them. Those "Hosannas"—redoubled as the city burst into view, clad in all the glory of the spring sunshine—meant "Save us!" But Jerusalem would not be saved, and was, instead, reeling headlong toward destruction. It trusted only in force, so force would destroy it in the end. These last few days before the Passover would see the Day of her Visitation passing into night, and the light of the world would soon be quenched in death's darkness. Then would follow God's inevitable judgment, since truth must prevail in the end.

Then suddenly, as if a blinding lightning flash from out that psychic storm had rent asunder the veil hiding the future, Jesus saw the doom day of the city with the clairvoyance of the Seer, every detail tragically clear, sharp-focused for one terrible moment. And what He saw overcame Him and 'whelmed Him in a flood of mounting tears. The city swooned and trembled before His brimming eyes till, convulsed and subsiding, it fell in flaming ruin, like a Valhalla of false gods, its flames mirrored in the crimson and carmine of the sunset.

The shouting mob turned to see what had held up the procession. Jesus had reined in His ass. Look! He was shaken with uncontrollable sobs. The people were terribly embarrassed. What sort of Messiah was this, heartbroken in His hour of triumph? Listen.

Words at last found outlet between the throes of His sobbing; those who were nearest never forgot the ghastly horror that glazed

His eyes as He cried, arm outstretched to the distant city, "Would that you had known—even today—the things on which your peace depends! But no . . . it is hidden from your eyes. But a time is surely coming—I see it clearly even now—when judgment will overtake you. I see you in that day: a city encircled with great ramparts and rings of trenches, besieged by the enemy on every side, buildings falling inward and towers toppling down on your descendants there within, till not one stone is left standing upon another; and all because you could not recognize the day when God Himself was visiting you."

Not only was He sorrowing for Jerusalem, which He so dearly loved, but also in that His self-identification with, and their recognition of, the Messiah had been utterly unavailing as yet to lift them from their ignorance of God. Not until He had further revealed Himself not only as Messiah but as the Suffering Servant, could they be in a position to face up to the crucial dilemma: *that either His claims were false (but Who else could raise the dead?): or else Messiah (and so God Himself) was utterly unlike their concepts of Deity.*

Chastened and subdued for a while, the procession moved on slowly forward again, down the long slopes of Olivet, past the enclosed garden of Gethsemane, with its age-old trees and its oil presses, over the Kedron brook and up through the frowning, deeply shadowed gateway into the teeming city streets. The whole city was stirred, saying, "Who is this?" and the crowds answered, "This is the Prophet Jesus, from Nazareth in Galilee!" And so He passed on and over the Tyropoean bridge into the Temple.

Annas and Caiaphas, together with Pilate and his captains, waited anxiously for the tumult that would be the first sign of the expected revolution. Their spies mingled with the procession. But all they witnessed was the interruption of a children's festival service, by the entrance of the procession. The Jewish authorities were scandalized not only at the obvious joy of the children at the distraction and its invitation to imitate the plaudits of the multitudes, but at the Messianic nature of the acclamations, now heard by them for the first time. Some of them approached Jesus Himself, as the high shrill voices of the children took up the cry: "Hosanna to the Son of David!"

"Don't You hear what these children are calling You?" they asked.

"Yes. I hear them well enough. Is it not written? *The most perfect praise is that which comes from tiny children.*"

This was the moment of acute crisis. The soldiers in the Temple and those in the Castle stood ready armed and only awaiting the call to march. Jesus had but to cry out and a *coup d'état* might have been achieved in a few hours. Everyone waited, tense and thrilled. But no cry was heard. He said and did—nothing. He looked around over the wide spaces of the Temple, as He stood there in the midst of the great courtyard. The animal pens were there as usual, the lowings and bleatings being suddenly heard in the hush of expectancy. The money changers were present, with their tables and their neat little piles of coins. The whole ghastly paraphernalia of sacrifice was once more cluttering up the Courts. But no longer did He feel any impulse toward violent precipitate action. Not by sudden impetuous clearances could graft and robbery, cruelty and cant, be swept forever from God's House. Only—He knew it now—by the slow operation of an infinite power released by an infinite sacrifice could the New Covenant be established. And as the sun flared low in the west like a world on fire, His gaze swept over the great spaces of the Temple and came back to rest on His disciples in a majestic and sovereign survey of the beauty and the evil—and the promise—so intermingled before His eyes. Then, slowly and deliberately, He turned round and walked out, followed by the Twelve. An incredible end to the triumphal entry—if He were an impostor. But He was the Heir: Heir of all the ages. He could afford to wait. And as the little procession descended the road and was lost in the evening glow, the disillusioned Pilgrims threw up their hands in despair and turned to leave. Another "Messiah" exposed.

And deep in the darkness of the heart of Judas a black fire smouldered, fed by the fumes of offended vanity and patriotism, till all restraints of loyalty gave way. The other disciples were silent as they retraced their way over the hill toward Bethany. It was all so strange; and they had never seen Jesus so severe in countenance, not even on the road hither from Galilee. Galilee! How far away, and how sweet! . . . Would any of them ever see it again?

III

The Heir

WHY did not the Priests arrest Jesus that night in Bethany? Even had they not known where He was to sleep, they might have guessed that He would be welcomed by His many friends in the village; or they might have had Him followed, the house surrounded and Jesus taken, any night during Holy Week. There were several reasons. To begin with, it looked as though He were not so dangerous after all, from Rome's point of view—and the death sentence was only possible with Pilate's concurrence. Perhaps He planned to withdraw from Judaea after this fiasco. Then there were the masses of His friends the Galileans in the city—and especially around Bethany, camping out there during the night.

But there was a deeper reason. Many were frightened of Jesus Himself. They knew He possessed supernatural powers. He, Whose voice (they now knew) could wake the dead, was not the sort of person the average soldier would care to tackle, nor his superiors hasten personally to condemn. The powers of Heaven might be shaken and the very earth dissolve into illimitable space.

Had Jesus not escaped mysteriously from the mob in Nazareth, passing through the midst of them at the very moment of crisis? Had He not dominated the hired ruffians in the Temple Courts when at a look from Him they had let the stones fall from their upraised hands?

So Jesus was allowed to sleep in peace, but His soul was troubled. He, the real Heir, had been forced to act almost as though impersonating a false claimant in order to be identified at all as the Heir; so that eventually He might be in a position to reveal the true nature of the Heir's character. He Who so hated play acting had been compelled consciously to fulfil a well-known Messianic Prophecy—how deeply it must have gone against the grain!—because only so could He be sure that His claim to be the Messiah was acknowledged publicly. His plan had succeeded in unmistakable fashion. The people *had* acclaimed Him as Messiah, but for the wrong reasons. They understood His claim—but misunderstood Him spiritually. As soon as they realized what His next step would be, they would inevitably desert Him. With the authorities it was very different. They understood much of His Teaching well enough, sensing as its inevitable result the end of intermediary sacerdotalism, as of propitiatory sacrifice, and of salvation through obedience to the minutiae of the Law. Nationalistically, they were largely indifferent to Israel's future. They had made terms with Rome. But spiritually they had to fight Jesus to the death. Not that many of them were not fanatically sincere in their antagonism to Jesus. That was the essence of their tragedy: that their spiritual awareness was often so atrophied that they were incapable of recognizing true Holiness.

Yes, Jesus saw it all so clearly, this inextricably tangled tissue of lies and truth, of reality and unreality, of sincerity and play acting, of understanding and misunderstanding. The irony of it all stung Him to restlessness and a sense almost of frustration. But He vowed that somehow He would make even this very frustration serve the Father's will. The plan had to go through to its destined end. Then God would vindicate Him.

There was yet another restless person in Bethany that night. Judas was wondering how best he could force Jesus into overt action as Messiah. Fancy tamely withdrawing from the city just when the goal of all their joint endeavour was within reach! If Jesus were the supernatural Agent of God He had seemed to be, He had only to raise one finger or utter one cry to call in supernatural powers, against which the Legions would be but as straw before a raging fire.

Jesus was also musing upon Israel's long history, in the light of His own coming against the shadowing darkness of His rejection. The vision of Isaiah came into His mind, of the vineyard of God, planted *on a very fruitful hill;* and of how God had *fenced it in and cleared it of stones, and built a tower there and a pit for the winepress; till, looking for grapes,* God *found only wild grapes. . . . What more could have been done for it? What have I left undone?* Why, when I looked for grapes, did I find only wild grapes?

Why, indeed? Jesus saw in vision the long history of that vineyard:

how God had entrusted it to successive husbandmen, and sent a succession of servants to gather in the fruit in its season. But the husbandmen took the servants and beat one, killed another and stoned yet another. All the martyred Prophets rose in array to testify against Israel. *What more?* Then the last and final appeal was made. God sent His own Beloved Son. "They will reverence My Son. . . ." But Jesus saw in vision Caiaphas and Annas and their fellow conspirators even now huddled together in a sinister group in Jerusalem. What were they saying? "This is the Heir! Come, let us kill Him! Then the inheritance will be ours!" Jesus knew how strongly they would fight against any Messianic claim—and in proportion to the strength of those claims, so much the more would they resist, since the dynasty of rule (and riches) would pass away from them were He once openly acknowledged. Jesus took the opportunity not only to apply this parable to the issues before Israel, but to tell it publicly next day in the Temple before His enemies; showing them how well He read their hearts and reminding them of the appalling doom they were calling down upon their heads. God would utterly destroy them and lease out His vineyard to other vinedressers, who *would* give Him His fruits in their season. He thought upon the masons at work there in the Temple, shaping, choosing, rejecting the stones they handled; He saw His Teaching, His Church, as a great rock, uncompromising, with no smooth edges, as rectangular as a corner stone—but rejected by the builders. But one day it would crown and hold together the Temple not made with hands.

Caiaphas and his friends were indeed in a desperate strait, faced with an unparalleled situation: that a direct claim to the Messiahship of Israel had been made, but that, so far, no rebellion had broken out. The Claimant, entirely uncompromising in His claim, was, apparently, entirely quietist in His actions. This had put them in a grave predicament. The Sadducaean Priestly party almost needed some semblance of a revolt—abortive, naturally—in order to induce Pilate to sentence Jesus to death. He was not likely to listen to the grievances that in reality underlay their hatred of Jesus. Besides, Jesus was still immensely popular. The people were convinced, so their own spies told the Priests, that Jesus was but biding His time. Therefore any premature attempt to arrest Him would be resisted violently by the

Galilean Pilgrims—and the authorities, not Jesus, might be blamed. The urgent necessity was to wean the people from their liking for Jesus. Then, provided He did not supernaturally resist arrest—which would have to be made at night, of course—the whole matter might be arranged . . . with a little persuasion of the Governor. There were ways, thought Caiaphas.

Then there was Herod, now in Jerusalem for the feast. He knew himself to be unpopular with his subjects on account of his murder of the Baptist, his treatment of his legal wife and the consequent threat of war with her father, Aretas of Nabataea. He was forced walk very warily in these dangerous days. Both races over whom he ruled (under Rome), Jews in Galilee and Arabs in Peraea, were hostile to him. And as for this Jesus, it had been reported to Herod that the Prophet had used a particularly insulting epithet about him— or, worse still for Him, about Herodias. And now had come the news of the Fellow's "triumphal" entry into Jerusalem. If only He were safely under lock and key—or better still, dead!

As the spring storms were slowly mustering about the city, even so all the forces of the world were inexorably converging upon Jesus to destroy Him. The air was to grow ever more sultry, heavy and still as the days followed one another and the Passover drew nearer. Physically and spiritually there was an oppressive feeling of tension in the stagnant, supercharged air of the Temple Courts. The first murmurings of the storms could be heard, nor were they very far away. The great piled-up thunderclouds were massing from all sides.

IV

The Master of Argument

. . . .

(I) TRIBUTE TO CAESAR

His enemies now had developed a plan of attack, deciding to assail Him on the threefold issues of His patriotism—or His lack of it— either way would serve their purpose; His belief in the Resurrection, vouched for by the witnesses of the Bethany miracle; and His well-known tenderness toward women, especially sinful women—with the Magdalene in mind, of course. They arranged to act in concert with one another; the Priests, the Pharisees and the Herodians.

The first of these unholy coalitions to go into action against Jesus was a deputation from the Pharisees and the Herodians. The idea was Caiaphas'; it had all the shrewd, incisive cunning of that astute brain. They had to be very careful, for they were treading on extremely dangerous ground. The people execrated Rome, and any questions involving defiance of Rome would have to be asked as if by a good Jewish patriot standing up for Jewish rights, else the crowd would be hostile almost to a man. An answer must be elicited from Jesus which would incriminate Him in Pilate's eyes—for only the Governor could impose the death sentence, and it was therefore imperative not only to prejudice Pilate against Jesus, but if possible to force him to arrest Jesus himself. It would save so much bother.

So the spies approached Jesus smoothly and ingratiatingly. "Master, we know that You are a truthful person, and teach the way of God in truth, and all You say and do is, beyond question, right. Besides, You are no respecter of persons, being afraid of no one. Tell us, therefore, what do *You* think? Is it right and lawful for us, as good Jews, to pay tribute to Caesar—or not?"

If Jesus answered "No," then Pilate could condemn Him for inciting to rebellion; if "Yes," then His popularity with the people would fade away. Jesus perceived the craftiness of the question. But there were certain facts He also knew: that the use of a foreign coinage implied, in the custom and belief of the time, subjection to the sovereign whose image the coins bore. He also knew that the Romans had been forced by the Jews to mint a special coinage for use in Palestine, from which the usual impression of Caesar's head had been expunged. He further knew that many Jews were in the habit of accepting and trading with the normal Roman coins, such as the denarius, bearing Caesar's image; also that it was the Jews themselves who had petitioned Caesar to make Judaea a Roman province. The facts played into His hands—if expertly used. With magnificent quickness of mind, He said, "Why try this on Me? Can anyone give Me a denarius?"

Not yet grasping the import of His move, someone unwittingly handed Him the coin. He looked long at it, holding it up for all to see—Caesar's head toward the people. "Whose is this image and superscription?" He asked.

"Caesar's," they replied.

"Caesar's? Well then, the lesson is clear. Render therefore to Caesar the things that you acknowledge, by using them, are rightly Caesar's; and to God the things that are God's."

When the spies heard His answer to what had seemed to them an unanswerable question, they marvelled greatly, being unable to seize on anything in His reply with which either to weaken His influence with the people or to prejudice Pilate against Him. So they said nothing in answer to His admonition and left Him. This was a victory for Jesus, and no mistake about it.

(II) THE COMIC CONUNDRUM

THE next battle opened with an attack in quite a different direction. It was an effort by Annas and Caiaphas to get Jesus into trouble with the orthodox Pilgrims. The Sadducees, from whom the High Priestly family were drawn, were unorthodox in refusing to believe in any Resurrection of the dead, regarding this as but an appendage of the Messianic hope, which they took pains to deny. On the other hand, the Pharisees put this belief in the forefront of their teaching. They were willing, however, to suffer the ridiculing of their own teaching rather than allow such a wonderful opportunity of discrediting Jesus to be lost. Besides, any denial of this belief would in itself help to show that Jesus was but an ordinary man.

The Sadducees chose a question which to them seemed one that was impossible of reply; a *reductio ad absurdum* of the whole belief in immortality, answerable only by admitting the lawfulness—eternally, too—of polygamy, on the one hand, or by denying the Resurrection or the validity of Moses' Law, on the other. The conundrum they concocted was really rather funny. There were many ill-concealed titters from among those in the audience who were in the know, as these grave Sadducees, so aristocratic and proud, slowly and unctuously tangled up the belief in immortality with a situation culled from the world of outrageous farce.

"Master," they purred, "Moses wrote a Law for us, saying that if a man died, having no children, then his brother should take his wife and raise up offspring on behalf of his dead brother. Well, in the instance we have in mind, there were seven brothers. The first married a wife, but died childless. So the second brother married her, but also died childless. And likewise the third, and indeed all seven, each marrying her in turn, but leaving no children. A very sad case. Last of all, the wife also died. Now at the Resurrection, whose wife will she be? For, you see, all seven had married her."

They cast their black, beady eyes down to the ground in grave, courteous enquiry, as though rather shocked at the scandalous nature of the story, while the crowd relished the absurd rigmarole and its unanswerable riddle. Jesus accepted the farcical question as an opportunity in which to deliver Teaching of the utmost spiritual significance. Greater issues were here at stake than His own popularity with the crowds. For they were assuming that either all the persons in the story were by now dead (dead, that is, without any other-worldly existence), or else the woman must have seven husbands in Heaven! In a world of solely spiritual values, such gross relationships as they were visualizing no longer existed; and so the question could never arise.

Had not God spoken through Enoch?

Therefore have I given them that be mortal and short-lived, wives and children; that thus nothing might be wanting them on earth. But you were formerly spiritual, in the enjoyment of Eternal Life. Therefore wives are not appointed for the spiritual; for they have their dwelling in Heaven, and they will all become Angels in Heaven.

"Is not this exactly where you go wrong," He asked His tempters, "in that you neither understand the Scripture—nor the power of God? The Scripture you quote legislates for this earthly life, wherein the children of this world marry and are given in marriage. But they who are counted worthy to attain to the spiritual world neither marry nor are given in marriage in the physical sense, but are akin to the Angels of God.

"So much for your misconception of the Scriptural passage. As for your misconception of the power of God, do you really think God cannot save His saints from death? Why, those who attain to that eternal world are forever immune from death, being children of the Resurrection. But if you want Scriptural proof of the belief in immortality, have you never read in the Law of Moses how God spoke to him, saying, *I AM the God of Abraham, and the God of Isaac, and the God of Jacob*—who were all dead in the earthly sense when Moses lived? Now, God is not a God of the dead but of the living! For all who truly live, live only in Him! So that, you see, the Patriarchs must at this very moment be alive! Really, you do very greatly err."

The crowds were delighted, for Jesus had proved Himself a master of orthodox belief; and the hated Sadducees had been put to ridicule in turn, and in answer to what had seemed an unanswerable question. Even one of the Scribes, listening to the debate, could not help saying, "Master, that was very well said!" Indeed, everybody was astonished at the wit and wisdom of Jesus, and the authorities found that His popularity was, if anything, increased by their questions rather than diminished.

(III) DAVID'S LORD

JESUS decided to turn the tables on His enemies by asking them an unanswerable question. He was resolved to end once and for all this conception of the Messiah as an earthly ruler, especially to discredit that "proof" of His calling that was thought to reside in an indispensable descent from David. Once again, Jesus lifted the whole matter on to a higher plane. He showed them that, far from thinking in terms of mere earthly descent, they ought to think—*even as David himself did*—in terms of spiritual pre-eminence and overlordship.

So He asked the Pharisees, "*Why* do you say that the Messiah *must* be a son of David? For if the Messiah be thought of merely as a descendant of David, how came it that David himself called Him 'my Lord' in that great passage: *Jehovah said to my Lord Messiah, 'Sit Thou on My right hand till I make Thine enemies Thy footstool'?* For, don't you see, that if even for one as great as David the Messiah is yet his 'Lord,' how can He, the Messiah Himself, be thought of as gaining any status or credit through being merely David's descendant?"

There could be no answer to that, of course. For it raised the whole concept of the Messianic role to the spiritual level where it belonged, and where the Jews could not follow Jesus. As for the crowds, they were delighted at the discomfiture of the authorities. Jesus' popularity was definitely enhanced by this battle of wits in which He came off so immeasurably the best. It was His turn now to speak and to show a new mastery, that in invective. But that was to wait for the morrow.

(IV) DENUNCIATION

So, on the Tuesday morning, Jesus opened up His great offensive against the errors of the Jewish Leaders. He would strip them of all their rich vestments of sacrosanctity and "authority" till nothing but the nakedness of their souls was visible. He showed them God's own scathing scorn of hypocrisy, His burning hatred of cant, His contempt for sanctimonious humbugs sheltering behind the ramparts of "religion."

He addressed the people, not the Rulers:

"The Scribes and Pharisees are now the accredited leaders of the nation—as Moses was in his day. So you have to obey them. *But don't copy them.* They talk a lot, but they do not act. Their work is to load up heavy burdens on the backs of the people—and they refuse to stir a finger to lighten them. All that they do is only done in order to catch the notice of their fellow men. Look at them there—with their extra broad leather Scripture text cases, and their huge tassels—preying upon the property of poor widows and delighting in making long unreal prayers! They fight for the best places at banquets and for the front seats in Synagogues. They love to be saluted in the market places and obsequiously called 'teacher.' "

Jesus turned to His disciples. "But don't *you* be called 'teacher'; for only One is your Teacher, and you are all brothers. And as for calling people 'Father this' and 'Father that'—drop it; for only One is your Father and He is in Heaven. And don't go calling anybody 'Leader'; for only One is your Leader, even I, the Messiah!"

Then He turned to the Jewish "leaders" and spoke directly this time to them. "Woe to you, you impious Scribes and Pharisees! For you shut the door of God's Kingdom in men's faces, and, while refusing to enter in yourselves, you do your best to stop anyone else from doing so. Woe to you, you play actors! Shams and humbugs, the lot of you! For you traverse sea and land to make one proselyte, and, when you succeed, you make him twice as bad a son of Hell as you are yourselves! Woe to you, blind guides that you are, saying to people, *If you swear by the Sanctuary, that counts for nothing; but if you swear by the gold on the Sanctuary, then your oath is binding.* You blind fools—which of the two is the more important, the gold or the Sanctuary that consecrates the gold?

"Woe to you, you canting Scribes and Pharisees! Making a big fuss about paying tithes on petty things like . . . mint and dill and cummin; while all the time you ignore the things in the Law that really matter, such as justice and mercy and truth. Blind guides, I say again—straining to eject a gnat, and then swallowing . . . a camel!"

There was a huge roar of applause here. The people were thrilled to hear Jesus lashing out at spiritual wickedness in high places. He went on: "Woe to you, you irreligious Scribes and Pharisees! Scrubbing clean the outsides of the cup and the plate, but gorging down the avarice and lusts with which they are filled—as if the inside were less important than the outside! Were not both made by God? Give alms of those inward things—judgment and the love of God, and lo! all things are clean to you! You remind Me of those whitewashed tombs in the valley; they look beautiful on the outside, but within they are full of dead men's bones and all sorts of putrefaction. And talking of tombs, I've noticed how zealous you are to rebuild, repair and decorate the tombs of the Prophets and of other just men of the past—and how you say, 'If we had lived in our fathers' days, *we* would never have been party to the persecution and murder of those great men!' But you are even now in process of filling up to the brim the measure of your fathers' guilt. For you reverence only the martyrs of *former* generations (who were killed by their contemporaries), and murder the Prophets of your own time. So that you are indeed following in your fathers' footsteps. That's the traditional mind all over. Truth which has become truism you are perfectly willing to accept, but new truth you reject. I tell you, therefore, that upon you, and such as you, shall fall the responsibility for all the martyrs' blood which has been shed from the time of Abel down to Zechariah the son of Barachiah, whom you slew—just over there, between the Sanctuary and the Altar. . . . Yes, it will all fall on you!"

All that Jesus prophesied of them came literally true, in that they added to the long list of martyrs the name of the Son of God. "His blood be on us and on our children!" they were to cry. And so it came to pass. *They called death to them*—and it answered their call.

V

Wednesday in Holy Week

. . . .

(I) THE WOMAN TAKEN IN ADULTERY

BAFFLED and defeated hitherto, the authorities prepared to open their third and final attack. This, they thought, could hardly help but be conclusive, for they were banking on Jesus' compassion—a safe hazard. He had claimed, as Messiah, to be judge of Israel; so they planned to bring Him face to face with a sinner, caught flagrantly, if possible in some open sin involving the death penalty according to the Law. And then they would see what sentence He passed on the sinner—or if, as they fully expected, He let her off with His crazy notion of "forgiveness." For a woman would suit their purpose best, Jesus, they well knew, being ever tender toward women, especially fallen women—look at the Magdalene! So with devilish cunning they somehow managed to produce—probably it was not so very difficult— a woman caught during the night, committing adultery. They dragged her to the Temple (her paramour doubtless having been left alone) and thrust her forward in all the shame of public exposure before the astonished and nauseated gaze of Jesus.

"Master," they said, "this woman was caught, in the very act . . . of committing adultery. Now *Moses* commanded us in the Law to stone such creatures. But what do *You* say?"

The full horror of their action swept over Jesus; not only the cruelty toward the woman, but their misreading of His real attitude toward such sinners. For no one before or since has so hated sin as did Jesus, just as no one before or since has so loved sinners. They thought He was lax in the Law. Little did they realize His utter purity, which was what had so wondrously cleansed the soul of Mary Though here was no repentant Magdalene, nothing but a coarse

356

sensual adulteress, yet they judged aright. He could not condemn her to death. For, even if Pilate did confirm the death sentence, stoning would do nothing to save her soul. But He was so desperately embarrassed by her shame and by His loathing of the whole sordid conspiracy, that not only was He silent but unable to look anyone in the face. To cover His distress, He bowed down and, stooping, found Himself nervously tracing little patterns with His fingertip in the sand of the Court.

At first the Priests were bewildered. Why couldn't He answer a straight question? Did He agree with Moses or not? Was He, after all, only a bemused absent-minded visionary, half-baked and quite harmless? Look at Him, oblivious of the world, tracing squiggles in the sand. . . . But you had to be careful with this Fellow. He was deeper—and cleverer—than you expected.

But while they were thus ruminating, the superb mind of Jesus was swiftly and intuitively finding the one course which, while vindicating His mercy, would at the same time rescue Him from His dilemma, ensnare His enemies in their own trap—and save the woman. Suddenly He raised Himself to His full height and, stretching forth an arm, pointed to the men ranged in a row before Him, crying: "Very well. Let him that is without sin among you cast the first stone!"

And this time He stooped down not to trace meaningless patterns in the sand, but to write, for all to read: *It is the* righteous *men who shall inflict the punishment of an adulteress.* They watched Him in silence. The moments, the minutes, passed. His eyes never once strayed from those characters He was tracing in the sand, but His ears were alert. Presently there came a hesitant, shuffling sound as one— and then two—of the Priests moved away as unconcernedly as they dared, to be quickly followed by others equally anxious to disappear unobtrusively. At last all the footsteps died away and there was a long silence. Then Jesus raised His eyes. The woman before Him was alone.

Very gently He spoke to her. "Woman, where are your accusers? Has *no one* condemned you?" There was the very faintest tinge of amusement in His eyes.

"No one, Sir."

"Well, neither do I condemn you." (He Who alone could have,

being the only One without sin.) "Be off now, *and never sin again.*"

The authorities had shot their last bolt. The triple thrusts had been met, parried and turned against themselves with ever deadlier power and accuracy. Another means to rid themselves of Him must be found. A secret arrest, after the feast was over—if an arrest *could* be achieved. If only they could know for certain whether or not He were a quietist and would allow Himself to be taken! There was some talk of a disaffected disciple . . . Judas by name. A Zealot, some said, a wild fellow, with a high place in the Apostolic band. He might possibly be useful. Bribery could do much sometimes. No harm in sounding him secretly, anyway. And he might know where Jesus slept each night, and, in especial, whether He were likely—or not—to resist arrest. That was the main point to clear up.

(II) JESUS AND THE GREEKS

ONLY a few short hours of daylight were now left to the Ministry of Christ, before the powers of darkness mounted up the sky and blotted out the last lingering beams of the sinking sun. No longer then would the Temple Courts echo to the sound of that golden voice. The feet of the Son of God were treading their paving stones for the very last time. An era was ending, going down into the darkness behind the vast night wrack that was even then looming up as if from all horizons, as storms will—suffocating, doom-filled, infinitely menacing. The afternoon was sultry and an airless unreality brooded over the scene. An immobility, not of mere rest or passivity, but rather as of extreme tension—as though balanced opposing strains were charging the atmosphere with explosive potentialities—held the world in a static hypnosis. Colossal clouds, jagged-edged, fretted with fire and baneful with coming terrors, were piling up high in the blood-shot heavens. The Courts and colonnades looked curiously flat and two-dimensional, as if earth were suddenly reduced to being a dimly lighted backcloth to some eerie stage play. The very sky seemed dream-bound, moveless even in its inexorable motion; as if the heavens were reflected in some deep-sided goblet, wine-dark with the life blood of the grapes of wrath; still, inverted, a world mirrored in a cup of suffering.

Jesus was still too; waiting, even as earth and sky, for the last crisis to break about Him in a dual release of material and spiritual thunder and lightning. Here, as the giant stormclouds slowly reared up against each other in the solemn majesty of cosmic battle, the last Messianic decision was upon Jesus, as He sat quietly, waiting . . . watching . . .

The hordes of Pilgrims swarmed mazily before His gaze. Near Him were the trumpet-shaped receptacles for the Temple alms. He noticed how differently people gave their money offerings. Some, obviously rich, and proud of it, ostentatiously selected the largest and most valuable coins and threw them in with the clattering publicity of apparent unconcern. He saw, too, how the more humble folk gave place to these wealthy Jews before they, too, approached the offertory trumpets and slipped in their gifts.

Then a bowed and broken figure attracted the attention of those compassionate eyes. She was in mourning, in a widow's habiliments, poorly dressed and nervous in her movements. She waited awhile till the rich men had moved away and there was a pause in the stream of almsgivers. Then, embarrassed and shy, she came slowly forward, clasping an old purse in her bony hand. Fumbling awhile within it, she eventually turned it upside down and emptied all its contents into her hand—two "mites," a ninety-sixth part of a denarius. It was all she had . . . and she looked long and wistfully at the two tiny coins lying there in her hand, all unconscious of the watching eyes of the Master seated there on the terrace steps near by; all unconscious, too, of her immortality. Then, with a last glance behind her to see if she were obstructing anyone else, she took the two coins from her hand and dropped them into the offertory trumpet. There was no clatter. They were too small for that. Then, hurryingly, she shuffled away over the marble pavement, a poignant figure of grief, still clasping her now empty purse.

Jesus was intensely moved. He called to His disciples: "Did you see that poor widow—with her two mites offered to God? I tell you she has cast in more than all the other givers put together! For *they* gave of their superfluity, but she has given—in her desperate need, too—all her livelihood!"

Although it was now becoming difficult to see clearly, the disciples were intrigued to see a party of Hellenic-looking Pilgrims approach-

ing them, eagerly scanning every face as they moved, as though looking for someone. They halted on seeing the disciples and eyed them
while consulting together.

Then one of them came forward and selected Philip among the
disciples as the most Grecian in his cast of features, and addressed
him: "Sir, we wish to see Jesus. Can you tell us where we may find
Him?"

Philip at once made himself known to them, and not only were
they glad that their quest was concluded, but also to discover that he
had a Greek name. Philip proceeded to fetch Andrew, his special
friend, and together they led the Hellenes forward to meet Jesus. As
they went, they explained to the disciples that they had come from
Edessa, in the far north, to invite Jesus to leave Jerusalem and accompany them back to their own city, at the express wish of their king.
Approaching Jesus, they handed Him an Aramaic scroll, which He
unrolled and read.

Standing there in the lowering twilit gloom, silent and still, Jesus
was swept by a flood of emotion as He realized that here was release,
full and free: release not only from death—and the cutting short of
the one and only fully integrated life on all the earth—but also from
the hatreds and enmities, the ignorance and misrepresentation, of an
unfulfilled Ministry. Release to a welcoming, cultured city that was
actually beseeching Him to preach the Good News of God to it, and
longing for the "Yes" that would rescue Him from the City of Wrath
and from His hour of doom.

But was this the release He really longed for? There was a starkly
tragic look in His eyes as He whispered, "Oh, now is My soul disquieted! *What am I to say?* Shall I cry to God, 'Father, save Me from
this hour!'? But surely it was solely for His very purpose that I am
even now come to this hour. For . . . unless a grain of wheat fall to
the ground . . . and die . . . it remains but a single grain. But if it die,
it can bear rich fruit. The truth endures: he who loves his life shall
lose it, and only he who cares nothing about his life in this world compared with that in the world to come, can preserve it to all Eternity.
It is the same for you all. Whoever of you would serve Me, he must
be prepared to follow Me—and *so* keep with Me . . . that wherever I
am, in this world—or the next—there shall My servant be. And who-

ever serves Me, him will My Father honour! So I can but cry: 'Father, glorify Thy name!'"

And then, at that very moment, the storm broke, the lightning flashed like a bright sword, and a shattering crash of thunder rent the air and reverberated over the far hills of the Wilderness. It was, for Jesus, the self-same Voice that had called to Him in the two former crises of His life: at His baptism and on far Hermon. And as the pealing echoes resolved themselves into supernal syllables, He heard God crying from Heaven:

"I have glorified it . . . and will glorify it again!"

This was for Christ the confirmation He had awaited of the rightness of the plan and the glory of it. Again, as in the raising of Lazarus, there came the reaction, the knowledge that He required no such affirmation or Divine stimulus; and He turned to the crowds and said, "This voice did not come for My sake—but for yours! The hour has struck at last—when the Son of Man is to be glorified!

"Now *will I rise, saith the Lord.* Now *will I be exalted!* Now *will I be lifted up!* Yea, *now* is the world on trial! *Now* is come its judgment! *Now* shall the Prince of this world be cast out!"

It was not He Who would be judged at His Trial, but Pilate and Caiaphas and the Jews. It was not He that would be expelled from God's Kingdom, but the Prince of Evil.

The faith of Christ soared on wings of exaltation as He cried, "Yea, and when I am *lifted up,* I will draw . . . *all men* . . . to Myself!" Not only those few disciples about Him now, not only the many Edessans He might have preached to, but all the souls who had ever been or who should ever be! And even as He spoke, John saw His arms stretched out not only as though in an agony of supplication or as embracing the whole universe—*but as if He Himself were hanging upon a cross.*

That the people listening had caught the drift of His thoughts was proved when, rather bewildered, they asked among themselves: "But the Law says that Messiah, when He comes, will remain forever. What then can You mean by this being *lifted up?*" They asked Him, "With Whom exactly do You identify Yourself when You refer to Yourself as the 'Son of Man'?"

But it was now too late—in a double sense—for explanations. So soon would even this eerie half-light fail and the last embers of the day be quenched in darkness. Then the gates of the Temple would have closed upon His departing figure for the last time. His words had the mournful solemnity of a tolling bell.

"Only for a little while longer yet will the light shine among you. Walk, then, while you have the light, that the darkness may not overtake you. . . ." Yea, if only man could always keep abreast of the sun, one would walk forever in the light. Darkness can only overtake those who fall back. . . .

"Whoever walks in the dark, knows not where he is going. While, then, you still have the light, believe in the light, that you may be sons of the light! I have come as light into the world, that no one who believes in Me should remain in darkness."

He began to move away from the Temple. As He ascended the steps leading up to the gateway, the sun's rays, breaking through a rift in the giant stormclouds, suddenly shone like a golden searchlight over the splendour of Herod's Temple. He turned to survey the scene. The roofs dazzled the eyes. The courses of great stones were brought into sharp focus as with a perfectly placed floodlight. Never had the Temple looked so glorious, so breath-takingly magnificent, as it did now against the black menace of the storm wrack.

The sight overwhelmed Jesus, and He cried aloud, "O Jerusalem! Jerusalem! Slaying the Prophets each in turn and stoning those that are sent to you! How often would I have gathered your children together, even as a fowl gathers her brood under her wings . . . but you would not let Me. See! *Your Temple is now left to you—desolate, empty.* For I tell you, it will never see Me again till it shall echo once more with the cry—*Blessed is He Who comes in God's name!*—and, this time, *mean it.*"

As they passed out under the mighty walls, the disciples ejaculated in renewed wonder, "Master, look! What terrific stones and what glorious buildings!" But with Jesus it was not mere size and splendour that had so moved Him. He saw the Temple as the fortress of an outworn system, the bastion of God's enemies, something doomed to inevitable and utter destruction.

"So you feel, do you, the power and strength of these great buildings? I tell you, soon there shall not be left one stone upon another that shall not be torn down!"

And He turned His back on the Temple and strode away toward the Mount of Olives.

(III) THE GREAT ASSIZE

ONCE out there, they sat down to rest awhile on its slopes, surrounded by the Pilgrims, getting ready to camp out for the night. The day was all but done and the city looked more lovely than ever now, in the wake of the great storm, with the golden roofs shining wetly in the late slanting sunlight against the indigo background of the departing clouds. The thunder yet rolled remotely over the Judaean hills, while yet the city, shining calm and beautiful, was seen against a setting of doom.

James and John were bewildered at this talk of Jerusalem's destruction and asked Jesus privately when these things would happen and what would be the sign.

Jesus answered, "No one knows—not even the Angels in Heaven, not even I, the Son of Man—only the Father Himself. But though heaven and earth were to dissolve into nothingness, the truth remains: My words shall *never* pass away!"

And then, there on the slopes of the Mount of Olives, Jesus rose and turned to address the assembled Pilgrims encamped in their thousands out on the hillside. Never was He in greater or more ultimate earnest; for this, He realized, was likely to be His very last public utterance: His final and most essential Teaching. Thinking still of ultimate judgment, He sought such a setting—poetic, concrete, sublime—as would invest this last discourse with supremely rememberable import and give it infinite solemnity.

Then, even as He gazed on the shining city, lighted to glory by the sundown, He saw, close at hand, the very setting for which He was seeking. There before Him was the Temple, resplendent and blazing in the fiery light of the setting sun, its golden roofs yet shining almost blindingly above the dark bastions of its walls. Behind, the terraced towers and domes and the level rows of rooftops, tier on tier, gleaming and glistening as the sunlight caught their yet rain-soaked surfaces, arrased the Temple as though with a lustre of innumerable celestial servitors. And there, in front, down in the valley before Him, a shepherd was dividing his flock for the night folds: the sheep to his right hand and the goats to his left. Peoples of all nations lay spread out on the slopes of Olivet; while to the far left, out of sight beyond the city, a tall column of smoke rose from the ever-burning fires of Gehenna, in the valley of Hinnom. Here, then, to His very hand, was the sublime setting for the immortal picture story Jesus was about to tell.

He saw in vision what Daniel and Enoch had seen: the blazing Throne of Judgment. . . . And there, behind and about the throne, tier upon tier, were massed the assembled Angels, stretching away into blue infinity. And before the throne stood the hushed multitudes— all men since time first began till time should end—waiting for judgment to be pronounced. Into the very centre of this full panoply of Heaven, even up and onto the throne itself, strode Jesus, the humble Carpenter of Nazareth, and dared to speak in His own name the ultimate judgment of the Almighty: to define the sole basis and criterion of Eternal Worth! In this superb assumption we see the full range of the confidence of Christ, and His sense of union with the Father at its most identifying.

But the significance of the parable cannot be measured solely by this contrast between the Outlaw of Jerusalem and the King of Heaven; it contains a further synthesis of contrasts: that between the Jesus of Galilee and the Christ of the Road. For here we meet a Christ Who integrates the two characters into One vast personality. Just when the Christ of the Road is at His most towering and apocalyptic, He, the Son of Man seated at the Assize of Eternity, passes ultimate judgment on every soul *by the sole test of its obedience to— the Sermon on the Mount!* The Message and the Mission: the Teacher and the Suffering Servant, and here integrated in one supreme revelation, bringing the Gospel story to full circle and completion to the Christ.

But there is even yet a further surprise. The inaugural cleansing of the Temple had been a magnificent gesture of sweeping reform. The sermon in the Synagogue at Capernaum was an almost incredibly bold revision of the Mosaic Law. The Great Sermon revealed an altogether new conception of ethics. But this parable stands alone for sheer audacity of reforming affirmation. So much so that ecclesiastics then and now regard it as dangerous, to be toned down and softened as best they can. Yet, as strong as steel, as sharp-edged as a knife, as warming and illuminating—and searing—as a flame, this Sword of Fire, hilted like a cross, sweeps in flashing terror forever before the Gates of Paradise. None may enter therein but those who can pass the one test—who belong as of grace to Eden. For it affirms that love of man *is* love of God, that love is more than belief, that active well-doing from a right motive is the truest worship. The test of the soul's Eternal destiny is decided by the ordinary, humdrum, everyday choices of life. Both the just and the unjust regard the test as irrelevant and their destiny with surprise. Neither can understand that it is love and not "religion" that matters in the end. Indeed, the just protest at being thought "pious"! But this is Jesus' final word. There is no arguing about it.

The parable of the last judgment is the high charter of love's freedom and the condemnation of sacerdotalism, of formalism and cant, in religion. This is how God Himself judges. As for Jesus, His preaching was done. The sacrifice awaited Him.

(IV) JUDAS

THAT night there was a momentous meeting in Caiaphas' house, attended by the Priestly party, the chief of the Scribes and certain Elders of the Jews, to decide how best they might effect the arrest of Jesus—by craft, of course, in view of His still great popularity with the people. It was agreed that nothing could be done until after the feast and the Galileans had gone home, since to arrest Him while they were yet in the city might well provoke a popular riot. In any case, there was always Jesus Himself to cope with. . . . If only they knew—for certain—whether He would resist arrest or not. . . .

Then it was that suddenly into the midst of this conference burst the dark figure of the traitor. He had never been quite comfortable in the Apostolic band. The only southerner in a group of northerners—sharing the sullen and hard characteristics of the Judaeans—he was a Zealot, a Nationalist, who had been, nevertheless, deeply attracted by the idealistic Teaching of the Galilean Prophet. Two conceptions of the Messianic role struggled for domination in his mind. The one was his by hereditary training and education; the other was based solely on his deep love for Jesus, Whom he had never really understood. But he had remained loyal when, after the Butaihan crisis, so many disciples had left Him. He had companied with Him through all these latter months, knowing the constant danger involved in following Him. He had been flattered by being chosen as treasurer of the Apostolic band, an important and most responsible post, of which the others were often envious—distrusting him on more than one occasion. Then had come the Bethany banquet, held at his own father's house, too. That had been desecrated by the mad behaviour of the Magdalene, and by Jesus' incredibly foolish apology for her lapse of good taste, and His rebuke of him, Judas, in his own house and before all his own town's folk. A rebuke, too, that rankled all the more in that he knew he had made it so perfectly clear that he had only been thinking of the Apostles' needs.

The entry into Jerusalem had roused all his nationalistic fervour to frenzy. Jesus was, after all, going to vindicate His Messianic role by a popular rising at the head of His followers! Then had come the tame anticlimax and the spineless failure to do anything at all. In the bitterness of his reaction his loyalty had snapped. He had waited awhile, brooding and smouldering, listening to Jesus discoursing on the necessity for death if full fruition were to be accomplished. Here was no Messiah. Only one more fanatic, dreamer, idealist. Better, far, to get Him out of the way before He deceived any more of the people. The magic had gone from life. There was only disillusion and despair.

Then it was that he decided to put Jesus to a test that would prove Him. The authorities could be told where Jesus was that night—Judas knew He was most likely to sojourn in the one place where some solitude could still be found in the thronged city and its environments: Gethsemane, the olive-press garden in the valley of the Kedron. He would tell Caiaphas that Jesus would not resist arrest—he had heard in a roundabout way that this was what the Leaders most wanted to know. Then, if Jesus did *not* resist arrest—*and God did nothing about it*—He could not be the Messiah. If He *did* resist—or God intervened—then all would be well.

So it came about that into that dastardly conference burst Judas, frenzied and far from sane. Stares greeted him from the astonished and offended Elders.

Then Caiaphas smiled on him and beckoned him closer. He spoke, silkily. "Come, my friend. Judas, I think, is it not? What have you to tell us?"

Judas edged nearer, nervously, then suddenly stopped and refused to advance farther. In a hoarse whisper, he asked, "Is it right that you want to know whether Jesus will resist arrest?"

"Yes, we would indeed like to know that—for *certain*."

Judas raised his voice. "Well, I tell you, He *won't*! He'll let you take Him—He's tame, meek, spiritless. He's no Messiah! You needn't be frightened of *Him!* I'll let you know where and when to take Him."

He threw his arm out suddenly. "Is it not written *Whoever* will *be lost—let him be lost!*—and *let the survivors devour one another—*" with a snarling glance at the assembled Sanhedrin—"*I took my staff 'Goodwill,' and broke it; and the day it was broken, I said to the hucksters who had hired me: 'If you think it right, give me my wages. But if not . . . well, never mind'?*"

He glared at them wildly, but Caiaphas was urbane and gentle in voice as he answered, "Let me see, how does the Scripture continue? *So they paid out for my wages thirty pieces of silver.* Shall we say, then, thirty pieces? Provided, of course, that you also let us know where and when we can take the Man secretly."

Judas nodded, hungrily, watching the treasurer as he slowly counted out the thirty silver coins. Then, turning suddenly, he fled away into the night. Caiaphas smiled and rose. "That makes it all quite easy and smooth-going. It was lucky I let that hint drop. I thought it would reach Judas. I had my secret channels. . . . Shall we depart?"

VI

Holy Thursday

. . . .

(I) THE LAST SUPPER

JESUS read the soul of Judas like an open book. He had strived so long and so hard to save him, and had largely succeeded; but it looked as though he were now lost. When, then, the Thursday dawned, Jesus was faced with the knowledge that Judas was about to betray Him. It would be on the eve of the Passover—tonight, and He had so greatly longed to share the Passover Feast with His disciples; but most probably that would now be impossible. He Himself, instead, would be the Passover victim: *God would provide Himself a Lamb.* In that case, the only opportunity to share a common Covenantal Meal with the disciples would be on this very evening. Therefore, if they were to be uninterrupted, Judas must not be allowed to know where the meal would be taken. So, when in Bethany the disciples inquired of their Master where they would be sharing the Passover Feast, they were met with the strange request that Peter and John be sent privately to Him. Alone with them, He unfolded His plan. As in the preparation for the Triumphal Entry, this was secret and depended upon the co-operation of certain allies in the carrying out of His purpose.

"Go into the city," He told them, "and as soon as you enter the gate you will see an unusual sight—a man, not a woman, bearing a pitcher of water: you can't mistake him. Don't speak to him, but just follow him home. And then go within and say to the householder: 'The Master says: "Where is My guestroom where I may eat a solemn Meal with My disciples?" ' And then he will show you a large upper room, furnished and prepared. There I want you to make ready for us all."

Peter and John at once proceeded to carry out Jesus' instructions and found everything as He had foretold; and they made ready the meal. Then, when darkness had enveloped the city, He came with the Twelve and, entering the house, ascended to the Upper Room, telling them that for Him this was to be their Passover Feast. This was perfectly in order, many Jews preferring to put back the meal by twenty-four hours because the Passover that year fell on the Sabbath. The owner of the house was not present at the meal, but stayed in the other part of the house with his family, knowing that the Master—for he himself was a secret disciple—wanted to be alone with His Apostles. All the arrangements had been supervised by the Beloved Disciple, who was himself also present at Jesus' special invitation.

As the disciples followed their Master up and into the Upper Room, there was much ignoble heartburning as to who would be honoured with the chief places at the feast—those on the right and left of the Master. The Sons of Thunder? Peter? Judas? Who should be "first"? Jesus noticed the constrained silence of the disciples. Not one of them would sit down at the table. The old trouble again—precedence, envy . . . He remembered having openly rebuked the Pharisee at Magdala for his lack of courtesy in not arranging for the foot washing of his Guest. Tonight, there being no servant present, for safety's sake, there was no one to undertake this foot washing, unless one of the disciples would volunteer for it. But they all sat still in moody silence on the stools or forms ranged against the walls.

Then Jesus rose up. John, the Beloved Disciple, watched Him with the keen awareness of spiritual insight. In afteryears, meditating on this sublime action, he said, "Jesus knew full well that the Father had placed all power in His hands; knew, too, how that He had come from God, and was about to return to God. Yet, knowing all this—think of it!—He rose from His place at the table, laid aside His outer robe, tied a towel around Him and, pouring water into a basin, prepared to wash the disciples' feet." The sheer wonder of it overwhelmed him. "He did it," he went on, "because He loved them so—loved them, even Judas, right up to the end."

The disciples were motionless from shame; and as Jesus went to each one and washed his feet and dried them, He gently chided the disciples for their envious thoughts.

"Didn't I tell you that your Lord would one day gird Himself and make His servants sit down to a meal and come and serve them? I seem to remember, too, that we once had some talk about who was the greater, the guest or the slave who waited on him. I think someone said it was likely to be the guest. But he was wrong. For, see, I am in the midst of you all as the Slave Who serves you."

He saw how shamed and humbled they looked; so, as He continued His task, He comforted them. "But *you* are the loyal ones—" for this had been true even of Judas—"who have been true to Me through all My trials. And even as My Father is giving Me a Kingdom, so I give you the right to eat and drink with Me in that Kingdom!" For this communion *was* the Kingdom, even then in being; and they *were* about to eat and drink, even as do all who today share in that selfsame Covenantal Meal—*in His presence, in that Kingdom.*

And so He moved from disciple to disciple; to Matthew, who knew what it had been to possess slaves to do this menial task in that house back there by the Lakeside which he had given up for Jesus; to John and James, smarting with shame for their former ambitions; to Judas, too, with a specially pleading look, as if love would break down the barricades of evil.

And so to Peter. Hot, generous, unstable (as yet), loyal at heart, deeply loving, he could not endure the constraint of this terrible silence as the foot washing went on. He felt he would burst if Jesus were to stoop and touch *his* feet. As the Master knelt on one knee before him and reached for the basin, Peter's defences broke down:

"Surely You're not going to wash *my* feet?"

Jesus made gentle answer. "You do not understand just now what I am doing; but you will realize it all later on."

Peter (as so often) protested, "I'll *never* let You wash my feet— *never!*"

Jesus paused, His hand still on the basin. "If I don't wash you, you will have no part in Me. . . ."

"Then, Lord—" in sudden impulsive reaction—"wash, not my feet only, but my hands and my head also!" not knowing much what he was saying.

Jesus smiled. "It's all right. It's quite enough to wash your feet, since I know you have already bathed in preparation for the feast. It's only the surface stains that need to be cleansed. But I cannot say that for all of you. . . ." But even then He never glanced in Judas' direction, but left them guessing as to whom He was referring. He then put on His outer robe again and sat down, saying, "Do you realize the inner meaning of what I have just done for you?"

There were bewildered looks and murmurs of incomprehension.

He resumed: "You do well to call me 'Master' and 'Lord'—for so I am. If then I, your Lord and Master, have washed your feet, you are bound to do the same for one another in future; for I have been setting an example for you to follow. The servant must not expect to be more highly privileged than his Master, and should therefore never be ashamed to do what his Master has done."

Jesus then settled their respective positions around the *reclinium*. Young John He placed next on His left—as was right, since he had provided the meal and was therefore in a sense the host, having on his right hand the chief Guest, as was customary. Jesus paused for a moment before deciding whom to place on His right. Then, with a beseeching look, He chose—Judas, who took his seat in strained silence.

Then, when they were all settled, Jesus said, "I cannot tell you how greatly I have longed for this moment—to eat this, My last Passover Meal with you all together!" After one of the disciples had handed Him the wine cup and they had all stood up for the blessing, Jesus handed it back, saying, "No . . . I mean what I say. You take it and share it out among yourselves; for I shall not ever again taste of the fruit of the vine till God's Kingdom shall have fully come."

As the meal proceeded the atmosphere became increasingly sombre and heavy with grief. The soul of Jesus was overburdened with sorrow for the approaching wreckage of the soul of Judas. He therefore roused Himself to make a final appeal to the traitor. He will let him know that his secret was already known to his Master—thereby easing and unsealing the oppressive, bursting constraint of guilt and preparing the way for the full unburdening of confession and the cleansing flood of tears. So love, taking, as ever, the initiative, went over to the offensive, but in so delicate and kindly a way that the guilt of Judas was screened from the others.

Deeply troubled in spirit, Jesus spoke—looking at no disciple— with the utmost earnestness. "In most solemn truth, I tell you, one of you is about to betray Me. . . ."

One after another they whispered, "Lord, is it *I?*" each of them, including Judas, expressing utter bewilderment on his face. Only Jesus knew in His soul the present truth of the Psalmist's words: *Even My own trusted friend*—he who shared My meals with Me— *even he is ready to trip Me up heavily.*

So, with this Psalm in mind, Jesus added pointedly: "It is even one who now shares this meal with Me. . . ."

The disciples were terribly distressed as Jesus continued in even more revealing frankness: "It is one of the Twelve—one who but a moment ago dipped his hand into this dish beside Me. That hand even now rests upon this table!"

He waited for Judas' response . . . but none came. A sense of the strange inevitability of His passion stole over Jesus: a feeling as though He were held in the grip of a fate foreordained before the foundation of the world. His thoughts eased themselves into sombre, murmuring speech, as He passed from appeal to solemn warning.

"Verily, the Son of Man moves to His destined end . . . even as it has been decreed of old. But woe to that man by whom the Son of Man is betrayed."

The Beloved Disciple was leaning over and reclining on Jesus' breast. Peter nudged him, whispering, "Ask Him whom He means."

So John looked up at Jesus and murmured under his breath, "Lord, who is it . . . ?"

Jesus whispered back so that only John—and Judas—could hear: "It is the first one to whom I shall give this morsel, after I have dipped it in the dish." And He took the morsel of unleavened bread, dipped it in the dish of sweet juices, and handed it to Judas on His right.

Judas took it, a wild startled look in his eyes and beads of perspiration starting out from his forehead. He now knew for certain not only that Jesus shared his secret, but that He was, nevertheless, going forward to betrayal, refusing, even with this provocation, to assert Himself. Again, no Messiah, this. Only an upstart charlatan, an impostor, forgetful of Israel's glory and of her destiny, and despising *him,* Judas, as a traitor to his cause! Well—better be loyal to Israel and a traitor to Jesus, than the other way round. There followed a stark moment of immobile horror, as young John gazed shudderingly at Judas and Judas gazed defiantly at Jesus.

Long afterward, as the Beloved Disciple related the events of that unforgettable night to his own followers, he said, "Do you know, when Judas took that morsel, at that very moment I saw Satan enter in and take possession of his soul. . . ."

Then Jesus—but so quietly that no one heard but those next to Him—spoke again to the traitor: "What you must do . . . *do quickly*."

And immediately Judas started up, stumbled dazedly across the room, opened the barred door fumblingly, and passed out . . . and the door slammed-to again. But not before the intensely poetic soul of John had seen and felt the deep significance of the black darkness glimpsed for a moment through the opened door. *". . . and it was Night. . . ."* he whispered to his friends long after, shudderingly; and they wrote it down in his memories of Jesus, an unforgettable sentence, filled with the deepest symbolism.

The disciples were dumbfounded. What on earth did all this mean? They had seen Jesus whisper something to Judas, who had hurried from the room; so that some supposed that he had been sent out to buy some missing provisions from those dealers who at Passover time kept their stalls open far into the night. Others guessed that Jesus had sent him off to aid some ailing beggar (they knew Jesus' ways). Only young John knew what had really happened, not only here on earth but in the realms of the spirit. He could not take his eyes off that door. The sound of its slamming-to still echoed in his ears; the signal of a soul self-ejected from salvation. Somewhere, out there in the black void, "walking in the night," Judas was stumbling, in the Outer Darkness. The tension was unbearable.

Then suddenly it was broken by a great cry from Jesus: *"Now* at last is the Son of Man glorified! And in Him God is glorified! God will glorify Him in Himself—and glorify Him *now!"*

(The refrain, "Glory . . . Glory," beats yet upon the ear as the far echoes of that tragic, triumphant cry are heard even by us today that listen.)

The tension was broken; limbs were stirred again, and eyes turned away from that closed door. There ensued a sublime sense of ease—and of purgation. The atmosphere, till now so heavily charged with psychic strain, was cleansed as though a cloud had been lifted from their hearts. Though they did not know the outcome of the strange prophecy about betrayal, each one of the disciples knew in his heart that nothing was further from his thoughts than any intention to betray his Master. And the slow, sweet smile of Jesus rested upon each of them as He entered at last unhinderedly into fullest communion with those whom He loved. A spirit of harmony and peace, poignant and tragic, but with the horror of evil purged from it, united them all in one perfect fellowship, a fellowship infinitely more deep and binding by reason of that very poignancy and brooding tragedy. The disciples, even then, did not realize the ghastliness of the inevitable catastrophe looming so nearly ahead. Surely, they thought, this despairing mood of self-oblation would pass and Jesus soon be again His own happy self. Danger, undefined and vague, seemed to threaten Him, and they could not escape the infection of His sombre mood . . . but He Himself would in the end triumph over His enemies, as He always had done.

As for Jesus, He saw Himself being slowly engulfed by a dark sea of death but, in astounding paradox, triumphing gloriously in that death. The time remaining to Him was so short. Only a few more hours now separated Him from the dread moment when the Lamb provided by God Himself would be slain for the morrow's cosmic Passover ritual: when all Heaven would be bowed down in abasement and wonder. The one sweet and consoling truth lay in this lovely fellowship: an organic union—more than unity; a communion of spirit transcending all barriers of time and space, even of personality itself, making all One in Love. Judas, the rotting diseased branch, had been self-separated from the Vine of God; for sin is separation and so death. For the fruit of the vine—this wine, now shared by them all— could only flow from healthy branches; and the one bond of union was this pulsating vibrating love, everywhere flowing forth and received, like cosmic rays binding the universe together. This was the final joy, unalloyed and complete in them even as in Him. From henceforth they were no longer Master and servants, but Friends. So let them always recall this communion, this joy . . . and, to seal it with a tangible recurrent token, to be apprehended in every renewal and in every generation of disciples yet to be, He gave them the supreme ritual of organic union, sublimating the Passover Rite and investing it with the universal and personal significance to which it had always pointed. God Himself the Lamb: the bread broken, the body of God; the wine outpoured, the life blood of God; God ever in Him, the Son of Man, His Son; and through His Son, and by this reciprocating love, God in them . . . and so, all One in Love. What He had failed to achieve in the great sacramental meal on the Butaiha Plain, with its teeming thousands and its material miracle, He here succeeded in achieving with this handful, behind closed doors and with no miracle. The Church was now in full communion with Him; for here was perfect love.

"Do you now understand? . . . Never mind. It is not the time for explanations. I must necessarily leave so much unsaid. But one day you will remember and realize, and rejoice. Meanwhile—and always—this is My command to you: *Do this in remembrance of Me*. Yes—go through this ceremony in renewed fellowship with one another and with Me, for I shall be present with you. For only in so far as you partake of My body and My blood will you be impelled in My spirit to break your own bodies and pour out your own life blood for your friends. For that is the uttermost that love can do to prove its quality."

And the disciples, one by one, on bended knee, received the broken bread and the outpoured wine, and were infused with the Eternal Life flowing from its sole source in God's heart. This was the New Covenant, at last mediated in perfect revelation. Not in itself new: indeed, older than time: coeval with God Eternal: but new in man's experience now; and this Love, sealed in sacrifice and mediated in sacrament, is Life: Eternal, Divine, unifying, complete.

But Jesus was very human. The pang of earthly parting smote Him as He looked on His loved companions. Did they even now realize the shortness of this present earthly companionship, the nearness of His departure?

"Very soon I shall be going back to My Father," He told them, pausing to see whether any of them would by a question show his desire fully to understand. "I notice," He went on, "that none of you asks Me 'Where are You going?' Perhaps it is because your hearts are too full of sorrow. But nevertheless, it is the plain truth. In a little while you will behold Me no longer; and then, after another little while, you will see Me again."

The disciples were out of their depth. "What can He mean by this talk of a 'little while' and 'going to the Father'?"

Jesus saw them discussing these questions and did His utmost to explain to them that sorrow and joy are cyclic in this earthly life, grief being a concomitant of birth as well as of death; and this crisis *was* one of birth as well as of death—a birth through death, to an endless joy, even to an Eternity of life.

"And as to the 'whither' of My departure, it is all-important to you to understand this: that I shall no longer be present in fleshly guise with you. You will then seek My *bodily* presence in vain; for, as I tried to tell the Jews, I shall be in a world where men cannot follow Me on earth."

Peter was troubled that Jesus was sad because no one had asked Him whither He was going. "Lord," he asked Him, "where *are* You going?"

"As I say, Peter, I am going whither you cannot follow Me—at present. But I promise you this: you *shall* follow Me one day!"

"Lord, *why* can't I follow You *now*—for You know I'd follow You anywhere, even through death itself!"

Jesus smiled a little sadly. "You will not believe Me, I know, but I tell you that very soon all of you will be scattered to your houses— yes, every one of you—and will leave Me alone." He added, in an afterthought: "No, not alone, for the Father will still be with Me."

There was a long silence. Then Jesus looked at Peter. He saw his inner weaknesses; and his still more central strength.

"Simon . . . Simon—" significantly dropping the loved name of "Peter," the "Rock man"—"Satan has claimed the right to sift you, even as wheat is threshed. But I have prayed specially for you, that your faith may not fail. And you, in turn, must be a source of strength to your brethren."

Peter was deeply roused, not only by the challenge to his courage implicit in Jesus' words about the coming desertion of the disciples, but still more by this singling out of him before all the others for censure . . . and for intercession. Also the renewed use of "Simon" instead of "Peter" hurt him deeply.

"Lord," he cried, "I am ready to go to prison or to death for You! Though all these others may in the end prove disloyal to You, that will *I* never be!"

Jesus gazed deep and long into Peter's eyes, reading his very soul. "Truly, I tell you, that today—even this very night—before the bugle sounds the second cockcrow, you will have denied Me three times over."

Peter was vehement in protest. "Even if it does mean death for me, I will never disown You!"

The others, stung by Peter's former words, hastened to concur. "Nor will any of us!" they cried.

Jesus thought it best to change the subject. He thought of Judas, at that very moment filling his purse (which was Jesus', really) with *thirty pieces of silver*, and meaning to desert with all it contained. Each of the disciples would need his own purse in future, and other essentials as well.

"Tell Me," He asked them in dreadful, searing irony, "when first I sent you out to preach, did you find you lacked anything?"

"No," they answered, "we were all right."

"Yes, but now all is different. He who has a purse had better keep it himself in future. He'd be wise to look after his wallet, too, and whoever does not possess a sword had better sell his coat, and go and buy one. . . ."

The words of Jeremiah had echoed in His mind: *Then I took a cup at the Lord's hand, and made all the nations to drink of it, unto whom the Lord had sent Me; but if they refuse to take the cup at Thine hand to drink, I will call for a sword.*

Then He smiled to Himself wearily. The fierceness of the Prophet was not of Heaven, but of man. Not so did the Suffering Servant cry. Nevertheless, He added, broodingly, a quotation from the great passage that did describe the Suffering Servant: "I tell you, the words of Scripture must be fulfilled in Me: *He was classed among rebels.* Yes, the things concerning Me move inevitably to their destined end."

The disciples were terribly literal. This call for swords . . . "Lord," they said, "look, here are two swords."

There was Peter's—you never knew when you might want one in this turbulent and antagonistic city—and Simon the Zealot also carried one.

Jesus swept round on them. He clapped His hands over His ears. "Enough, enough!" He cried, with disillusioned finality.

The disciples utterly failed to follow His seeming changes of mood, and were deeply distressed. Jesus smiled in compassionate love upon them.

"Don't be overworried. . . ." He returned to the subject of the "whither" of His departure. "See, I will tell you plainly where I am going. You believe I came out from God? Well, just as I came from the Father and entered the world, so now I am leaving the world and returning to the Father. Is that plain enough? Is it not written? *On that Day Mine elect shall sit on the throne of His glory and make choice of men's deeds, and their resting places will be innumerable.* Yes, in My Father's abode there are many resting places—there'll be room for you all. I am not deceiving you. If it were not so, would I have told you that I am going away to prepare a dwelling place in Heaven for you? I promise that I will come back and fetch you, so that wherever I am, there you can all be with Me! Then you'll know for yourselves where I am going . . . and in any case you already know the way to it."

Thomas protested: "Lord, we don't even yet know *where* You are going, so how can we know the way?"

"*I* am the real and living Way. No one can reach the Father but through Me . . . for if you really knew Me you would know the Father too. But you have had full opportunity of both knowing and seeing Him."

It was Philip's turn to protest. "Lord, how can we know the Father—unless, as He was to Moses and the other prophets, He is revealed in vision to *us?* Lord, let us see the Father! That is all we want." *All*—as casual as that!

"Philip, have I been all this time with you, and yet you still don't know Me? I tell you once again: whoever has seen Me has seen the Father."

It troubled Jesus that the disciples should still have failed to identify Him with the Father.

"Why is it that you ask thus to 'see the Father'? All the words and works that you have heard and seen in Me are due to My complete possession by the Father; they are therefore the Father's words and works: words and works available to you and to all who shall believe in Me hereafter, since in Me death releases greater power—and so leads onward to even greater works. For in dying I shall be able to release to all believers the full power of the Spirit: even the Spirit of Truth: that ultimate truth which is beyond mere proof and more than any theophany: Which the world just cannot apprehend because it cannot *see* it—relying, as it does, on merely sensory impression. But *you* will know it, for it will dwell within you always. I shall soon be disappearing from your bodily sight, but I shall not be leaving you forlorn; I shall be returning to you. But what the world cannot experience *you* will know, for you will be sharing in the life and power that the Spirit gives to men. The proof of anyone's love for Me is obedience to My commands, and whoever loves Me will be loved by My Father, and I will love him and appear to him."

"Why," asked a disciple, "should You only appear to us and not manifest Yourself to all the world?"

Jesus was very patient, even with this further evidence of their expectation of an earthly Messianic triumph.

"The Father and I *can* only manifest Ourselves to those who love Us and obey Our commands. But wherever We *can,* We will enter into men's souls and abide there. So, you see, My going is for your good. If I do not depart, My spirit cannot be fully released. But when it is, *then* will come also the conviction of the world; for the Spirit of Truth will convict and convince men as to the real nature of sin, of righteousness, and of judgment. For sin will be revealed when true holiness is at last apprehended. Righteousness will be revealed when this seemingly disastrous end to My sojourn here on earth is seen to be in reality a going to the Father. The true nature of judgment will be revealed when the Spirit shows to all the world that it is the prince of this world who will be judged and sentenced when they judge and sentence the despised criminal of Galilee. So always trust in the guidance of the Spirit, for it will lead you to the inner truth of all things; drawing ever upon what is Mine (for all that the Father has is also Mine) and revealing it to you. And now, while yet I am still with you, I bequeath to you My peace; such a peace as the world can never give. So let not your hearts be disquieted or afraid.

"That is, I think, all that I can well say to you now. I have yet so much I want to say to you, but you can't bear it just now; and after this, the opportunity will be gone. *For the prince of this world is even now drawing near.* But he has no hold on Me. His coming will but serve to let the world see that I love the Father and that I am but acting as the Father ordered. I have said all this that in Me you may have peace. In the world you will most certainly have tribulation. But be of good cheer! I have overcome the world!"

There followed a hush of wonder as the great discourse came to its sublime full close. Then Jesus stood up. "Rise!" He commanded them; and they, awestruck and silent, stood in their places, waiting. Then He lifted His eyes and hands to Heaven and prayed, as the High Priest of all humanity.

"Father, the hour is now come. Glorify Thy Son, that Thy Son may glorify Thee; for Thou hast granted Him power over all flesh to give Eternal Life to all whom Thou hast given Him. I have glorified Thee on earth by completing the task that Thou gavest Me to do. Now, O Father, glorify Me in Thy presence with that glory which I enjoyed in Thy presence before the world began. I have made Thy name known to those whom Thou hast given Me out of the world. Thine they were, and Thou gavest them to Me, and they have held to Thy word. They know now that whatever Thou hast given Me comes from Thee; for I have given them the words that Thou gavest Me to utter; and they have received them. They are now sure that I came forth from Thee, and they believe that Thou didst send Me. I pray for them, for they are Thine—since all Mine is Thine, and Thine is Mine; and I am glorified in them. I am to be in the world no longer . . . but they must remain in the world. So now I come to Thee, and pray, O Holy Father, that Thou mayest keep them by the power of Thy name, that they may be one even as We are One. I pray not that Thou shouldest take them out of the world, but that Thou mayest protect them from the evil in it. They do not belong to the world; but as Thou didst send Me out into the world, so do I even now send them out into the world. And it has been for their sakes that I have consecrated Myself to the truth. Nor do I pray for them only—but for all who *shall* believe in Me through their testimony: that they may *all* be one! As Thou, O Father, art in Me and I in Thee, so may they be one in Us. Yea, I shall give them the self-same glory that Thou gavest to Me, that they may be one in glory even as We: I in them, and Thou in Me, that all may be perfectly one. Father, it is My will that these, Thy gift to Me, may be beside Me where I AM . . . to behold My glory given to Me by Thee—for I have been loved by Thee from before the foundation of the universe. O just Father, though the world has not known Thee, *I* have known Thee; and they have known that Thou didst send Me. So, I have declared—and will yet declare—Thy name to them, that the love with which Thou lovest Me may be in them and I in them. . . ."

Then, after a long silence, passing all expression for profundity of import, Jesus said in sudden decision, "Come, let us be going," and they all filed out through that same door and down the outer steps into the night of the powers of darkness. Words had reached their utmost limit of expression; only the deed remained to be accomplished; and as they moved in silence through the moonlit streets and out through the dark shadows of the gate and down the steep defile of the Kedron Valley, this accomplishment of the deed was already begun.

(II) GETHSEMANE

CAIAPHAS was in a flurry of activity. The visit of the man Judas to the Council Room that evening had altered all his plans. Evidently Jesus was an out-and-out quietist. He was just waiting to be arrested. In Gethsemane, the fellow said. Well, that would suit very well. This was a unique opportunity, not to be lost, even if the feast would not be over. It would be wise to obviate the danger inherent in the partisans of the Prophet by getting a condemnation *before* the Galileans were astir—they encamped mostly outside the city, anyway. Tomorrow evening was the Passover Celebration, so that time was short and the need for haste urgent. Of course, a condemnation necessitated the willing co-operation of the Governor, since he alone was empowered to inflict the death penalty. So Pilate must be asked— and at once, before the arrest were made—if he could arrange for the Trial to take place in the earliest hours of the morning. Better still, if he could be induced to arrange beforehand for a condemnation. That should not be utterly impossible, if rightly set about. . . . Caiaphas cupped his chin in his hand. Pilate—most conveniently as it turned out—owed him, the High Priest, a considerable sum of money. That would be a lever; for Pilate was no strong character, as everyone

knew. It would be still easier to fix if Jesus could be somehow impli-
cated in rebellion against Rome. For Pilate was thoroughly scared
of Caesar, having already suffered one scathing rebuke from the Emperor—and that was for defying the wishes of the Priests. Yes,
Pilate should be manageable, rightly handled. It must be only one
person, however, who handled him—and Caiaphas began to rehearse
in his mind what he should say to him.

Then it was that Judas burst in upon Caiaphas: frenzied, insane.
Jesus was in a mood of utter surrender. He was going very soon now
to pray in the Garden of Gethsemane. You never knew . . . better
take a posse of Temple Guards if one could be got together at this
late hour. No mistake must be made this time. Caiaphas dismissed
Judas and at once rose up to visit the Governor.

He found Pilate yet astir, together with his consort, Claudia
Procula, in their sumptuously hung apartment in Herod's palace, with
a fire of coals burning in a brazier in the midst. Pilate was watchful
and wary. This was a very unexpected visit. He signalled his wife to
remain . . . and waited. These Jews—crafty, cunning and greedy.
That debt . . .

Then Caiaphas, smoothly, deferentially, began. Not a word of the
debt, as yet. This Galilean Prophet . . . a pestiferous nuisance. Had
Pilate heard about the procession last Sunday? Setting Himself up to
be King—King of Israel—riding on a white ass like a conqueror;
palms, cloaks, laid before Him on the ground; a menace not only to
the nation but to the empire. Well, you see, the people were hypno-
tized, spellbound. The Fellow could undoubtedly perform miracles—
the Bethany affair . . . four days dead. The sooner He Himself was
dead the better. No, no—by the power of Beelzebub, without a
shadow of doubt. God was outraged in everything He did: defying
the Law, breaking the Sabbath, ridiculing the Temple customs, casti-
gating the Priests. (That was a false move. Caiaphas caught Pilate's
sidelong glance, quizzical, amused.) And now this "Triumphal
Entry" with its open and arrogant assumption of sovereignty, betokened a defiance of Rome which, he was convinced, the Governor
would not take lying down.

Pilate listened, silent, thoughtfully frowning. He had, of course, heard all about this entry—and its tame ending. Queer, that, when you came to think about it. One had to be careful with all these inflammatory Galileans swarming in and around the city. Apparently the Man was just another crackbrained fanatic. It certainly looked as though the Fellow might be easily apprehended tonight, and, if He could be despatched as early as possible tomorrow, all the anxieties attendant upon a potential riot might be allayed and so Caesar would be pleased. It would make a good despatch, especially if the danger were slightly exaggerated. It was, in any case, a wonder that these Jews were for once on Rome's side, and it might be a good thing for the people to see what would happen to any challenger to Rome's authority.

But the matter of the Trial was purely a Jewish one. The Sanhedrin must judge and condemn if they wanted to. He himself would but ratify. He could not be bothered with ridiculous wrangles about Messianic claims.

Caiaphas was secretly exasperated. This would mean a dreadful hindrance to his plans. Messages would have to be sent out at once to every member of the Great Council, convening an extraordinary meeting at the very earliest dawn, since no trial on a capital charge could be legally heard during the hours of darkness. But he agreed with Pilate and hurried out. His next move was to arrange for a crowd of paid agitators to stand in the forefront of the Praetorium courtyard when the Trial opened before Pilate on the morrow. Everything seemed now arranged—except the vital matter of the two necessary witnesses. Here he was met by an almost insuperable difficulty. What exactly had Jesus ever said that could possibly constitute a charge of blasphemy—the easiest indictment involving the death penalty? He must get in touch with other members of the Sanhedrin and get his facts correct.

All this while Another was also waiting, down there in the shadows of the Olive Garden, in almost unbearable suspense listening for the sound of the guard that did not come. Jesus had asked eight of His disciples to be close at hand somewhere near by while He and His three most intimate Apostles withdrew into the central shadows of the ancient trees. He felt the need for human companionship and sympathy, yet He would be alone. So He asked His closest friends to watch and wait, near at hand. His voice was trembling as He told them, "My heart is almost breaking . . . even to the point of death. Stay here awhile, and watch."

Then He moved away from them about a stone's throw and they lost sight of Him in the shadows. After a while they lay down and waited, and were silent and nodded—and slept.

But there was one who, in spite of the disciples' sleepiness was watching and listening, and overheard the prayer of Jesus. A young man of the name of Mark was there in the garden, hiding in the gloom. His curiosity had been aroused by the unusual stir in his father's house that night, and by the insistence of his parents that the large party of men who tramped upward toward the Upper Room was not to be disturbed. He had listened . . . but could hear only a soft voice speaking, save once when there was a great shout. Just before they had left, there had come the sound of Psalm singing, quavering low. Then had followed the sound of feet descending the outer steps.

He had been so interested that, leaping out of bed and throwing a sheet around him, he had ventured out after them, hearing soon after the tallest of them saying: "All of you will soon be scandalized in Me—yes, this very night. It is not written? *I will smite the Shepherd, and the sheep shall be scattered abroad.* But after I am raised up again, I, your Shepherd, O my little flock, will go before you northward out of this blood-soaked city, into Galilee—Galilee!" And His voice sank to a whisper and His eyes shone. "You will see Me there!"

Mark had followed them into the shadowed recesses of the garden, and lay crouching down near to where Jesus was praying. Soon he overheard that same voice crying in agonized entreaty, "Abba . . . Father . . . all things are possible to Thee. Remove this cup from My lips." And then, a little later: "Nevertheless, not what I will, but what *Thou* willest."

A whole hour passed, and Mark could not escape, for near to the only entrance to the garden some of the men had lain down to rest. After a while he saw Jesus rise from prayer and rejoin His three chosen disciples, finding them still and silent. They were fast asleep. He saw Him rouse Peter.

"So not even you, Peter, could watch with Me for one short hour! Watch and pray with Me, all of you; lest you, too, enter into temptation. The spirit is indeed willing, but the flesh is frail. . . ."

Again He went away and prayed: "O My Father, if this cup cannot pass from Me except I drain it, Thy will be done." And after another long wait He came to them, and as before found them sleeping, for their eyes were terribly heavy. They could think of nothing to say in answer to His gentle rebuke. The silence was unbearably oppressive.

The long vigil was so intense a strain that, being in an agony of supplication, He prayed ever more earnestly, until Mark could see—in the sheen of the moon—beads of perspiration dropping off His forehead onto the ground. One of the disciples sleepily roused himself and thought he saw an Angel come down to strengthen Him—not knowing that it was Mark in his white sheet, shivering, his teeth chattering and his knees convulsively knocking together, too frightened to move or cry out and unable to escape.

All this long while the moon was dropping slowly behind driving clouds, till it was at length hidden by the dark mass of the wall and was not seen again till it reappeared far out and over the Judaean hills to sink at last to rest beyond the rolling black line of the horizon. And then there was, suddenly, utter unrelieved blackness.

Why this delay? *Was* it after all (thought Jesus), God's will that Messiah should thus suffer and die? God's will that His enemies were cutting short His life on earth and ending His influence and work in the world? Could this delay mean that God, seeing His complete willingness to offer Himself in self-oblation, was, as with Abraham's sacrifice of old, at last intervening to save Him?

Besides, had He not Himself arranged for His arrest, thus possibly presuming upon God's initiative? Had He any right thus to determine His fate? He remembered the pinnacle of the Temple—with a shudder—and again, temptation, subtle and intense, assailed Him as He waited. But He went on waiting. Nevertheless, with every long-drawn minute the striving of sense against this lunatic surrender which cut off all His helpfulness to the world became stronger and more insistent. Perhaps Judas had repented and His appeal to him at the supper had borne fruit after all. Perhaps God had already overruled

Jesus' possible presumption and determined fate according to His Almighty will. *"Thy* will, not Mine, be done. . . ."

But He went on waiting . . . waiting . . . His own will triumphant.

Then, at last, a long way off, somewhere behind where the wall was, there shone a dim glow which grew ever more fiery and before which the dark mass of the gateway was for a moment outlined. Then there was darkness again for a space. A short sharp call penetrated the silence and suddenly many torches and lanterns appeared on this side of the wall. Soon there could be heard the far sound of measured tramping, and the glint of light on spears and swords was seen before the glow alone remained to reveal the movement of the column as it descended the Kedron Valley and was lost to sight behind the palisading of the garden.

The traitor was here. Jesus rose. God had decided not to intervene. His own plan was ratified of Heaven. The machinery of "justice" had been set in motion to move inexorably to its destined end. There was no escaping the inevitable interaction of character and circumstance. It was an ironic touch—and evidential of His nerve strain, that Jesus roused the disciples—to tell them to sleep.

"Sleep on now! Rest yourselves. Enough. The hour is come. Look! The Son of Man is betrayed into the hands of wicked men." Then, more sharply: "Come. Get up. Let us go forward to meet them! Lo! Here is My betrayer, close at hand."

While He was yet speaking, Judas came into sight, leading a great crowd of men armed with swords, spears and cudgels. He had arranged a signal. "The One I shall kiss," he had said, "is the One to arrest. Lay hold of Him, and lead Him safely away." So he came forward and going straight to Jesus said, "Hail, Master!" kissing Him with seeming affection.

Jesus answered, "Friend, do what you have come to do. But would you, Judas, betray Me—with a *kiss?"*

Judas and the soldiers waited. . . . But nothing happened. Not a man of that great crowd moved.

Jesus seemed surprised. "For *whom* are you looking?" He asked of the centurion in command.

"Jesus the Nazarene," he replied.

"Well, I am He."

Whereupon they were all so terrified of Him that those nearest to Him shrank back suddenly, in their retreat overbalancing some others behind them, causing them all to stumble and fall to the ground. Judas watched, spellbound. . . . Was Jesus, after all, impossible to arrest? He stared at Jesus, his eyes dilating in the glare of the torches, as the men shamefacedly got to their feet again.

The voice of the Master was heard again, level and clear: "Whom did you say you were looking for?"

Once again came the answer, but in an awestruck whisper this time: "Jesus of Nazareth . . ."

"I tell you, I am the Man," answered Jesus again. "See, you can arrest Me. If it be I Whom you are seeking, all I ask is that you will let these My friends go free," for the terrified disciples were surrounded by the soldiers.

Then someone advanced to effect the arrest of Jesus; and in a flash Peter, impetuous as ever, drew his sword and striking at the man cut off his ear as the blow was partly dodged.

Jesus immediately and in the sternest tones denounced the action. "Put your sword back into its sheath," He cried, "for all who draw the sword shall die by the sword. What! Do you think I cannot, if I want, appeal to My Father to provide Me at this very moment with over twelve legions of Angels—instead of twelve men—to protect Me? Only, how then could the Scriptures be fulfilled, the Scriptures that say this *must* be so?"

He at once went over to the injured man and with a touch healed his wound. Then He turned to the concourse of soldiers and Temple guards. "Do you think I'm a rebel, thus to sally out after Me with words and cudgels? Day after day I sat teaching in the Temple, and you never seized Me. But this *had* to happen, as the Prophets foretold. This is *your* hour, and the dark powers'."

The captain of the guard, more daring than the rest, broke the brooding stillness by advancing toward Jesus, and, being a good Roman Centurion, stretched forth his hand and dared to lay it upon Jesus' shoulder, saying, "What are you all so scared about? Come, you are my prisoner."

Everyone held his breath. But nothing happened. The Hosts of

Heaven, even in this extremity, were obedient to His will. This was the full proof of His Divinity—that they laid hold of Him and nothing happened. But the Eleven—and Judas—could not see this inexorable logic. For them, this was indeed the end. How could He be the Messiah? They had been deceived. Turning in a group they all took to their heels and fled away into the darkness, surprising the soldiers, who in the general scramble could only find poor Mark—an easy target in his white sheet. But he slipped, terrified, from his would-be captors, leaving but the sheet in their hands.

Then they bound Jesus and led Him away; and the garden story was ended. But there was another garden story yet to be told: not of night and gnarled roots and horror and the dark power, but of dawn and flowers and joy and an unbelievable brightness. And in between these two gardens stood a gaunt rock shaped like a skull . . . and they who would pass from the agony of consecration to the joy of Resurrection must pass by Calvary's stark gibbet.

VII

The Trial of Jesus

. . . .

(I) THE ENQUIRY BEFORE ANNAS

ANNAS was rightly regarded by the Jews as the head of Israel. He had been deposed from the office of High Priest not by the Jews but by Valerius Gratus, the predecessor of Pilate, being succeeded by his son-in-law, Caiaphas. But he remained the virtual ruler of the Jews, and was undoubtedly the brain behind the family's fortune and the wily schemer who planned all policy. Caiaphas was himself busy with the arrangements for the meeting of the Sanhedrin to take place later in the night—as soon as the first light of dawn appeared in the east. Besides, he trusted to his father-in-law's astute brain to extract some incriminating admission from Jesus, with which they could later charge Him when the full Council met.

Annas, old, crafty and infinitely sinister, gazed searchingly at Jesus, and questioned Him about His disciples and about His Teaching. Why did He want to go about always with a bodyguard around Him? Were they the nucleus of a revolutionary organization? And why did He assail the Law and ridicule it in the eyes of the people? And what did the Triumphal Entry portend?

But Jesus held His peace. He knew that the enquiry was altogether illegal, as Annas had no right, not being the titular High Priest, to hold any enquiry at all. So, after a series of futile endeavours on the part of Annas to make Him speak, Jesus at last objected, speaking sharply and with inherent moral right.

"Why are *you* questioning Me at all?" He asked. "If you really want to know about My Teaching, ask anybody. I talked openly to all the world, having always taught in the Synagogues or in the Temple—wherever the people forgathered. Nothing that I have said is secret. So ask these My hearers if you wish to know what I said to them. They know full well what I have taught." He pointed to the Jews grouped about Annas.

The Master gazed at the cunning old serpent with superb courage, showing up his illegal status and his hypocrisy; and the absence of witnesses. But one of the Temple Guards lost his temper, being anxious to appear zealous before Annas. "How dare you speak to the High Priest like that?" he asked Jesus, giving Him a cruel blow.

But Jesus maintained His dignified aloofness, answering with incisive urgency: "If I have said anything wrong, prove it. If what I have said is true—why strike Me?"

Annas soon realized that nothing was to be gained by this preliminary enquiry, but that rather precious time was being wasted. Besides, a messenger had just arrived bringing an intimation from Caiaphas that the Sanhedrin had assembled and were ready to hear the case at the very earliest hour that was legally possible—that was at the third watch of the night, when the Roman bugles sounded the second *Gallicinium* or cockcrowing. So, the moment that Annas heard the bugle fanfares ringing from the Castle of Antonia, he rose and ordered the soldiers to take Jesus away to the High Priest's official palace. The onus of finding agreed testimony upon which to frame a charge according to the Jewish Law which would involve the death penalty, together with a further charge capable of rousing the Procurator to the ratification of that death sentence, remained now with Caiaphas. It was no easy task he was set, especially as Annas had failed in it.

Meanwhile, Peter and young John had found themselves together after the departure of the soldiers with Jesus. Far away toward the city the torchlight procession could just be descried—a dull red glow in the distance. The two disciples watched it till it disappeared within the walls. Then something in Peter snapped. He could not crouch any longer there in the shadows while his dear Master was dragged away to shame and to death. He must be near Him, come what may. He and John began to run toward the city; and John recalled that he was known to the family of the High Priest and might very probably be able to obtain entrance for himself to the Trial of Jesus—possibly

for Peter, too. So the two disciples followed the Master afar off—
significant of all men's following of Christ. This new chance friendship of Peter and John continued henceforward; and it was not long
before they were running once again together—but this time away
from the city.

Arrived at the house of Annas—for some onlookers had directed
the disciples—John knocked at the portals and after a while passed
within, having told Peter to wait outside till it should be known
whether or not permission for him also to enter could be obtained.
Soon the door opened again and John could be seen talking to the
maidservant who kept the door. Peter was beckoned within, his face,
scared and distraught, illumined by the lamplight. The door clanged-
to behind him and he found himself facing a courtyard, with a gallery
running along one side. In the middle was a large brazier glowing
with a charcoal fire. Most of the soldiers and some of the Temple
officials were grouped around this fire, the night being chill; and the
maidservants were mingling freely with the soldiers, bandying chaff
and enjoying the excitement of this strange midnight trial.

Peter was loath to leave the shadows of the portal, but even while he
hesitated to follow John within, the maidservant's lantern was lifted
and swung in his direction. The glow fell full on his face, and the
maidservant, eying him closely, said, "You're not, by any chance, one
of this Fellow's disciples, are you?" She felt sure she had seen him
with Jesus somewhere—in the procession last Sunday, possibly.

Poor Peter was taken unawares, and before he had recollected his
wits he heard himself answering "No." With a shock he realized his
commitment, and a subtle voice seemed to suggest to him: "It's all
right. You can act the part of a spy now, and so help to get Jesus
out of His trouble!" and he found himself walking boldly up to the
brazier and mixing rather overaggressively with the soldiers.

But he was a dreadfully poor actor; his face gave him away every
time. The maidservant's suspicions were definitely aroused. She came
over to the fire and scanned the faces grouped around it. Peter's was
lighted to a telltale clarity, the highlights and shadows thrown into
sharp relief by the bright flames. She nudged one of the bystanders
and whispered (but Peter overheard her): "This man *was* with Him"
with a jerked finger toward where Jesus was being examined.

Peter was appalled at the danger suddenly looming up before him. "Why," he exclaimed, "I don't even know what you're talking about." And he at once moved away into the shadow cast by another group on the further side of the fire. Then, when he thought no one was watching him, he sidled as nonchalantly as he could back toward the porch. But the door was shut and the maidservant had the key. The girl saw through his manoeuvre and began to say to those about her: "See that man lurking in the shadows over there? Well, I'm sure he's one of the Nazarene's disciples!"

Someone went up to Peter. "I hear you're one of this Fellow's disciples."

Peter uttered a great coarse oath—he was forced, he thought, to play the part now. "I don't even know the Man!" he shouted.

For a while the matter died down and he was almost compelled, to avoid any further suspicion, to rejoin the group about the fire. But one man in particular was watching him carefully. Peter was certainly out of luck, for this happened to be a relative of the very man, Malchus, whose ear Peter had cut off in the affray in the garden. After a while he went up to Peter. "Let me see," he snarled, "didn't I see you with Him—in the garden?"

Peter was panicstricken at this sudden change of fortune, just when everything seemed all right again. "No!" he cried.

But another joined in. "Why, of course he's one of them! You can't mistake that north-country accent!"

All Peter's scruples were thrown to the winds. He cursed and swore violently. "I tell you, I don't know anything about the Fellow!"

And suddenly the strident notes of a bugle blast rang out in the cold night air. It was the second cockcrow, sounded at 3:00 A.M. Almost directly after, a door opened in the gallery above and Jesus was led out, still bound with thongs. In the hush which fell on the crowd following the bugle blast and the opening door, Jesus came down the steps and passed right through the courtyard. He turned His face and looked long and earnestly at Peter; and as the farther door was thrown open for the procession to pass out again Peter rushed through and was lost in the darkness. Somewhere out there in the night, he wept his heart out. He had failed his Lord. All his discipleship was ended forever. He could never trust himself again.

"My Rock!" . . . A stream of cleansing tears gushed out from the "Rock," where it had been struck by the rod of conscience. And thus Jesus' prayer for him was answered.

(II) BEFORE CAIAPHAS

WITHIN the official residence of the High Priest the Sanhedrin was assembled in full session. The Trial proper had begun—illegally. For the arrest should only have been made at the instigation of at least two accusing witnesses. Caiaphas had done his best to obtain a suf- ficiency of testimony, but time had been against him. Those who now appeared to witness against Jesus contradicted each other—and there were two members of the Council who were being unpardonably ob- structive: Nicodemus and Joseph of Arimathea. They demanded strict legality on a capital charge—and the silence of the accused was not helping Caiaphas. It began to look as though Jesus might be acquitted—after a public trial too. This would be fatal, for it would inevitably focus enormous publicity upon the Prisoner. Caiaphas all but claimed that the disagreeing witnesses be stoned for perjury, so exasperated was he at the delay.

At last two witnesses came forward and offered to give further evidence, that is, to lay another charge. They averred that they had heard Jesus say—though it was two years before—that He would destroy the Temple "made with hands" and raise up another "not made with hands." Jesus had not said exactly this; what He had said was: "Go on as you are doing, destroy the Temple. . . . Never mind; in a short time I will raise up another Temple." It was deeply ironic that a simple metaphorical saying should have been (rightly) inter- preted spiritually; and then that this spiritual interpretation should in turn have been accepted literally—and made the basis of a charge of sorcery! But this newly improvised indictment also failed. Nicodemus and Joseph refused to allow such a charge to go forward, for they well remembered what Jesus had actually said.

So Jesus was still a free man legally. Caiaphas was at his wits' end. Then his quick, shrewd brain saw a possible way out. It was not a legal one, but he hoped no one would notice or challenge its irregu- larity. It was illegal to obtain grounds for a conviction by directly questioning a prisoner; but, being exasperated at the continued silence of Jesus—so aloof and dignified was He that He put all His judges to shame—Caiaphas rose in his seat and cried, "Can't You speak? What then was it that You *did* say?"

But Jesus was still silent and Caiaphas sank back again, defeated. Jesus had chosen that the one issue upon which He willed to be judged was that on which He had challenged Israel: His claim to be the Messiah. Therefore He would not take notice of any other issue.

Then Caiaphas decided to force Jesus to speak; for if anyone were adjured by the Oath of the Testimony—and especially if by the High Priest himself—He would *have* to speak; for, by the Mishna's law, no one could refuse to answer. Caiaphas further decided so to frame his question that the answer must be fatal, either way, to Jesus. So he once more rose from his seat; gorgeous in his robes and resplendent with jewels.

"I adjure You—*by the Living God*—that You tell us plainly: are You the Messiah, the Son of the Blessed—or not?"

This was crucial. Caiaphas watched Jesus. If He answered "No," then His hold on the people was finished. He would sink at once to the contemptible position of a self-exposed charlatan. On the other hand, if He answered "Yes," then this was, legally, blasphemy and deserving of the death penalty—*unless it were true*. But that were unthinkable. Yet a last struggle tore the soul of Caiaphas as he waited for the answer. For if Jesus *were* the Christ, the Son of the Blessed, then to treat the claim as blasphemy would be itself the most ghastly blasphemy possible. He looked at Jesus and Jesus stared back at him. Here was the one issue both were at grips with. . . .

Then the answer came at last: "I AM . . . and one day you will see the Son of Man at the right hand of power and coming on the clouds of Heaven!"

A hushed expectancy, awful and fearful, held everyone spellbound. Would the Heavens *now* open and the Angel Legions pour through the blinding gap in fulfilment of His words?

But nothing happened. The long silence was suddenly broken by a strange sound, rasping, tearing, nerve-shattering. For Caiaphas had with a violent movement thrown all scruples to the winds and challenged his fearful doubts (and his future destiny) as, clasping his robe in his two strong hands, he, with a mighty effort, tore it in twain; to be followed in turn by the other Elders present: the accepted reaction to blasphemy spoken and condemned. Two robes, however, remained untorn. Ignoring this, Caiaphas swung round upon his companions.

"What more evidence do you want?" he cried. "You have heard His blasphemy for yourselves. What's your verdict?"

There followed an immediate shout: "We sentence Him to death!"

Then the Jews threw over all restraint. The long suppressed hatred of Jesus was vented on Him now. They crowded round Him, and some even spat in His face. Others blindfolded Him and began to buffet Him, crying, "Tell us, O You 'Messiah,' who was it that struck You?"

And so, in rioting and shameful ridicule, the Trial before the Sanhedrin ended.

(III) BEFORE PILATE

WITHIN the great Palace of Herod—now the official residence of the Procurator—Pilate tried to sleep. What had Caiaphas exactly meant by this evening's strange interview? What was he getting at with all his talk of the dangerous new Galilean Prophet and this queer insistence upon an early morning trial? Most annoying, that. What hour was it he himself had to rise? Then he recalled that a messenger was to arouse him if all went according to plan. And the plan was? . . . To sentence the Fellow to death somehow. On what charge? Now he came to think of it, no actual charge had been mentioned. That was queer. He must get that put right, the minute the Trial opened. Couldn't afford to annoy Caiaphas just now. Besides, it was probably wise in any case to get the business over and done with before the crowds were about. There might be excitement, even a riot. But "at dawn or thereabouts"! It was the limit. He wouldn't stand for any more of this sort of pressure from Caiaphas or any other Jew. *And* the fellow needn't think he could arrange in advance for Rome's justice to be trampled on. There was no fathoming their blessed "Law"; but Rome's Law was crystal-clear. He would uphold that at all costs. Wonder what sort of fellow this Jesus was? "Messiah

King," so they said He claimed to be. Dangerous, that. Probably He was mad. Not so dangerous in that case. Either way, it was a good chance to teach the "King" and His "subjects" a salutary lesson. "King," indeed!

Near by, Claudia Procula, Pilate's high-born wife, was in the throes of a frightful dream. The strange figure of the new Prophet haunted her. In her nightmare she saw Him seated in Majesty on some vast mountain . . . and before Him Pontius was reeling back into a lake of deep indigo water, dark and fathomless. As she stared, horror-struck, into the water, she saw his white and swollen body re-emerge, deep-drowned and with closed eyes . . . and as it eddied in the unseen currents, rolling round in horrific semblance of life before it sank again, the hands seemed to clasp and unclasp as if in the act of wash-ing. She actually saw them sinking down through the swirling waters, still moving convulsively in each other's clasp before they too sank whitely and disappeared. It was at that moment that she awoke, too frightened to waken Pontius, too shaken even to cry out.

Morning came at last and Pilate was aroused and reluctantly dressed for a State Trial. The Jews, he was told, were already massed in the great courtyard before the Praetorium, where justice was dispensed. This space was known as the Pavement, its floor being formed of marble mosaics.

Pilate came out and seated himself on his chair of state. The Pris-oner was already there, awaiting him. The Representatives of Rome and of Heaven eyed each other a moment in silent appraisal. Con-tempt wrestled with surprise on Pilate's face. Then a message was brought to him. The Jews, it said, refused to enter the Hall of Justice, because for them to enter any heathen house was a defilement which would jeopardize the correct keeping of the Passover. Pilate was fur-ious. Defilement, to enter Rome's Court! His irritation, begun by this tiresome early rising, was intensified by this ridiculous scruple. He, Rome's Vice-Regent, was thus forced to go outside his own court, into the open air, this cold morning, merely to pander to these petty provincials. Well, he would show them he was not to be trifled with. If they meant to be difficult, well, he could match that, and with interest.

He appeared above, in a gallery, and a sudden hush fell on the expectant crowd. Then his voice was heard asking in harsh, sharp tones: "What accusation do you bring against this Man?" That would shake them.

Caiaphas was amazed and exasperated. Was the Governor—after all the careful priming of the night before—going to insist on the lengthy process of the Law: the *Accusatio,* the *Interrogatio* and lastly the *Excusatio?* Had he not tacitly agreed to ratify the Sanhedrin's sentence without retrying the case? Every moment counted if Jesus were to be crucified before the Galileans were astir in the city; and, in any case, He had to be dead before sunset, when the Passover began. Yet here was Pilate asking a question which implied that *he* was going to try Jesus!

Caiaphas rapped out an extremely impertinent reply. It was a brazen attempt to evade the framing of any formal charge, as well as a reminder to Pilate of last night's interview—and its personal implications.

"If He were not a criminal, we wouldn't have handed Him over to you to sentence." In other words: "Why can't you be satisfied with the finding of *our* court? And don't you realize that it's bad enough to *have* to ask you to execute the death sentence?"

But Pilate was not to be drawn. He pretended to be entirely ignorant of any secret compact with Caiaphas. He well knew that the Jews had already tried and sentenced Jesus; but he airily made answer: "Take Him, yourselves, then, and sentence Him according to *your* Law."

In this he was not only embarrassing Caiaphas, who dared not reveal his secret talk with Pilate, but also checkmating him in his real purpose: to kill Jesus. For the Jews could not execute any criminal.

The reply he was forcing from the Jews came at length: "You know very well we can't put anyone to death."

Pilate chuckled. So they had been forced to disclose their secret aim—to kill the prisoner before he had been tried by Rome! So they thought to flout the *Jus Romanum,* did they? Pilate enjoyed their embarrassment—and especially this public exposure of their dependence upon Rome. So he continued to wait for the *Accusatio* . . . and Caiaphas was forced to improvise one. He glibly lied, crying out, "We caught out this Fellow busily perverting the people by forbidding them to pay tribute to Caesar, and furthermore, alleging that He Himself was the real King of Israel!"

Pilate was interested. He would have another look at this "King." So he re-entered the Judgment Hall and called Jesus to him. "So *You* are the 'King' then, eh?" he asked, in faint amusement.

But this happened to be the very issue upon which Jesus wished to be tried; so He was prepared to answer. But first He had to know whether this were a genuine or a prearranged enquiry. Suspicious of Caiaphas' part in this, He asked Pilate, "Are you asking this of your own accord, or did . . . someone else . . . tell you this of Me?"

Pilate shrugged his thick shoulders. He was not going to be cross-examined by the Prisoner. "Am *I* a Jew?" he retorted, in withering tones. "It is Your own nation—and their High Priests—who have handed You over to me. What have You done?"

But Jesus was unconcerned with any defence of concocted charges. He was only anxious to make clear that He was the Suffering Servant Messiah and not the Warrior Prince.

So, in lofty calm, He answered, "My Kingdom is not of this world. If it were, My soldiers would even now be fighting that I should not be delivered to the Elders. But, as I say, My Kingdom is *not* of this world."

Pilate was puzzled. This strange, mystic-looking Prisoner *was*, then, claiming to be a "King" of sorts. There was a hint of fear in his reply: "Then, you *are* a 'King'—*You?*"

"Yes, indeed, but not in your sense. I was born into this world—to bear testimony to the truth. Everyone therefore who belongs to the truth acknowledges My voice."

There was a moment's silence. Then Pilate murmured sardonically, "What is . . . 'truth'?" and rose. Evidently this Fellow was harmless enough. Facing the mob once more, Pilate raised his hand to command silence. "I cannot find anything criminal about Him."

There was a rising tide of protest at this, led by the packed ruffians in the ever-growing crowd. Pilate shouted down the tumult. He was very angry.

"I tell you I cannot find anything criminal about Him," he repeated, so proclaiming the formal acquittal of Jesus, Who should have been at once released and no doubt would have been had not the Priests made a retort.

"He stirs up the people by inciting them to rebellion—starting, of course, in Galilee but now reaching here."

The cries redoubled till the babel caused Pilate to clap his hands over his ears and withdraw behind the great doors again. Jesus was still there, with His guards. Pilate looked at Him . . . and listened to the tumult outside, clearly audible here within.

"What have You got to say for Yourself?" he asked Jesus. But only silence met his question. "Can't You hear their cries? Listen! Do You hear how many charges they bring against You?"

But Jesus chose to ignore all charges save the one He was prepared to meet. Besides, they were lies, in any case. "Forbidding to give tribute"—when no small part of the people's resentment was caused by His having specifically ordered that tribute should be paid. "Inciting to rebellion"—when He had preached love even for enemies. So He remained withdrawn and indifferent. Pilate was astounded and not a little afraid. Perhaps the gods did sometimes come down to earth. Who could tell?

It was at this moment that a messenger arrived from his private apartments and hurriedly handed the Governor a wax tablet. Pilate looked at it in astonishment. It was in the handwriting of his wife. The Latin letters were ill-formed and hastily written, for she had just awakened, terrified by her dream, and, remembering with a shock the talk with Caiaphas last night, had reached in panic for her tablet and with a metal stylus had scrawled her hurried message, rung for a slave, given her the tablet, and then had lain back in exhaustion, her breast rising and falling quickly in agitation. She had done all she could. It was for Pilate to act.

Pilate stared long at the creamy scratches on the wax; and his mind suffered a great shock, his fears of Jesus being suddenly increased tenfold. For on the tablet were scrawled the fateful words: "Don't have anything to do with that innocent Man—for I have suffered greatly in a dream about Him."

Pilate recalled in horror Calpurnia's dream, which foretold Julius Caesar's end, and glanced again from the tablet to the Prisoner, silent and still. There was a dignity—inherent, undeniable—about the Man.

Better keep clear of Him. You never knew when the gods might interfere. Fate had a trick of hounding down whoever defied the omens. Then the words "starting in Galilee" from one of the random accusations hurled at the Prisoner struck his mind. "Galilee?" The Man, then, was probably a Galilean. Pilate turned to the Tribune. "Is this Man, by any chance, a subject of Herod's?"

"I understand so, your Excellency."

Good. That solved everything, most conveniently. All he had to do was to hand over the Fellow to Herod. It would get him out of all the trouble—and the danger, too. Moreover, such a course could, if subtly managed, be read both as a tactful compliment—and as a possible insult to Herod! On the one hand: "I recognize that you, as King of Galilee, rightly retain a primary interest in all your subjects. I am but Procurator, under Caesar, of Judaea. Therefore in the matter of this Prisoner, a Galilean Whom I now send to you, I humbly surrender my rights of judgment to your Majesty."

Excellent! That would tend, too, to mollify Herod's ruffled feelings over that unfortunate affair of the Galileans' riot, when so many of these ridiculous hotheads had got in the way of the Roman spears and swords. Also, Herod could thus be led to laugh with Rome over the absurdity of any rival claim to sovereignty.

"Centurion, you are to take this Prisoner called Jesus to King Herod, now. Say that I send him my compliments, that this Man is a Galilean, and that I forbear to try any subject of his Majesty. So, instead of dealing with Him myself, I am sending to Herod this— *The King of the Jews.* Don't forget that last sentence. *The King of the Jews.* Understand?"

The centurion saluted, a ghost of a smile playing for a moment on his lips as a quick glance of cynical amusement passed between him and the Governor. Then he gave an order and Jesus was led away in the custody of the cohort. Pilate returned to his wife. That was a nasty corner neatly passed. He knew how to steer his chariot.

(IV) BEFORE HEROD

THE old Maccabaean palace was not far away. It faced the Hasmonean courtyard, through which a messenger was soon running to give

Herod a warning of the arrival of the cohort, which waited in the dark portals till summoned within by a court official. Herod had received Pilate's message with mixed feelings. He had refused to take any notice until he had heard the word "Jesus." Then all his anger at the infernal cheek of Pilate in thus rousing him at this unearthly hour had suddenly been replaced by a burning curiosity to see for himself this new Prophet of Whom he had heard so much. Once he had thought Him the avenging reincarnation of the Baptist, but that was now a thing of the past. Nevertheless, they said He was a clever Fellow, talked well and was a wonder-worker. It would be most amusing if a miracle or two could be performed for his own special benefit this very morning! Though that entry into the city the other day was distinctly improper. . . . Not that it signified anything much, in its·issue. Just as well to let the people, always excited at festivaltime, get rid of some of their energy, especially if it ended tamely. Curious, though, Pilate sending Him along like this, at this unconscionable hour. Decent of the fellow, anyway, coming to his senses at last. It would never do, however, to be in too much of a hurry to let the Romans in. Keep them waiting a bit. Show them, too, that others could muster a brave array of soldiers besides them. He rose and rapped out a sharp order, donned his military uniform and entered the hall of the palace. Beastly dark and cold. Why should Pilate occupy his own Herodian palace, banishing him, the King, to this dank, foul-smelling place? His soldiers looked well, however, grouped around the throne, awaiting his arrival. Moving slowly along the length of the hall, he seated himself and ordered a messenger to bring in the Prisoner. Just as well, perhaps, the soldiers were here. You never knew when miracle-workers were about. But though he was all agog to see Jesus, he was not going to let Pilate shift the responsibility for order and justice in Jerusalem on to him. Rome had caught the Man; Rome would have to deal with Him. By all accounts, a popular hero. Might cause a riot any day. Besides, the murder of one Prophet was quite enough, thank you, for any man. He wasn't going to have the blood of any more of them on his hands. Meanwhile, he would be enjoying the satisfaction of a great curiosity—and a little sport, possibly, a unique entertainment.

Then the doors opened and the tall white-robed Prisoner was led up the length of the hall toward Herod. His hands were bound and on His face was a great weariness—and yet a greater majesty. There was a moment's silence, while the puppet King of an obscure Roman Dependency stared at the King of all the universe. Then the centurion delivered Pilate's message, a slight inflexion of humour informing his last words:

". . . I have the honour, therefore, to present to your Majesty— Jesus, *The King of the Jews!*"

Herod started in sudden annoyance, his thoughts racing ahead in an effort to understand. Unable at once to fathom the mystery, he tried to gain time by asking a string of questions of the Prisoner, among them an airy request that He should perform a miracle. When at last he paused, he was met with an unyielding silence. Herod's thoughts strayed from the Prisoner to the Procurator. *The King of the Jews.* It sounded remarkably like an insult to his own sovereignty. But maybe Pilate was merely laughing at the absurdity of anyone challenging his, Herod's, sway. Best to treat it as a rich jest and to laugh with Pilate over it—and then to return it with interest.

"So *You* are . . . *The King of the Jews* are You? Dear me, Pilate is vastly droll today. A magnificent jest, centurion! Never heard a better!" And a little tardily, the weak indulgent King went off into peals of laughter, holding his sides and rolling about on his throne, imitated, of course, by his courtiers. He called an attendant.

"Go, fetch me one of my old robes—the purple one for choice, which I so seldom wear. For, after all, *I* cannot afford to ape the honours due only to great Caesar! Whereas *this* Man, well, it will suit Him admirably!"

The robe was brought and Jesus was arrayed in it, and Herod and his courtiers bowed to Him in mock reverence, while all the time, Jesus stood silent, detached, motionless. Herod beckoned the centurion.

"Thank His Excellency, the Procurator, for this, his so rich a jest. Say Herod, *the King,* deeply appreciates his subtle sense of humour, but he would not dream of usurping the Procurator's authority here in Jerusalem. So I am sending the Prisoner back to him. You might add that I have done my poor best to supply any lack in the Prisoner's

'Regality,' and therefore send Him back, arrayed no longer as a 'King,'
but as an *Emperor!*"

He turned away abruptly and disappeared; and Jesus was once
more led between files of Roman soldiers out into the brightening
daylight. Herod, behind closed doors, scowled in fury. *King of the
Jews* indeed! Pilate would smile on the wrong side of his mouth when
he saw his precious "King" returned to him arrayed in the Imperial
purple. Two could play at jesting. If any insult were intended the
last laugh would not be with Pilate; and Herod suddenly went off
again into peals of uncontrollable laughter, which echoed mockingly
along the empty corridors.

(V) BEFORE PILATE AGAIN

MEANWHILE, in the new Herodian palace, Pontius Pilate and Claudia
Procula were once more together, discussing this unpleasant episode,
so happily and wisely—and amusingly—disposed of. She looked at
her husband, safe, now, from fate and brooding tragedy. Those hands
of his, which were clasping the arms of his seat in strong, possessive
power, would, after all, never wring themselves whitely in a swirl of
waters.

There was a knock at the door. The centurion entered. The Prisoner was back again, and there was a message from Herod. The
Prisoner was dressed up in a toga of the Imperial purple! Pilate rose
in wrath. The thing was an outrageous insult. But the message was
couched in the friendliest terms. One could hardly object without
exposing one's own joke. Best to pretend to keep in with the old fox.

What was that rising roar outside? The crowds following Jesus?
No? Swarms of people have been collecting during the Prisoner's
absence? What for? Ah, yes . . . that custom of theirs, by which a
prisoner was released every Passover at their demand—one of Rome's
tactful ways of keeping on good terms with the people. A very sound
custom—and one which could be used at times most conveniently.
He glanced at Claudia Procula. There was a most abject fear in her
eyes. Her dream, of course. Something in it, perhaps. But what if
the mob could be induced to choose Jesus as the Passover release?

That would simplify everything, and the Man was obviously popular.

Pilate went out into the Judgment Hall, but Jesus was not there. He passed out through the great doors on to the gallery. A vast crowd, swelling every second, faced him. At one side stood Caiaphas and the Priests, near the cohort guarding Jesus, in His purple mockery of the Imperial regalia. On the other side were many rough-looking men, scowling. A confused roar greeted Pilate's appearance, and in the excitement he failed to distinguish between the two separate factions. His mind was on Jesus, and it was to the Priests that he addressed himself, after having obtained silence by a raising of his right hand.

"You brought me this Man as being an inciter to rebellion among the people. I have, however, examined Him and can find nothing criminal about Him, for all your accusations. No, nor yet has Herod, to whom I sent Him, being a Galilean; for, as you see, he has remitted Him again to me. He has undoubtedly done nothing worthy of death, merely been, shall we say, a little indiscreet. So I shall discharge Him."

The crowd jeered and catcalled Pilate, who, to placate it, added a rider to his verdict. "In view, however, of His indiscretion, I shall order that He be scourged before being discharged."

The greater part of the crowd now gathered in the Praetorium were bewildered by Pilate's words. Who, anyway, was this *other* Prisoner? They, Zealots, had come there solely to demand the release, this Passovertide, of their beloved champion Barabbas, now languishing close by in the dungeons of Fort Antonia—not to argue about some Prophet or other. Evidently this other Prisoner was no rebel; Pilate's words made that clear. So much the worse for Him, for in this He was unlike their brave Barabbas, who had killed several Roman soldiers before being finally overpowered. So they shouted out, "We have come for the Passover release! The Passover release!" The cry, "Barabbas!" was taken up and echoed by a growing number of people.

Pilate, mystified for a moment, remembered the man. He had not known quite what to do with that first-class rebel. Execute him? But that might incite a riot—though of course, Rome could not pass over open revolt. Best wait till after the festival, anyway. This untimely demand for his release was most dangerous. It was, in fact, an open defiance of Rome's authority. Whereas this Jesus was obviously a dreamer, harmless, other-worldly. But Claudia Procula's dream? *Other-worldly*—now, what exactly had he meant by that? It became imperative that he must induce the people to demand the release of Jesus rather than of Barabbas, providing no one remembered that He had just been acquitted; for, if so, they might demand, and rightly, the release of *both* prisoners. He was glad now that he had ordered the scourging of Jesus. It gave Him the status of a criminal, and so made His release at the demand of the people seem perfectly in order.

There was however one fatal flaw in Pilate's reasoning. He did not realize that the great majority of the people now gathered without cared nothing about Jesus, having come specially to demand the release of Barabbas. A closer scrutiny of their faces, ruffianly and coarse, would have told him. He thought that the greater part of the crowd would welcome his offer to release Jesus, for the High Priest was hated and Jesus, he understood, was popular. Indeed, he had only that morning heard that Caiaphas had accused Jesus solely out of envy. Pilate also failed to appraise rightly the degree of disillusionment with which the masses of the people regarded Jesus' own apparent failure to implement His Messianic claims. For the aftermath of the entry had been fatal to the claims.

Meanwhile the astute brain of the High Priest was alive to this new development. He had never bargained for this great gathering so early in the morning, having, indeed, gone to tremendous trouble to forestall any such embarrassment, in asking Pilate to hold the Trial before the Galilean Pilgrims were likely to be astir in the city. But this assemblage of Zealots altered everything. He quickly realized that it could, wisely handled, be turned to good account. Moving swiftly over to the leader of the Zealots, he struck a bargain. "If you will join with us in demanding Jesus' death, we will join with you in demanding Barabbas' release."

Thus it came about that the subsequent cries were unanimously raised by the whole assemblage, a fact that amazed and frightened Pilate, when, on advancing to the forefront of the gallery, he cried to the people, "I know that it is your custom that I should release to you one prisoner at the feast. Which of the two, then, will you have,

Barabbas or Jesus, the 'King of the Jews'?" and was at once answered by a mighty shout of "Barabbas! Barabbas!" Pilate winced, but repeated his question, for fear it were misunderstood, and was answered with the same cry.

Pilate's obstinacy and weakness impelled him to ask, "Barabbas? Why, what then am I to do with Jesus, Whom you call the 'King of the Jews'?"

"Let Him be crucified! Crucify Him! Crucify Him!"

Pilate was deeply distraught. He felt he was losing grip. Caiaphas was besting him after all. He appealed to the crowd's sense of justice: "Why, what crime has He committed?"

The crowd, however, had learned their part, and the demand for Jesus' Crucifixion arose in ever-increasing volume. Pilate dug his heels in. He would *not* give way to this rabble. It was obvious, now, that it had been got at—by Caiaphas, most likely.

He repeated his previous decision, therefore. "I hold to my judgment. I tell you, I have found nothing about Him that deserves death. So I shall do as I have said: scourge Him, and then let Him go. Officers, take the Prisoner and carry out my order."

Amidst howls of execration from the mob, Pilate disappeared once more behind the great doors of the Praetorium, and Jesus was led away through a side gate into the inner courtyard, the soldiers' quarters where scourgings were carried out. The mob refused to disperse, because Barabbas had not been released to them. Had they but got their way then and there the Priests would have been robbed of their chief allies in the post-scourging scenes. Pilate's obstinacy in this, as well as in other ways, thus contributed to the final tragedy.

Within his inner room, he brooded, hurt, angry and confused. He wished passionately to score off Caiaphas, and yet at the same time to ridicule this "King of the Jews," provided His death were not his own responsibility. While the lictors bound the Victim without in the courtyard and strapped Him over a low pillar and thrashed Him with a leather-thonged *flagellum,* weighted with lead and jagged pieces of iron and bone, Pilate fretted impatiently, uneasy and ill-tempered. He loathed his office at times like these. The most difficult post in the whole Empire. He thought anew upon Jesus' strange silence, and upon His even more strange breaking of that silence. "My Kingdom is not of this world." . . . And there, outside, He was being lacerated and torn by the cruel scourge. He remembered several prisoners going raving mad under the lash—unless unconsciousness interposed. It was a beastly world.

When the lictors had completed their dread task, they unleashed the ropes from about the torn and still quivering flesh and set Jesus down upon a derelict bench against a wall. Then someone picked up the fallen purple robe and flung it jeeringly over Jesus' shoulders; and His blood, soaking in, dyed even more deeply crimson its blazing Imperial hue.

"Calls Himself Almighty Caesar, eh? He only lacks Caesar's bays! Let's make Him a coronal like Caesar's—only of thorns!" He snatched up some of the firing lying in a heap near the brazier. Quickly it was twisted into a circlet and thrust brutally on to Jesus' head, making the blood flow down His face. Then, one by one, they marched up to Him (having got the idea from Herod and going one better) and saluted Him, crying, "Hail! King of the Jews!" and striking Him in the face with their fists.

One soldier, more ingenious than the rest, cried out, "Why, He hasn't got a sceptre!" and thrust a tall rush from a great vase into Jesus' right hand, resting the top of it against His shoulder. "Now He's a proper King!" the soldier cried, kneeling before Him and, mumbling a mockery of the Roman Sacramentum or Oath of Allegiance, spat viciously at Him, taking the bulrush and striking Him with it, while others helped to prop up the poor tortured body, only semiconscious by now, lest it fall over sideways.

Suddenly an upper window was thrown open and the face of the Governor was seen looking out. He stared down at the Prisoner. The soldiers were confused and tried to snatch away the symbols of mock royalty. "Stay," ordered the Governor; "when He recovers a little, bring Him in to me, *just as He is,* into the Judgment Hall; and I will myself release Him to the people."

He had been struck by the scene in the courtyard. In Pilate's heart was a mixed motive: pity for an innocent Victim and contempt for Herod's returned "Emperor." Perhaps the mob outside (they were

still there, he could hear them yelling) would share his own feelings,
mixed though they might be, and go away quietly home when they
saw this "rebel" in His misery.

Pilate's reappearance upon the gallery brought a redoubling of the
insistent cries of "Barabbas! Barabbas!"

But the Procurator raised his right hand for silence and was heard
to say, "Look! I am bringing Him out to you!" his hand pointing to the
side door, through which was filing out a posse of soldiers. The
crowd's hopes were to be realized! The cries turned into cheers . . .
till suddenly Jesus, not Barabbas, was seen. Pilate cried, "Look!
There's the Man!" and waited, arm outstretched to see the effect of
his plea upon the people.

But he had entirely misjudged his audience. A tremendous uproar
broke out and a cry rose, "No! Not this Man, but Barabbas! Barabbas!" and "Crucify Him!" was once again hurled at Jesus.

Pilate was furious, and, as at the beginning of the Trial, he once
more taunted the Jews with their powerlessness to execute the death
sentence apart from him. "Very well. If you so want Him to be crucified, take Him and crucify Him yourselves—that is, if you dare! For
I find no fault in Him!"

The Priests were for a moment baffled. This looked like being a
deadlock. They knew very well that they could not take up Pilate's
challenge. Evidently the political charge had failed. They were,
therefore, thrown back again upon the religious charge. The brain of
Caiaphas was hard at work. How could he so frame a charge of
blasphemy that this time even the proud pagan before him would
respect it, and fear it?

Then he spoke: "But *we* also have a Law as well as you—*and* one
that involves the death penalty. And by *our* Law He is bound to die
because He has claimed to be . . . *the Son of God!*" with a cleverly
timed pause and a sudden lowering of the voice and a little catch of
breath. The shaft went home; there was a perceptible shudder of awe
as every eye, including Pilate's, turned to gaze at the still and silent
Figure between His guards. Claudia Procula's dream returned in
enhanced terror to Pilate's mind. "God's Son!" Words ominous
beyond all reckoning. He turned slowly in the tense silence, pointed

the guards wordlessly to the doors and walked within yet once more, followed by Jesus.

There, once more in the Judgment Hall, he eyed the Prisoner long from between lowered eyelids. He was desperately afraid, and his fear came out in his half-whispered question: "Where . . . do You come from?"

But only silence met his query. Jesus, Who was fully conscious once again, knew that this was not the time to teach this earthbound soldier anything about Heaven and the Father's presence—if ever he could learn.

As so often with the panicstricken, Pilate grew irritable and blustering in an endeavour to bolster up his courage. "So You will not deign to speak to me? Don't You realize that the whole issue of Your condemnation or acquittal is entirely in my hands?"

Then Jesus answered. His voice was calm and without rancour. "You would have no power at all over Me, were it not allowed you—from Above!" pointing upward with His finger. Then, still eying Pilate, He compared his character with that of Caiaphas. The eyes of Jesus hardened as He, the Prisoner, passed Eternal Judgment on His judges. With His arm pointing toward where the Priests stood without, He cried "Therefore he who delivered Me to you has a greater guilt than you."

Pilate understood and secretly agreed. He knew, none better, that the whole prosecution was a faked-up affair. He resolved all the more to be free of the guilt of condemning this noble mystic. So once again he went out to the people and repeated his decision to set Jesus free. But Caiaphas rightly saw in this very insistence a sign of inner weakness, and at once struck in with his last weapon, the one thing, he well knew, most feared by Pilate—the threat of Caesar's displeasure.

"If you set Him free, you prove yourself no friend to Caesar! Whoever calls himself a King—or shall we say, an Emperor?—sets himself up as a rival to Caesar!"

There was a desperate hatred in Caiaphas' voice, even a hint of Pilate's possible impeachment before Tiberius. He waited as the shaft went home. Pilate winced and the colour mounted and drained from his thick neck. In that moment he knew he had lost the battle.

Jesus was now a doomed Man. But one thing Pilate obstinately would not allow—that Caiaphas should thus shift the issue. If Jesus were to die, then it should be as "King of *the Jews*" and not as any possible rival of Caesar's. The ultimate issue (in his eyes) should be made clear for all to see: that so perished any claimant to their Jewish Messiahship. So, in very truth, from Pilate's as well as His own, motive, Jesus died indeed for His claims to be the Suffering Messiah—and as that Messiah.

The Procurator gave an order, and once again the great doors opened and Jesus was led out. And this time Pilate himself went before Him toward the front rail of the gallery and ordered a great chair of state to be dragged forward, and set Jesus thereon, as if in regal state.

"Behold—your *King!*" he cried to the people, packing all his Roman contempt for their superstitions, fables and fooleries into his taunt.

Caiaphas fully sensed Pilate's scorn for Jewry, and yelled, "Take Him off that throne! Away with Him! Crucify Him!" a cry taken up with a wild yell by the whole crowd, driven to desperation by Pilate's refusal so far to release Barabbas to them.

"What?" asked Pilate, sarcastically, "What—crucify your *King?*"

"We have no King!" cried Caiaphas.

Pilate's eyebrows lifted in ironic surprise. He waited . . . till Caiaphas grudgingly added, "No King, that is, but Caesar."

Pilate's brows relaxed in complacent triumph. The hated High Priest had thus been driven—here, in front of all these people, most of them Zealots, too, as Pilate now realized—to acknowledge Caesar as Israel's sole and rightful King! In his pitiable and self-compensatory pretence, Pilate thought he had won the final battle, avoided a tumult, ridiculed the Jewish Messianic pretensions, and bested Caiaphas.

There remained, he remembered with a start, the Prisoner: still seated there in the chair of state. The Prisoner and the little matter of his own complicity in the Prisoner's fate. Claudia Procula's dream . . . Better to placate whatever gods there might be. He felt himself a participator in high tragedy. With an impulse begotten of the theatre, he clapped his hands and ordered a slave to bring him a basin of water; and there, in full view of all the people, he plunged his hands into the water and washed them ostentatiously before the multitude. Then he turned to Caiaphas and the Priests and made doubly sure that the responsibility for Jesus' death should rest where it belonged.

"See! I wash my hands before you all, in token that not on me, but on you lies the guilt of this Man's blood. I am entirely innocent of it. It is your affair."

Back came the ghastly shout: "His blood be on us, and on our children!"

The demand for the release of Barabbas arose again, and Pilate, exasperated, gave an order; not long after a great bull mastiff of a man was led out onto the gallery, where Jesus had risen from His seat and stood between His guards. The two prisoners stared at one another for a moment, while the crowd yelled itself hoarse with excitement; the one, a rebel and murderer, was to be released; the Other, because He had done no violence, neither was any guile found in His mouth, was to be crucified. Pilate looked at the two men, and then at the papers in his hand. Curious, the two of them having the same first name—"Jesus," which meant "Saviour." "Bar-Abbas," too, meant "Son of the Father." Most extraordinary. Pilate looked again, long and intently at Jesus. . . . But the soldiers were already unbinding Barabbas' arms, the great muscles straining while he smiled hugely at the shouting crowds and shouted back at them in turn. Jesus was brought forward and formal sentence was passed upon Him; but no one heard, so great was the tumult of joy at Barabbas' release, as the people surged round the rebel and bore him away amid sounds of shouting and singing.

Longinus the centurion meanwhile led Jesus away to disrobe Him and to dress Him again in His own bloodstained garments, the soldiers being busily engaged fetching a cross from the store always kept in the castle. Pilate was occupied superintending the writing of the Titulus or Accusation, which was by custom affixed to a white wooden board and carried in front of the condemned prisoner by a herald. When the inscription was completed, it was held up for all to see.

Headed by the official Latin *Accusatio,* the latter was also written in Greek and Aramaic. It read: "This is Jesus of Nazareth: *The King of the Jews!"*

Caiaphas was furious. It was the last deliberate insult offered this day by Pilate to Israel. He pressed forward toward the gallery, where the Procurator was about to withdraw within.

"Don't write 'The King of the Jews' " he protested, "but *'He said:* "I am the King of the Jews" '—a very different thing."

Pilate glowered at him over his shoulder. Obstinacy was the last refuge of defeated pride. "What I have written—I have written!" he growled, his jaw thrust out in self-persuasion of strength. Before he disappeared, he gave a final order. Even though Barabbas were free, by Jupiter, his two confederates should suffer! All three of them had been languishing in the dungeons only awaiting sentence following arrest and accusation by the Romans themselves, who had been attacked by them in the execution of their duty. So, rapping out a sharp command, Pilate ordered that Gestas and Dysmas should suffer alongside Jesus. Thus there were three processions to drag the weary length of the *Via Dolorosa,* each headed by a Titulus-bearing herald and followed by a cross-bearing victim, guarded by soldiers.

Pilate, wretched, beaten, oppressed by a sense of doom, having finished this dread morning's work, moved across the gallery and the huge doors of the Praetorium swung open for the last time and closed behind his retreating figure. And the pavement with its lovely marble mosaics were left untenanted, its patterned symmetry broken only by patches of blood and drippings of water; evidence, for all to see, of the guilty Prisoner and the guiltless Procurator. But not all the water in the world could avail to wash away those stains on Rome's judgment floor; and to the end of time Christians the world over will repeat the accusing words: "Suffered under Pontius Pilate."

VIII

The End of Judas

ON the edge of the crowd during the Trial of Jesus was a figure, wild-eyed and haggard, on the verge of raging madness.

When he saw his Master led out to be crucified—Jesus' glance for a brief moment resting upon Judas' horror-stricken face—he broke away in panic from the crowds now gathering about the procession to Golgotha (for the Galileans were coming up into the city in increasing numbers) and ran frantically toward the Temple, to that same place where he had made his compact with Caiaphas. As he ran he felt from time to time for the wallet containing those cursed pieces of silver. He could hear them jingling as they loosened with his running, and, arriving, he untied his girdle and held the wallet in his right hand, while with the other he rained desperate blows at the closed doors of Caiaphas' house. At last a servant appeared and started back. No, the High Priest had not yet returned.

Judas rushed away to the Temple. As he crossed the Tyropoean bridge an impulse called to him to throw himself over and make an end of it all. But first he must dispossess himself of this damning price of treachery. Besides, he knew, there was only one place for lost souls—Gehenna. Breathless, and now stark staring mad, he tore through the vast Temple Courts and came to the porch of the very Sanctuary itself, beyond which none but the Priests were allowed to pass. The latter had by now returned from the Praetorium and were filled with self-satisfaction. They had got their way at last and could now get on again with the Passover preparations. The sudden intrusion, impetuous, Satanic, of this ghastly figure startled them, till someone, with a shock of surprise, recognized it. Judas lifted high the hand that held the wallet and clasping the end of it, swung it sharply round, and thirty silver coins scattered ringingly over the marble pavement. His voice rose to a scream as he cried, "I have sinned! I have sinned! I have betrayed innocent blood!"

The haughty Priests looked coldly at this man who had served their ends and was now no further concern of theirs . . . save that he was at this moment odiously profaning the sacred mysteries of God's Holy Temple.

"What does that matter to *us?*" they asked sneeringly. "That is your affair, not ours." (They had soon forgotten their own terrible: "His blood be on us and on our children!")

Judas, with his arm hiding his bowed head, turned away stumblingly at those cruel words, rushed through the open porch and was lost to sight. A servant was ordered to collect the scattered pieces of silver. No one knew what to do with the money. The matter of its disposal must be brought up at the next meeting of the Sanhedrin.

Meanwhile, Judas was on his way to "his own place," as Luke afterward described it: the terrible valley of Hinnom, the Tophet of old and the Gehenna of Christ's warnings of ultimate judgment. Here, where the vast refuse heap was always burning, were flung all the carcasses and offal and other filth from the city. Here, too, in ancient days, were cast away the ashes of false gods; and here, more distantly still, living human sacrifices were burned. Into this desecrate solitude stumbled the Waster, the Son of Loss, still clutching in his hand the unwound girdle with which the wallet had been secured. Down the ravine he plunged, over the smouldering refuse, leaping and bounding in his terror, up the steep precipitous rocks on the farther side, till he saw ahead of him a stunted tree growing out of the mountain face and overhanging the valley far below. Here was the ideal place for self-immolation. Deliberately he affixed his girdle to the gnarled branches, knotted it into a slip loop, thrust his head into it and hurled himself forward into the void. But the girdle snapped and with a ghastly echoing cry he crashed into the yawning chasm below. Falling at length there onto a jagged rock, he burst asunder and was disembowelled.

When the Sanhedrin met, it was decided after a full discussion, that the thirty pieces of silver, regarded (conveniently) as a gift from Judas, could not legally be put into the Korban or Treasury since it was the price of blood. So they agreed to purchase with it the plot of ground adjoining the very height from which Judas fell, to be used as a cemetery for the burial of strangers. The disciples afterward remembered Jeremiah's reference to this very spot. *Behold, it shall no more be called Tophet or the valley of the sons of Hinnom, but the Field of Slaughter. For they shall bury corpses there till there be no more room left; and their carcasses shall be meat for the birds of Heaven and for the wild beasts.* They also recalled Zechariah's prescient words: *So they weighed for My hire thirty pieces of silver. Yes, the Lord said unto me: "Cast it into the Sanctuary—the goodly price that I was priced at by them!" So I took the thirty pieces of silver and cast them into the Sanctuary.* So the field was thereafter always called Akeldama, the Field of Slaughter, even as Jeremiah had prophesied. It was almost as if echoes from ancient prophetic cries yet reverberated along that desolate ravine; as if inexorable Destiny drove the Traitor toward Gehenna—the dread image of ultimate Hell. So passed the Traitor to his own place.

IX

The *Via Dolorosa*

THERE was another watcher at the condemnation of Jesus—a bowed and greying woman, stricken with overwhelming grief, Mary, the mother of Jesus, leaning on the arm of her sister Salome. It seemed to her a lifetime ago when a messenger had burst in upon her there in far Nazareth with the alarming news that her Son had entered Jerusalem in triumph as the King-Messiah. (Had he not heard of it from a traveller who had but now watered his camels at the well?) Then James, who had departed for the feast, returned unexpectedly, furious beyond words. Yes, it was all true, and so dreadful that he himself could not even stay for the feast.

This could mean nothing but that Jesus' hour had come; and Mary remembered with heart sinkings the normal end of all such claimants to Messiahship. Would it be otherwise with her Son? Of one thing only was she certain. She must go to Him—now, at once. So, quietly and determinedly, she set about making immediate preparation for departure, sending a secret message to her sister Salome in Bethsaida, and ordering steeds and a guide for them both.

Almost as soon as she had arrived, word had gone round that Jesus had been condemned—to be crucified. She saw in the distance the pikes and spears of the Legionaries over the heads of the crowd. She followed in their wake despairingly, trying in vain to get nearer to her Son. Would none pity Him? *Is it nothing to you, all you that pass by? Behold and see if there be any sorrow like unto My sorrow. . . .* She became aware, somewhere ahead of her, of a group of women— surely these were His friends—wailing in their grief.

Then she heard His voice, coming as from a great distance: "Daughters of Jerusalem, weep not for Me, but weep for yourselves. For, behold, the days are surely coming when men shall say: 'Blessed are the barren and the wombs that never bare, and the breasts that never gave suck.' Then shall they begin to cry to the mountains, 'Fall on us!' and to the hills: 'Cover us!' For if they do these things in the green tree, what shall they not do in the dry?"

She heard the words about the barren and the childless. How true they were! He was surely, even now, thinking of her! Then she caught sight of Him, a little way ahead of her. He was stumbling and falling under the great weight of the ghastly Cross He had to bear. Even as He stooped to ease Himself, the lash of the lictor descended upon His wealed back. But Mary screamed and hid her face. When next she looked up, He had collapsed under the load and the lashes were raining down on His prostrate form. There were angry shouts from the Galileans, now in a majority in the crowd. Word having reached them that Jesus was being tried for His life, they had rushed out of their camping places around the city, only to arrive too late. Had they come a little earlier, when first the Zealots had departed with Barabbas, they might possibly have rescued Jesus. But the Romans were taking no chances now, and Pilate had despatched a double guard under the command of Longinus the centurion, to escort Jesus to Golgotha. Seeing Him fallen down, the Galileans rushed forward, only to be checked by the spears of the Legionaries. The centurion hastily scanned the crowd, searching for someone whom he could impress to carry Jesus' Cross. Better not have a Jew. Only cause trouble—defilement, again, probably. Ah! There was a great burly Negro, trying to get through the press of people, on his way to market—the very fellow! And he was at once seized upon by the soldiers, the Cross was lifted from Jesus, tied to his back, and he was ordered to rise and carry it for Jesus. The huge muscles strained; he rose, and the pitiful procession moved forward once again.

The disciples afterward learned that the Negro's name was Simon and that he hailed from Cyrene. He had been passing by on his way in from the country when he first met Jesus in such tragic circumstances. He became a disciple of the Master, being among the teachers in Antioch. His two sons, Rufus and Alexander, were also converted to Christianity, and his wife "acted as a mother" to Paul. So it was that he went with Jesus "outside the camp, bearing His reproach," and won for himself and his family immortal honour in Heaven. But he always disclaimed any credit for his action, saying that he just happened to be on the spot when Jesus fell down. "Besides, they made me, I tell you. . . ."

X

At Golgotha

COULD the people only have known, this was the true Triumphal March; not an entry this time, but, as Moses and Elijah on Hermon had foretold, an exodus. There He was, hemmed in by soldiers, in the grip of Rome, on His way to death. But of this moment might it truly be written: "He, going through the midst of them, went *His* way."

The procession passed out through the gate and made its slow way to the place of execution, known as Golgotha, or simply "The Skull." This was a rounded knoll, in the rocks of which were deep caverns, giving it its strange and gruesome name. They arrived here, at about the third hour, that is, nine o'clock.

The horrible preparations for crucifixion—the fixing of the upright wood in the ground, the nailing of the Sufferer to the transverse, the unimaginably agonizing lifting of this to the upright and its affixing there—were enacted in a growingly mournful light, drained of colour and warmth, with every detail startlingly clear and yet becoming increasingly silhouetted as the light continued to fail and such a darkness began to cover the earth as matched the gross darkness of the people.

The thoughtless cruelty of the soldiers, who were but obeying orders, was set against the forgiving love of the Son of God. Even as they were driving home the nails, He prayed, "Father, forgive them . . . for they know not what they do. . . ." He refused the anodyne mercifully provided by the women of Jerusalem in order to deaden the senses of those crucified. He would have His mind alert and His consciousness undimmed. The Titulus was set up over His head, with its threefold inscription, and the soldiers sat down to watch for the end. The four men told off to watch each gibbet shared out, as custom allowed, the raiment of the condemned man, casting dice for the one article which was too good to tear up among them.

There, in the fading light of a dying world, in the last few moments
of an era, groans of agony—and the rattle of dice—were the only
sounds that disturbed the silence. The Pilgrims, alive at last to the
fait accompli of Jesus' condemnation, were streaming out toward
Golgotha, bewildered and hurt. But when they came near the crosses,
standing starkly on the knoll against the greying sky, they fell silent
and forebore to gaze at too close quarters upon His agony. A few,
however, hired for the purpose the day before by Caiaphas (as ever,
thorough) tried, as they passed by, to lead a chorus of derision directed
against Jesus, repeating part of the rejected testimony, not knowing it
had been legally overthrown at the Trial. "Ha! You Who are able 'to
destroy the Temple, and rebuild it in three days' come down from the
Cross and save Yourself—if You can!"

This concerted effort to ridicule Jesus did not make much head-
way, and Caiaphas himself was forced to venture out of the Temple,
together with Annas. And seeing the people so stricken with grief,
they did their utmost to make fun of Jesus, crying out for all to hear,
"He saved others—but He cannot save Himself! *If* He be the 'King
of the Jews,' let Him now come down from the Cross, and we will
believe on Him!"

Jesus had indeed saved others, but it was precisely because He *was*
the Messiah, the King of Israel and of all the world, that He could not
save Himself and come down from the Cross. He—and Caiaphas, all
unconsciously—had made the issue perfectly clear. He was dying as
Messiah; suffering as the Son of God; revealing the heart of the
Almighty.

One of the rebels, crucified alongside Jesus, railed on Him, saying:
"Are You not the Messiah? Then save Yourself—and us."

The other rebuked him with the words: "Have you no fear even of
God? We are, after all, suffering the same punishment as He is—and
we justly. We are only getting what is the expected penalty of rebellion. But He has done no harm."

He had heard Jesus' wonderful prayer for His tormentors, had
seen His bravery and endurance, His silence under unjust taunts, His
gentleness of eye. He glanced at the Titulus. *"King."* What did that
portend? Was He indeed a King? As he watched Him his thoughts
raced on through time and space till he saw the inevitable vindication

when such regal love should at last come into its own and reign in glory forever.

To his own utter amazement, he heard himself imploring the Victim on the Cross next to him: "Jesus . . . when You come into Your Kingdom . . . don't forget me!"

This was the sublimest faith yet shown in all the Gospel Story: the first-fruits of the Cross, the initial attracting of one man that will one day include "all men" drawn into Jesus through His "lifting up."

Back in a flash came the equally astounding answer: "I tell you truly, you will, before this day is out, be in Paradise with Me!" It was as if the sound of trumpets was echoing from beyond the fosse of death: as if a bright sword had cloven the darkness in twain, letting the light stream in from Heaven.

As the victims more nearly approached death, the soldiers allowed some of those more intimately connected with them—women mostly— to come closer to the crosses. With the strange failing of the light, the crowds had largely departed. It was almost noontide now, and at last the mother of Jesus was allowed to come near. With her were her sister Salome, Mary of Cleopas and the Magdalene. One man was also allowed to accompany them, John the Beloved Disciple, known to Longinus personally.

Jesus knew, however, that the victims were no fit sight now for anxious and loving relatives. He looked the last time into His mother's eyes and a trembling smile of sad but infinitely loving understanding passed between them. Then, still looking at her, He signed toward John with a slight inclination of His head, saying to her, "Woman, behold your son!" and then to John: "Behold your mother!" and John was quick to understand and act. He at once went across to Mary, took her by the arm and led her, bowed and broken, away out of sight of the crosses.

Slowly he and she ascended the road into the city . . . but, oh! she knew that no "son" could ever take the place of her Firstborn, now so nearly gathered into the shades of the Unseen. Her heart was transfixed by the sword of fate. All the mystery, the rapt and enthralling promises, of Jesus' birth; all the proud stirrings, the uneasy riddles, of His development; all the glory of His short-lived triumph in Galilee—what meant they in the end? Was it thus that God worked—to raise up, only to cast down? As she dragged herself up the long road back into the city, she shuddered and nearly fainted. It was so dark. Where was the sun? Look! There was a man with a lantern. Not sundown yet? Then she turned for the last time to glance back before entering the gateway. There, to the north, could still be just descried the rocky knoll and its three crosses, against a faint glow low down on the horizon. Then, even as she watched, that suddenly failed, and there was darkness over all the land.

Into that darkness no human sight could—or can—penetrate. Somewhere in it, near to the Cross, now that the soldiers could no longer see him, was Peter. He was the most wretched man on earth. Not only was all his world crashing about him, but his soul was lost. Not a sound came from Jesus. Even the defiant rebel was at length silent. The soldiers were awed and not a little frightened . . . for strange subterranean rumblings at times disturbed the enveloping gloom. The centurion listened uneasily. Then there was a sudden shudder in the rock masses on which Jerusalem was built. The awe of the supernatural oppressed him. He glanced toward Jesus. Calling Himself "the Son of God"! Might well be, too, the way He behaved. Magnificent courage . . . and forgiveness . . . and royalty. The rumblings died down and renewed stillness descended once more upon that sunless world, terrified by the darkness of the day.

Then, suddenly, that darkness was shattered by the most awful cry that ever came from the lips of man. Peter never forgot the sound of those dread, inexplicable syllables, issuing from the central Cross, but coming as though from the fathomless depths of the abyss: *"Eloi, Eloi, lama sabachthani?"*

The words died away into the darkness and were echoed along unseen defiles and ravines about the hidden city. He had never heard Jesus' voice sound like that before. There was in it a ghastly clarity and an utter void of sense that set him shaking with fear. It was as though the very darkness had found expression, as though all the suffering of all the world echoed that "Why?"—and was answered only by further echoes . . . and a silence. The more he (afterward) thought upon it, the more tragic and bewildering it seemed. Had Jesus then reached the ultimate end of disillusionment and despair? Was He going down to the dust of death realizing at last that His reliance upon God and His faith in His plan were both misplaced—that the Powers of Darkness had won finally and irrevocably—that His life was in vain, His Teaching a lie, and death the End?

He looked, and there was none to help. . . . And it came to pass, when midday was past, that there was neither voice, nor any to answer, nor any that regarded. There was—nothing . . . nothing. . . . Jesus had thus to endure even this final agony—so infinitely greater than any physical pain—and be alone, even without the conscious presence of the Father; had to face the crash of all His hopes, the failure of all His plans. It was the Father's will that He should taste for one stark instant the ultimate loneliness and separation of sin . . . for only so could He redeem the whole universe—including even the very pit itself.

But even in this supreme agony, His faith held. He still pinned His trust to love, whether or not God had abandoned Him. He faced the abyss in the superb consciousness that though this be the utter end, His course had been right, His plan accomplished, His Mission and Message fulfilled and vindicated by the last criterion: *His own judgment.* If the throne were empty, there were *none other gods.* There was only right . . . and love. So that, with this ultimate disillusion menacing Him in all its horror, He could yet cry with a loud voice, in the most triumphant cry in all history: *"It is finished!"* His concept of Divinity had been lived out in death as in life—whether there were a God or not. This was overcoming the world indeed—overcoming not only earth's uttermost rejection and agony, but Heaven's abandonment, too. Faith could go no further. There were no victories possible beyond this supreme victory over even God's seeming desertion. *I wondered that there was none to uphold. Therefore Mine own arm brought salvation to Me!*

Others heard this cry beside Peter. Some thought Jesus was calling out against the darkness. *"Eli!"*—"O sun, why hast thou forsaken Me?" Others again, thought He was crying for Elijah to help Him, and when, in His agony, He was heard saying "I thirst," and a soldier ran to give Him a drink from a sponge dipped in vinegar, holding it aloft on the end of a spear, another cried out: "Stop! Let's see if Elijah comes to save Him!"

Then suddenly the black mood—and with it the darkness of earth—

lifted. Christ knew that the Father *was* with Him, with Him as never before; and the glad relief and comfort of God's presence again flooded His soul, and Heaven was lighted again to glory.

The poor tortured body was all but dead by now and the Spirit was about to depart to Him from Whom it proceeded. As Peter had withdrawn from the sight of Jesus' eyes, now that the daylight had returned, John, who had come back, was the only one who heard the whispered words of Jesus, as in sweet confidence and intimate trust, He spoke to God, "Father, into Thy hands I commend My Spirit." And with that His head, held erect for so incredible a time in spite of all the pain and utter weariness, fell forward at last, and Jesus was dead.

XI

Aftermath

AT that very moment (it was afterward discovered) "the Veil of the Temple was rent in twain from the top to the bottom"—strangest, swiftest and most dramatic of all comments on the death of Jesus on the Cross. For this death that was the end was also the beginning. This symbolic destruction of the ancient exclusive sanctities was the opening up of the new accessibilities. As the writer of the Epistle to the Hebrews put it: "Having, therefore, brothers, boldness to enter into the Holy Place by the blood of Jesus, by the way which He dedicated for us—a new and living way, through the veil—let us draw near with a true heart in fulness of faith." So God Himself in nature provided the perfect comment on the death of His Son. The earthquake that shook the world shattered also the barriers of hatred. Love was loose at last.

The centurion, now that the daylight was creeping back once more, saw the sudden sagging of all Jesus' muscles. He moved forward and listened, and touched Jesus nervously; and backed away from the Cross, saying, "Truly, I do believe this Man *was* a Son of the gods!"

The few that were left, watching from a distance, seeing Jesus was dead, turned away, beating their breasts in grief and desolation; and Peter went home at last—that is, to the house of John, where Mary was lying ill. Salome had also returned to comfort and tend her sister. But the Magdalene stayed on there by the Cross, together with that other Mary, the wife of Cleopas, the mother of two sons who afterward became disciples of Jesus, James and Joseph. What, thought the Magdalene, will become of Jesus' body? Where will it be laid? For she had a plan already formed in her self-dramatizing way. Had He not said of her phial of perfume there at Bethany (dear God, was it not yet a week ago?), "Against the day of My burying has she kept this"? Well, that was all gone and the cruse broken;

424

but, once the Sabbath was over, she could buy some more—unless they threw His body into a felon's grave.

Meanwhile Caiaphas, in the Temple, was wondering if his enemy were dead by now or not. He could not bear to think of Him still lingering in life while the Passover was being celebrated. If He lingered till evening, He would die on the Day of the Sacrifice—the "Lamb of God" indeed! That would never do. So he sent a messenger to Pilate asking that the *crurifragium*—the breaking of the legs of the victims in order to hasten death—might be applied to the three criminals, lest the Feast Day be defiled. A messenger told the centurion in charge, and the dread but merciful method of final despatch was applied to the two rebels. But Jesus was already dead, though one of the soldiers pierced His side with a spear to make doubly sure. The Beloved Disciple, long afterward, told his friends: "I was there, I tell you. I saw it . . . and there came out blood and water. God knows I am telling you the truth, blood and water. . . ."

And in his allegorizing manner, he ruminated upon this twin mystery of Baptism and Communion, the mixed Chalice of Suffering.

At length the messenger returned and the Sanhedrin learned of Jesus' death. One of its members, Joseph of Arimathea, a rich man and much respected, who had never consented to the condemnation of Jesus, being in secret a disciple—but fearing the Priests—went in boldly to Pilate and asked the Governor for permission to remove the body of Jesus and dispose of it, telling him that he meant to inter it in the rock-hewn tomb he had intended for his own use one day.

Pilate was astounded. "Dead, you say, already? Is the centurion returned from Golgotha? No? Would you mind waiting till I have his report?" And Joseph was ushered into an anteroom and waited.

Presently he was visited by an official. "His Excellency's compliments, and he has now received the full report at firsthand from the centurion in command. He wishes me to tell you that permission is granted you to have possession of the corpse of Jesus." And a written order was handed to Joseph, who left the palace forthwith. He then joined his friend Nicodemus, who was awaiting him outside, and together they went down the hill toward the gate and so out to Golgotha's ghastly scene. Joseph had brought with him a new linen embalming cloth, and Nicodemus had earlier that day been to the

Bazaar of Spices and had purchased a hundred pounds' weight of a mixture of myrrh and aloes, the finest embalming materials procurable. They came to the Cross of Jesus. Joseph presented his written order to the sergeant in command, and together and with the utmost tenderness and reverence these two members of the Sanhedrin removed the body of Jesus from the Cross. Then they carried all that remained of the Master they both so deeply admired (but succoured too late) away to an enclosed garden near by which belonged to Joseph, wherein was a newly made tomb cut out of the solid rock, and having laid it on the ground, wrapped it in the linen cloth, after placing about His body and in among the folds of the cloth the pungent sweet-smelling spices. His head they swathed in a separate cloth, wrapping it tightly round so as to leave the face free. Then they laid the Prophet to rest, rolling a great circular stone, which had been cut specially and set ready on a little level platform, till, descending the hollowed-out groove, it finally settled itself over the rounded opening to the tomb, completely sealing it. Then they departed.

The two Marys had followed them from Golgotha, keeping out of sight till they had disappeared. Then Mary of Cleopas also went home; but the Magdalene stayed on by the tomb, resting upon a rock near by. She could not bear to leave this sacred spot. Nor had this attempted embalming by the two Councillors, for all its obvious lavishness, deterred her from carrying out her own plan. It was *she,* not these men, who should tend the body of her Lord, and no one should stop her. Her Lodestar had fallen flaming from the sky. She had but one purpose left: to tend and care for the body of Jesus, in her planned and special way. Directly the Bazaars reopened on the Saturday night she would go out and buy the costliest spices with what was left of her former wealth, and, since it would be too dark then to do anything in the tomb, she would wait for the first glimmerings of early dawn to give her an opportunity. She would need help, though, in rolling away the great stone. Better ask some of the other women to give her a hand.

Mark was only a boy, troubled and excited by the queer goings-on in his father's house, terrified by the events in the Garden of Gethsemane. His mind was obsessed by the words he had overheard the clear voice of Jesus saying as He walked from the house to the garden. "After I am raised up, I will go before you into Galilee."

What had that meant? "Raised up . . . " They said He was dead now. But He had said, *"After* I am raised up . . . " Mark's father knew where Jesus had been laid. The boy haunted the tomb and its environs. "Raised up . . . "?

Young John's house was filled the long Sabbath through with sorrowful, despairing disciples. There was not a ray of light anywhere. Who could any longer believe in a Jehovah Who could let Jesus die? And who could any longer believe in a Messiah Who did so die? They had been deceived all round. But their love for Him remained. Jesus, the Friend, the Comforter, the Master, this was a memory that could never be taken away from them. Ah! if only Heaven had burst asunder and the thronging Angels had rescued Him from the Cross, the world would know that He were indeed God's Anointed One!

But now Jesus was dead. The Light had gone out.

POSTLUDE

POSTLUDE

POSTLUDE

I

"Now in the place where He was crucified there was a garden." The tall cypress trees could be just descried against the blackness of the sky. The moon had withdrawn and the far stars looked down from the remote heavens. It was very still . . . and very peaceful. Away to the east, the merest glimmer of light fluttered a moment and faded and swelled again . . . and soon the distant outline of the mountains of the Wilderness was visible beyond the bulk of Olivet. Then the near-by flowers rose in startling clarity out of the dew-hung mists, their white blossoms seemingly poised in midair. A morning freshness, cool and sweet, breathed in the low-stirring breeze.

From somewhere in the darkness came suddenly a low, choking sob. It was the Magdalene, sunk down in grief inconsolable by the side of that tomb wherein lay all that was dear to her on earth, the body of Jesus. In her arms was a parcel of precious spices and ointments, bought last evening—her last gift to her dear Lord.

There was a sound of footsteps and the low speech of them that mourn, as Mary of Cleopas and Salome came to help her in the rolling away of the stone that sealed the tomb. Together they waited till suddenly the sun's rays streamed out over the sky and lighted by reflection the grey mists in the garden. They glanced around them to see whether the gardener might by any chance be yet arrived to give them a hand. But they were quite alone. From far away a bugle sounded. Their eyes inevitably went to the stone which they would have to move unaided . . . and lo! it was rolled back right to the top of the grooved ledge again, and the entrance to the tomb was open! The Magdalene rushed, leaned down and peered within . . . but her own form excluded the light, and it was, in any case, not full dawn yet. She then stepped boldly within through the rounded opening, followed by the others. As their eyes accommodated themselves to the darkness within, the beam of growing light from the circular entrance making a violent contrast with the black recesses of the tomb, they realized with a shock of fear that they were not alone. A white-robed figure could just be made out, seated somewhere at the further end of the rock ledge whereon the body had been laid. Shrieking with terror, they rushed toward the exit.

Then a voice—high-pitched and eager and very young—arrested their stampede.

"Don't be frightened. I know Whom you are looking for—Jesus of Nazareth, Who was crucified. I tell you, He is risen! Look! There's the place where they laid Him!" And following his pointing hand, they stared at the rock ledge . . . but no body was there.

The boyish voice was heard again. "Go and tell the disciples—and especially the one called Peter—'He is going before you into Galilee! There you shall see Him, even as He told you!' Tell them that—they'll remember!" And he pointed with both hands toward the entrance. "Quick! Go!"

They did not need telling. They fled through the narrow opening into the daylight again, clutching one another breathlessly. The Magdalene, being younger than her two companions, sped toward the city and knocked violently at the door of John's house, where she knew Peter was. Panting, she was ushered in and blurted out her story. But all she was concerned with was the removal of the dear dead body which she had so eagerly promised herself to anoint and tend. "They have taken away the Master out of the tomb, and we don't know where they have laid Him. . . ."

Peter and John rose in consternation. Waiting for no fuller discussion, they were up and away in a moment, flying with all possible haste to the garden tomb. John, the younger, outstripped his companion and arrived first at the tomb. He stooped down and peered in at the open entrance, and could just make out, in the now stronger light of morning, the body wrappings lying on the rock ledge . . . *but no body*. Then Peter rushed up, and thrusting John out of his way, stepped into the tomb. After a moment or two, he too could make out the bandages lying collapsed on the ledge, and the rolled-up napkin that had been swathed about Jesus' head lying exactly where it had lain when the head had been in it; its very shape—cupped still, though in part fallen in—showed that the body had not been extricated by human hands from its wrappings, but had just vanished, leaving the graveclothes as they were, but tenantless. There were no littered spices to be seen—had the wrappings been disturbed they would have scattered about the floor. Peter called John, who now entered; and together, awestruck and greatly wondering, they gradually became aware of the import of what they had seen: the first indisputable evidence of the incredible fact which was beginning to hammer at their minds.

Baffled and perplexed, they made their way back to the city. Arriving at John's house, they found Mary of Cleopas and Salome there, telling their strange story to a sceptical audience. It was regarded as sheer nonsense. These hysterical females! But now here were Peter and John with confirmation of the fact. No talk, this time, of a voice in the tomb or of any apparition; but they were both firm about the graveclothes—and their implication. No criticism could shake them. They had seen for themselves. The body had *not* been extricated. It had vanished. But what about this special message for Peter? "I will go before you into Galilee. . . ." Yes, Jesus *had* said that. What could it all mean? No message (thought Peter) could be specially for him *and be authentic,* not after his denial of the Master. Yet . . . ?

Meanwhile Mary of Magdala, having followed Peter and John back as fast as she could (after all, she had only just now run all the way uphill into the city) arrived at the tomb again—to find the two disciples gone and herself alone again, disconsolate in the garden. She began to sob convulsively once more.

Then there came a Voice from the rising mists. "Woman, why are you weeping?"

To which Mary answered, chokingly, "Because they have taken away my Master, and I don't know where they have laid Him."

It was kind of the gardener to sympathize with her. She turned to glance at him . . . but she could only just make him out in the still misty sunlight. Then the Voice spoke again: *"Why* did you say you were weeping? Were you looking for anyone?"

She blurted out, "Oh, Sir, if *you* have carried Him away, tell me where you have put Him, and I will take care of Him!" What she meant by this was not clear even to herself. All she wanted was to be alone with the body, to tend and kiss and caress it . . . and of course, to anoint it as she had planned.

Then one miraculous word came from the figure standing in the luminous mist—Himself seeming somehow to be the source of the light about Him: "Mary!"

It was *His* voice! It was He Himself! Startled with excess of joy, she cried: "Rabboni!" and ran toward Jesus, all her love leaping out to Him. Then her arms were wildly clasped about His feet as she prostrated herself upon the ground in utter abandonment of devotion. The voice of Jesus was a trifle sterner. "Cease clinging to Me!" He ordered. The ever-emotional Mary must learn to express her love less physically and more spiritually.

For He had from henceforward three main aims in His Resurrection appearances: to prove His continued existence, to show its changed expression, and to prepare the disciples increasingly for the withdrawal of mere sensory evidence of that existence, so that they might learn to cling only to His Spiritual Presence, eternally with them. The Ascension would finally teach them that the time for sensory appearances was past because they were no longer necessary, something infinitely better having been grasped: that He was indeed with them "all the days—even unto the end of the world."

He had this supreme lesson in mind when He added, to Mary: ". . . for I have not yet ascended to My Father. But go to My brothers and tell them: I am ascending to My Father—and your Father; to My God—and your God!"

And Mary went. She, of all people, left her Beloved Lord, standing there in the garden in the cool of the morning, to walk all the way once more to Jerusalem to find the others and give them His Message. This was indeed a new Mary, and her obedience the first-fruits of the lesson He was teaching.

She burst in once again upon the disciples: "I have seen the Lord! Actually seen and spoken to Him!"

Thomas reserved judgment. It sounded so hysterical. Her overwrought condition—and the morning mists—accounted for everything. But Peter felt that it was only just that Mary, who, whatever her past sins, had never denied her Lord, should take precedence over himself. If only Jesus would appear to *him*—to him alone—so that he could sob out his penitence and receive His Divine pardon! But that was unthinkable.

His dream came true. But of what happened he never spoke, nor where it was that Jesus appeared to him. The sacred intimacies of that reconciliation were for him—and his Master—alone. But, afterward, he wrote to some friends of the joy of being—"according to His great mercy—born anew to a life of hope through the Resurrection of Jesus Christ from the dead." The Love of Jesus was never shown in greater tenderness than in this lovely condescension. And it made a new man of Peter, courageous, valiant, cheerful, passionately loyal, even if so human still. Jesus lived—and still loved him. That was all that mattered in all the world.

II

That same evening Cleopas was on his way home, walking, together with a friend, toward the village of Emmaus, about eight miles from Jerusalem. They were busy talking about the tragic happenings of these last few days, culminating in the Crucifixion. Soon a Stranger joined them, and seemed puzzled by their earnest talk.

"What is all this you are discussing on your walk?" He asked them. They were so amazed that this Traveller should have asked them such a question that they pulled up short.

Cleopas replied, "What—do you mean that you're such a lonely stranger in Jerusalem that you really don't know anything about the dreadful happenings there?"

"What things?"

"Why, about Jesus of Nazareth! He seemed to us, and to all the people, such a mighty Prophet, strong in action and utterance; but the High Priests and our Rulers sentenced Him to death—and crucified Him. We had hoped that He would have redeemed Israel—but alas, He is dead. Not but what there were some queer tales going about the city just before we left it—about some women belonging to our group, who astonished us by saying that they had been early in the morning to His tomb and couldn't find His body, but saw, instead, (or so they said) a vision of Angels who declared that He was alive!

As a matter of fact some of our company did go to the tomb to test the women's story, and sure enough they found the tomb empty. But Him they never saw."

The Stranger was not so much concerned with proving the truth of His Resurrection as the import of His Sufferings. It was this overwhelmingly stressed issue underlying His Passion and Death that was for Him—and so should be for all His disciples—the most important of all truths: namely, that He suffered and died as the Messiah in order to reveal the true nature of the heart and being of God. So now once again He unfolded the full significance of His Divine plan, placing it in line with the most inspired of all the sacred writings, and thereby revealing the destined role of the Messiah.

So talking they ascended to a high plateau from which the city could be seen bathed in the mellow afternoon sunlight. Soon they were falling gently into a beautiful well-watered valley and again rising after a mile or so through a ravine cut between mountains covered with fruit trees, afterward passing by many olive groves and orchards as they neared their destination. But the two friends hardly noticed the scenery, so thrilled were they with what the tall Stranger had to tell them. He gently chided them: "Are you not really showing yourselves rather dull-witted in being so reluctant to believe, and understand, these things?" Cleopas felt a pang of remorse, but it wasn't easy to credit every rumour, especially when your own wife was the source of a strange tale. The Stranger went on: "Why not, instead, believe all that the Prophets have foretold? Can't you see that the Messiah was destined to suffer thus, and *so* to enter into His glory? Don't you realize that all this was inevitable—and *fitting?*"

He told them about Moses, the hero of the Exodus of Israel from bondage; and about the Unknown Prophet of the Exile and his dreams of the Suffering Servant; dwelling upon Zechariah's Prophecies of the lowly King, the pierced Victim and the smitten Shepherd. Psalm Twenty-two was also quoted, and its strange correspondence with the Passion. And at last their incredulity gave way to a new-found realization of truth, of God's love and of Messiah's glory—*in Jesus.*

Suddenly they found themselves near at home and as they drew up by their portal, the Stranger prepared to say farewell and to go forward on His journey. They felt that they could not let Him depart;

they would fain hear more. So they pressed Him, saying, "Stay with us! For, look, it is getting toward evening and the day is now far spent." So He went in with them; and as the sun dropped, red and glowing, toward the distant hills veiling the Great Sea, they hastily prepared a supper for their Guest and for themselves. And so, after a while, they sat down to eat.

Then a strange thing happened; for it was the Stranger, not one of themselves, Who took the bread in His hands and blessed it . . . And even as they watched, wonderingly, something in His demeanour and gestures reminded them suddenly of the Supper at Bethany—a trick of breaking the bread and, with arms outstretched, looking up to Heaven while He prayed for a Blessing to rest upon their meal. And with a start of infinite wonder and surprise they fell on their knees before Him. But even as they gazed adoringly upon Him He began slowly to vanish into empty air . . . and they were alone once more. Directly they knew He had indeed been present with them, the need for further sensory proof was at once obviated. He was teaching them the lesson of the Resurrection and the Ascension; that He is Eternally Present with those that believe on Him.

The two disciples were so overwhelmed with joy that they could not bear to wait until the morrow before imparting their marvellous news to the Brethren in Jerusalem. So they at once set out to do the very thing they had dissuaded their Guest from doing—undertaking a night journey. Their natural fatigue after an eight-mile walk was forgotten, and there in the gathering darkness and the rising moonlight, they retraced their steps with hurrying pace through the ravine again and up the long defile toward the Holy City. Rapping on the closed doors of the Western Gate, they entered the city and made their way along the moonlit streets to the house owned by the father of John Mark, where they knew the disciples were meeting that night. Gaining admittance by a secret knock—for the doors were barred for fear of the Rulers—they found the Apostles still gathered together, with some of their friends, only Thomas being absent. Before they could get a word out regarding their having seen Jesus, they were met with a cry: "The Lord has really risen—He's appeared to Simon!" and there was Peter, embarrassed, overwhelmed, tears of joy brimming up into his eyes and coursing down his weatherbeaten face. Then they themselves related their own experience on the road and how they had recognized Jesus when He broke the bread.

Even as they were yet speaking, the eyes of the disciples were drawn off from them and staring across the room. Turning, the two disciples saw Jesus Himself! And out of the hush of wonder His voice was heard: "Peace be unto you." He lifted His hands in blessing . . . and lo! there were the nail prints. For most of them there, this was their first sight of the Risen Lord. No wonder they were scared and thought they were seeing an apparition.

Jesus sensed their bewilderment. "Don't be afraid!" He said. "Why are you so upset and sceptical? See! It really is I Myself!" He showed them anew His pierced hands and feet. Having unfolded the grand panorama of the past—its Messianic dreams, now fulfilled—He went on to open up their part in the future Mission of His Church.

"Repentance and remission of sins must be preached in My name to all the nations, beginning here in Jerusalem. To this you must all bear testimony. Even as My Father sent Me out, so send I you. And I will send down upon you that which My Father has promised. In this very city you will before long be endued with Power from Above."

Then, with intense solemnity, He recommissioned them for their colossal task, repeating with added emphasis what He had said on that rock above Caesarea Philippi, when He had first founded the Church. With bated breath they heard again those awe-inspiring words about the eternal distinction between right and wrong and the ministry of forgiveness and of judgment—and even of condemnation—to be exercised in His name and through His Divine Inspiration by His Church: words that exalted and yet cast down; of the glory of commission; of the terrifying responsibility that was theirs—and yet again not theirs but His; and they were filled with a humiliating sense of unworthiness to essay so great a task. But of one thing were they sure—their eyes still upon Jesus—that only in His power could the gigantic task be ever undertaken.

III

A week had passed, and once again the disciples were gathered together in the Upper Room in an instinctive desire to be together again, there, on this, the first weekly commemoration of the day on which He rose. But this time their number was increased by one, Thomas the Twin being now present with them. They had found it all but an impossible task to convince him of the truth of their stories. To their reiterated affirmation: "We have seen the Lord!" he countered with: "Unless I see for myself His hands with the prints of the nails in them, and even put my finger through the nail holes—yes, and thrust my hand into His pierced side—I tell you I will never believe you!" There they had been forced to leave the matter, so that today there were ten joyously happy disciples and one gloomy sceptic. At any rate they had been successful in persuading him to be present with them tonight. They secretly hoped that Jesus might appear to them on this Sunday also.

And their hope came true. Though the doors were shut once again, Jesus was suddenly seen standing in their midst, saying, as before, "Peace be unto you!" Then He turned to Thomas. "Look at My hands. Come, put your finger through here . . . and thrust your hand into My riven side, if you still want to . . . and be no longer sceptical, but believe."

Embarrassed and put to shame in front of all his fellow disciples, Thomas yet showed himself for what he really was—loyal and devoted in spite of all his pessimism. Falling down at Jesus' feet, he cried, "My Lord and my God!"

Gently chiding him, Jesus answered, "So you believe—now that you've seen for yourself!" He turned to the others. "Blessed be those who shall believe on Me even though they shall never have seen Me."

IV

It was young Mark who had reminded the disciples of Jesus' words: "Behold, I will go before you into Galilee." They talked the matter over and came to the conclusion that this Message could only mean one thing: that they had themselves to move to Galilee, whither Jesus would precede them. So one day Peter and the others set out for their own beloved north country once again, shaking the dust of hated Jerusalem from their feet and with every step feeling an increasing joy in homecoming. And so the dread southward journey to Jerusalem—balancing that earlier joyous onset northward to open the Ministry—was itself balanced by this last journey back to the gladness of Galilee. And just as Jesus led the way on those two so greatly contrasting journeys, so once again He led the way now. Though they could not see Him, He was there in the forefront as always, "going before them . . . and they were amazed . . ." only, this time, as they followed, they were overjoyed! It was glorious to be going home—why, look, there in the far distance, between the walls of yonder ravine, was a patch of the vividest, deepest blue—their own beloved Lake! Mary went back with them, together with young John, who would not leave her side. But she was anxious for James and her other sons. It would not be easy to persuade them that Jesus really was the Messiah—*and was alive.* The brothers were deeply hurt and angry; and these tales of His "Resurrection" would only serve further to embitter their contempt for any who "believed" in Him.

Some considerable time had by now elapsed since their return to Galilee. But nothing had happened. It was all very puzzling. One afternoon, young John, wearying after a while of Nazareth, came over for a short visit to Peter and the others at Capernaum. He found them curiously lax and disgruntled. This waiting had apparently got on their nerves. Thomas was there, reflective and none too cheerful as usual. Nathanael Bartholomew had come over from Cana and the two sons of Zebedee were also present.

They were chatting desultorily together when suddenly Peter, impulsive as always, squared his shoulders and rose up. "I don't know what you fellows mean to do," he said, "but this waiting about has got me down. *I'm* going fishing! Anyone coming with me?"

In a flash they all agreed to accompany him; so they went down to the shelving beach near the hot springs just south of Capernaum, where they found their boat still drawn up at the head of the little bay. A long time had elapsed since last Peter was on the Lake.

Many a time, since they had returned to Galilee, he had wandered down to stare from a distance at his boat and turned away disconsolately. After all Jesus had called him from his fishing to follow Him. But now . . . Surely Jesus would not mind them having a night out on the Lake. So they all sailed away as the sun went down, and the water, paling to emerald and then to silver, gently lifted the boat and let it subside again as the long smooth swell rollers bore southward along the central deeps of the sea.

But not a single fish did they catch. It almost looked like a judgment on Peter's impetuosity. The hours of night slowly passed and still there was nothing in their nets. They had repeatedly dragged them partially in and examined them in the cold moonlight, but only dripping meshes could be seen, and reluctantly they released them again into the dark watery depths below them. And now it was nearly dawn. Already silver streaks were gleaming on the Lake's smooth surface and the gathering light revealed a morning mist as the soft-blurred line of the shore could be faintly descried.

Peter and the brothers were irresistibly reminded of another similar occasion . . . two long years ago, when after an almost identically fruitless night of attempted fishing they had drawn close to the shore and had seen Jesus standing there. There was a strange atmosphere about this fishing trip—almost as if a loop in the long coil of time were enfolding them and they were close to moments long gathered up into the past. Indeed, it seemed as though at any moment now they might expect to see Jesus on yonder shore. But that was a foolish thought . . . and Peter turned his eyes away from the shore and busied himself energetically with the tackle. But the longing grew on him to hear once again, here on the Lake, that beautiful voice floating out to him over the waves . . . and not, oh, not as though from some remote world of spirits, but in the dear familiar accents of ordinary everyday life.

Then something in young John's demeanour struck Peter as queer. He was staring—rapt, excited—toward the shore, straining his eyes to pierce the pearly haze softening the line of the beaches. The splashing sound of breaking wavelets echoed from the shore toward which they were gently drifting. The early sun was beginning to filter through the mist and light everything to shimmering luminous beauty. Then a voice—oh, so like that other voice!—echoed over the calm clear water.

"My children, have you caught anything?"

"No!" answered a disciple unthinkingly from the forward part of the boat. He had not seen young John's strange gazing.

"Then try the other side of the boat and you will net a good catch!"

Peter's heart nearly stopped beating. It must be a dream, an illusion. . . . He dared not turn to look at the shore. But as all the others save young John were busy taking the stranger's advice (after all, it was a quite usual thing for some interested passer-by, who could see the shoals of fish more clearly from the shore than the fisherfolk from the boat, to call out a friendly suggestion), Peter gave a hand with the nets, transferring them with much labour to the other side of the boat—and lo! they were, in a moment or two, weighted down with a great inclosure of fishes! See, the cork floats were dipping under the grey rollers even as they watched!

But young John had not moved nor had he taken his eyes off the shore. (They had never expected him to be of much use in a boat.) And when Peter heard him whisper: *"It is the Lord!"* he could restrain himself no longer and, dropping the net, clambered frantically out of the boat, and was swimming, floundering, splashing to reach the tall majestic Figure standing on the shore, hastening to be the first to greet his beloved Master.

But when at last he waded ashore something restrained him from clasping Jesus. Perhaps it was the everyday voice with which Jesus spoke, saying so prosaically—as though nothing had happened to sever the past from the present—"I've made a fire already; so go and fetch some of the fish you've caught," adding half-humorously: "By the way, how many do you guess there are in the net—big, proper fish, I mean; not little ones, of course?"

"I say a hundred," said Nathanael, entering into the strangely everyday atmosphere with an effort.

"A hundred and twenty-five, at least," laughed James.

"A hundred and fifty!" cried Peter.

Excited and flushed—and filled with a curious feeling of unreality, as if they were re-enacting a stage play—they rushed down to the beach again and counted the fish with many laughing wranglings and recounts.

"A hundred and fifty-three!"

"Splendid!" cried Jesus. "And now come and breakfast."

The homeliness of it all completely baffled them—that Jesus should talk thus, after His Resurrection, just as though it were two years ago and not today. They finished the meal in an atmosphere of constrained joviality. This was a new side to the Risen Lord. What did it mean?

It was not till long after that they came to realize that Jesus in His wisdom and love was proving to them that the best of the past was *not* lost, but treasured up, enhanced and glorified; that beauty and love are eternal and not transitory.

Later, too, they knew that the rest of the story also held its lesson for them. Jesus had to make it clear to them—and especially to Peter—that, even if the past be not lost, no one should live solely upon memories, no matter how beautiful nor how successfully recaptured; that life must be lived breast-forward, not facing the past, like a man walking backward. Paul was so persuaded of the dangers of this wrong attitude to life that he resolved to "know Christ no longer after the flesh," lest such a study of His earthly life should blind him to the presence of His living Spirit "all the days." So now with Peter, nostalgia for the past must not be allowed to impede the carrying out of the tasks that lay ahead. He was given, in this Appearance of Christ, an assurance that the past was not lost; but only so that he might turn his back on it for the last time—sensible of its safety to all Eternity—to embark on his real life's work as leader under Christ of the Church of God.

So it was that Jesus, after a pause, turned to Peter and suggested a quiet walk up the sloping hillside; and Peter rose eagerly, and the others, feeling suddenly very lonely, stayed where they were. Only young John, after a time, got up and, hesitant and shy, followed after his Master and Peter, keeping his distance, for Jesus was obviously in deep conversation with Peter.

Jesus was leading Peter toward the heights behind Capernaum. For a space there fell a silence between them. From where they were strolling the busy western shore of the Lake shone clear in the morning sunlight; the fishing boats in midstream, the little bay down below, with some boats drawn up on the shingle and the nets by them. Near by on the green hillside, grazed a flock of sheep, the young lambs frolicking together.

Jesus asked Peter a question: "Tell Me, Peter, do you love Me more than . . . all this?" His gesture embracing the boats, the Lakeside and all Galilee. Peter quickly sensed the import of the question. He felt somehow guilty, as if his so great love for the Lake were somehow a hindrance to his love for Jesus.

"Why," he faltered, "You know that I love You."

"Then feed My lambs," said Jesus; and they strolled forward in silence a few more paces. Then Jesus once more asked Peter, "Simon, son of Jonah, do you really love Me?"

Peter was deeply troubled at the use of the more formal "Simon" in place of the special name given him by Jesus. Was it a tacit reminder of his innate weakness?

He glanced at Jesus in wistful bewilderment. "But, Lord, You *know* that I love You!"

"Then be a shepherd to My sheep," returned Jesus.

To Peter's intense dismay Jesus a third time asked him the selfsame question. So much was he grieved that there was a sharp tone of protest in his answer, "Lord, You know everything. You know perfectly well that I love You."

"Then feed My sheep."

It was, again, not till long afterward that Peter realized with a start that what had seemed at the time an irrational—and indeed exasperating—repetition was in reality the tenderest of kindnesses. For Jesus was intent not only on proving that the best of the past was stored up in Eternity, but that its worst was capable of redemption— an even lovelier thing. He was giving Peter the chance of actively cancelling out that manifold denial of his Master by an equally manifold avowal of loving loyalty. He was not only demonstrating Peter's forgiveness—that had come when he first saw his Risen Master—but bringing back his self-respect. Peter himself sensed this long after, when he wrote of one who had gone astray like a sheep that was lost, and was returned unto the Shepherd and Bishop of his soul, himself tending the Flock of God willingly, as of a ready mind, not lording it over the charge committed to him, but making himself, even unto death, an example to the Flock; that when the chief Shepherd should appear, he might receive the crown of glory that would never fade away.

But Jesus was not only concerned with the past, and its effect on the present. He also saw clairvoyantly into the future. Turning once more to Peter, He said, "Here, by the Lake, in the days that are past, you were free to do as you liked and to go where you liked. You were independent—putting on your own girdle! But when you grow old, you will stretch out your hands—" as He spoke, Jesus stretched out

His arms as if on a Cross—"for someone else to gird you . . . and you will be taken where you've no wish to go. . . ."

John, long afterward, recalling the scene, said to his friend, "In this, Jesus was indicating the kind of death by which Peter did in the end glorify God."

But Peter, happily for him, was not able fully to understand these mystic words. Instead, he found himself irritated to find how close young John had drawn. Catching sight of him, he turned and asked Jesus, "And what about *him?*" Couldn't Jesus switch His questions and His forebodings on to someone else for a change?

But Jesus made an enigmatic and half-humorous answer. "Even if I should choose that he should survive till I come back in glory, why is that any business of yours?"

It was unfortunate that these words should have been made the basis of a rumour that the Beloved Disciple should never die; and John, in his old age, was careful to point out that not only was this an entirely unjustifiable interpretation, but it was based on a popular misquotation.

As for Peter, had not Jesus once told him, "You cannot follow Me *now* . . . but you *shall* follow Me hereafter"? And His words came true. "Following afar off," Peter walked in the tracks of his Master, even down his own *Via Dolorosa,* through the Gates of Hades, and along its tortuous passes, climbing gloriously the steep ascent of Heaven until he came out at last into a large place and his soul was face to face with the glorified Christ seated at the right hand of the Throne of Glory. There all the beauty, all the happiness of all the days was restored and treasured forever; and all bitter regrets wiped out and vanquished eternally in the love of Jesus.

v

Deeply impressed, as the disciples were, with the beauty of this token recovery of the day on which they had first been called to Christ's service, mention had been made of that other great "day of the Son of Man" when they had been ordained and Jesus had preached to hundreds of His followers on the mountainside, high over the

Lake. So it was that Jesus had asked that all who had been present on that latter occasion should, if possible, gather together at the same spot on an appointed day. Peter thus began his shepherding at once, finding first those members of the Apostolic band who had not been present by the Lakeside, giving them the Message regarding the proposed reunion with their Lord. He then had to reach the wider circle of Galilean followers, especially those who had been present to hear the Great Sermon.

When the day came the hillside was filled with disciples rallying to the level place from where the crowds had heard Jesus preach on that unforgettable summer's day. Arrived there, they waited for a space, till suddenly Jesus appeared in the midst. They soon sensed that this time Jesus was no longer the recovered everyday Companion of the past, but rather the Eternal King of all the universe. He spoke to them of that earlier day when He had ordained the Twelve to preach in Galilee. But this time He commissioned His hearers to a far greater task, even to the conversion of the whole world. Never before had He been so superbly regal, so majestic. The sovereign confidence of His discourse revealed Him as King of kings and Lord of lords. There was sorrow in His voice as He looked back on His earthly Ministry, especially on the failure of that earlier preaching. "I was in the world, and I appeared to man in the flesh . . . but I found all men drunken and none thirsty; and My soul sorrowed for the sons of men." Towering over them in supernal authority, He cried, "But *now,* all power has been given to Me in Heaven and in earth! Go, therefore, and make disciples of all nations, baptizing them in the Name of the Father, and of the Son, and of the Holy Spirit. Teach them to obey all those commands I have laid on you—" this, with special reference to the Great Sermon—"and lo! I am with you *all* the days, even to the very end of the world!"

Even as they gazed, awe-struck, upon Him, He faded from their view . . . and the story of this experience was afterward told in hundreds of homes, so sealing the certainty of His Resurrection.

The story reached Nazareth. Here dwelt James, the Lord's brother, troubled and miserable, implacable in disbelief, trying to win from an even stricter observance of the Law that ease of heart that had left him ever since that terrible day when he had gone with his mother and brothers to fetch Jesus back from Capernaum. And now, not only was Jesus dead, but his mother had again left him, permanently to reside with some young stranger in Jerusalem, so people said.

But Jesus loved James, in spite of those taunts of cowardice, in spite even of His own reluctance to leave His mother in his care. So He appeared specially to him, whose zeal for the Law could be turned into an equally zealous care for the Church. So deeply was James converted to belief in his own Brother's Divinity—an astounding fact, and one of the most convincing evidences of the truth of the Resurrection—that, afterward, in a letter to his converts, he was to refer to himself expressly as "a servant of God and of the Lord Jesus, the Messiah," urging his readers to "be patient until the coming of the Lord," Whom he called *the glory*. . . . He left his business in Nazareth to go up to Jerusalem, persuading his other brothers to go with him—to stay for a while, at any rate, in the Holy City. There they were welcomed by the Apostles on their return from Galilee—for the latter had been ordered by Jesus to gather together in the capital, to await the great Feast of Pentecost, an ideal occasion for a Christian crusade, since the city would once again be thronged with visitors from all over the world. In spite of the real danger of persecution, the disciples obeyed their Lord, many of those who had seen Jesus on the mountainside accompanying them, there being about one hundred and twenty followers of Jesus assembled in Jerusalem.

VI

Not long after, Jesus appeared again to His followers, first in the city itself, then leading them thence as far as Bethany, the scene of so many precious memories. Once again He opened to them the sense of the Scriptural references to Himself, with special regard to those foretelling His Sufferings and Resurrection. He told them that they were to preach repentance and remission of sins in His name to all nations, beginning from Jerusalem.

"Do not leave Jerusalem till you have been endued with Power from Above. Wait therefore for what the Father has promised you—

the coming of the Comforter, the Holy Spirit. For before long, you will be baptized with the Holy Spirit."

It was not till long after that the disciples fully realized not only the omnipresence of Jesus with them, but His presence also, could they but apprehend it, in the "least of their brothers" in the everyday world around them. Had not Mary mistaken Him for the gardener, Cleopas for a fellow traveller—and most of the disciples for a fisherman by the Lakeside? Was there not a gracious congruity in each of these slow recognitions—a leading-up to the consciousness of the Christ in every man?

But now the thoughts of some of them were still set upon earthly triumphs and the Restoration of Israel. Hearing of Jesus' promise of the Holy Spirit, they asked Him: "Tell us, will that be the hour when You *will* restore the Kingdom again to Israel?"

He was very patient with them. "It is not for you to know the times or the seasons. All you need to realize is that Power will be given you, and you will be My witnesses, first in Jerusalem and then throughout all Judaea and Samaria—and so to all the ends of the earth!"

Thus He bade them carry, in widening arcs, the Gospel of Love not only to the Jews but also to the Samaritans—even to every nation and race. By now they had at last learned the supreme lesson of His ever-present companying with them. So, on the very spot where not long before He had burst into tears as He beheld the city from the shoulder of the Mount of Olives, He lifted up His hands and blessed them as they knelt around Him. Then, while they were yet gazing upon Him, He was lifted up from the earth and a cloud received Him out of their sight. So came the Ending which was also the Beginning. The task, gigantic and incredibly difficult, loomed before them; but Power was promised soon. When would He return?

As if in answer to their ponderings there came a message from two men, dressed in white, who were suddenly seen to be standing beside them: "Men of Galilee, why do you stand here still looking up to Heaven? This same Jesus, Who has been taken up from you into Heaven, will one day come back—just as you have seen Him depart into Heaven."

Accepting this message, they returned to the city, filled with an exceeding great joy. There was no sadness of farewell about this good-bye. Instead, there was a sense of His abiding presence that irradiated all life. There, in Jerusalem, they resorted with one mind to prayer, together with the womenfolk of their company, led by the mother of Jesus. The brothers of Jesus were also there—*worshipping their own Brother. . . .*

And in Heaven the portals opened once more, as on Mount Hermon; but this time to receive the Conqueror, amidst the plaudits of all the Angels and Archangels, as Jesus strode toward the great white throne and sat Himself down, by the Father's command, at His right hand, the Redeemer of all the universe, having fulfilled His Mission, poured out His soul even unto death and won for all men the chance to enter Heaven and dwell with Him forever.

Lift up your heads, O ye gates, and be ye lifted up, ye everlasting doors, and the King of Glory shall come in! "Who is the King of Glory?" Even the Lord of Hosts—He is the King of Glory.

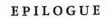

EPILOGUE

EPILOGUE

. . . .

(I) THE WITNESS OF THE BELOVED DISCIPLE

. . . and the Word was made flesh . . . and dwelt among us . . . and we beheld His glory: glory as of the Only-Begotten of the Father, full of grace and truth.

That which was from the beginning: that which we have heard: that which we have seen with our eyes: that which we beheld and our hands have handled, concerning the Word of Life (the Life that was manifested and that we have seen: of which we bear witness, and declare unto you—that it was the Life, the Eternal Life, which was with the Father, and was revealed unto us): that which we have seen and heard, declare we unto you, that you may have fellowship with us; yea, that fellowship of ours which is with the Father and with His Son Jesus Christ.

For God is Light, and in Him is no darkness at all. If we walk in the Light—as He is in the Light—we have fellowship one with another and the blood of Jesus Christ, God's Son, cleanses us from all sin. God is Love; and herein was the Love of God manifested for us, that God sent forth His Only-begotten Son into the world, that we might live through Him. For we have beheld and bear witness that the Father sent the Son to be the Saviour of the world. Whosoever shall confess that Jesus is the Son of God, God abideth in him, and he in God. Our witness is this: that God gave unto us Eternal Life— and this Life is in His Son. He that hath the Son hath Life. And he that hath not the Son hath not Life. For we know that the Son of God is come, and hath given us an insight to know Him Who is the real God; and we are in Him Who is real; even in Jesus Christ. This is the true God, and this is the Life Eternal.

(II) THE WITNESS OF PETER

Blessed be the God and Father of our Lord Jesus Christ, Who, according to His great mercy, begat us again unto a living hope by the Resurrection of Jesus Christ from the dead; unto an inheritance incorruptible, undefiled, that fades not away, reserved in Heaven for you who by the power of God are guarded through faith unto a salvation ready to be revealed in the last times; so that your faith might be found unto praise and glory and honour at the revealing of Jesus Christ; Whom, having not seen, ye love; in Whom, though now ye see Him not, yet believing, ye rejoice greatly with joy unspeakable and full of glory, receiving the end of your faith, even the salvation of your souls; concerning which salvation the Prophets sought and searched diligently, who prophesied of the grace that should come unto you, searching what time and in what manner these things should come to pass, when the Spirit of Christ that was in them prophesied of the Sufferings of Christ and of His afterglory: a mystery now revealed in the Gospel preached unto you in the Holy Spirit sent forth from Heaven; which things the Angels desire to look into. . . . For we are redeemed, not, indeed, with corruptible things, such as silver and gold, but with the precious blood—as of a Lamb without blemish and without spot: even the blood of Christ; Who was foreknown, indeed, before the foundations of the world; but was manifested in these latter times for your sake, who through Him are believers in God, Who raised Him from the dead, and gave Him glory.

(III) THE WITNESS OF PAUL

Who shall separate us from the Love of Christ? Shall tribulation, or distress, or persecution, or famine, or nakedness, or peril, or sword? Nay, in all these things we are more than conquerors through Him that loved us. For I am persuaded that neither death, nor life, nor Angels, nor Principalities, nor Powers—nor things present, nor things to come, nor height, nor depth, nor any other creature, shall be able to separate us from the Love of God which is in Christ Jesus our Lord. We give thanks, therefore, unto the Father, Who made us meet to be partakers of the inheritance of the Saints in Light; Who also delivered us out of the power of darkness and translated us into the Kingdom of the Son of His Love; in Whom we have our redemption, the forgiveness of our sins: Who is the Image of the Invisible God, the Firstborn of all creation. For in Him were all things created, in the Heavens and upon the earth, things visible and things invisible, whether Thrones, or Dominions, or Principalities, or Powers: all things have been created through Him, and unto Him. For He is before all things, and in Him all things consist. And He is the head of the body, the Firstborn from the dead, that in all things He might have the pre-eminence. For it was the good pleasure of the Father that in Him should all fulness dwell; and through Him to reconcile all things to Himself, having made peace through the Blood of His Cross—through Him, I say; whether things upon the earth, or things in the Heavens.

Blessed be the God and Father of our Lord Jesus Christ, Who hath blessed us with every spiritual blessing in the Heavenly places in Christ; having fore-ordained us unto adoption as sons through Jesus Christ, unto Himself, to the praise of His glorious grace, which He freely bestowed upon us in the Beloved; in Whom we have redemption through His blood—even the forgiveness of our sins according to the riches of His grace; having made known unto us the mystery of His will, according to His good pleasure which He purposed in Him, unto a dispensation of the fulness of the times: to sum up all things in Christ—the things in the Heavens, and the things upon earth—even in Him Whom He raised from the dead, and made to sit at His right hand in the Heavenly places—far above all rule and authority and Power and Dominion, and every name that is named, not only in this world, but also in that which is to come. For He hath put all things in subjection under His feet, and given Him to be the head of all things. Unto me, who am less than the least of all Saints, was this grace given—to preach the unsearchable riches of Christ— to make all men see what is the stewardship of the mystery which from all ages hath been hid in God, Who created all things; to the intent that now unto the Principalities and Powers in the Heavenly places might be known through the Church the manifold wisdom of God; according to the Eternal purpose, which He purposed in

Christ Jesus our Lord. For He that descended is the same also that ascended far above all Heavens, that He might fill all things.

For there is but one God, the Father, of Whom are all things, and we unto Him; and one Lord, Jesus Christ, through Whom are all things, and we through Him.

So we preach not ourselves, but Christ Jesus as Lord; and ourselves as your servants for Jesus' sake; seeing it is God that said: "Light shall shine out of darkness"—Who also shone in our hearts, to give the light of the knowledge of the glory of God—in the face of Jesus Christ . . . Who, being in the form of God, counted it not a thing to be grasped at to be on an equality with God; but emptied Himself, taking the form of a servant; and, being found in fashion as a man, He humbled Himself, and became obedient unto death— yea, even the death of the Cross. Wherefore God has highly exalted Him, and given Him a name which is above every name; that at the name of Jesus every knee should bow, of things in Heaven, and things on earth, and things under the earth; and that every tongue should confess that Jesus Christ is Lord, to the glory of God the Father.

Christ Jesus, Who before Pontius Pilate witnessed a good confession; Who is the blessed and only Potentate, the King of kings and Lord of lords, Who alone has Immortality, dwelling in light unapproachable, to Whom be honour and power eternal.

(IV) THE WITNESS OF THE EPISTLE TO THE HEBREWS

God, Who of old time spake unto the fathers by the Prophets, has in these latter days spoken unto us by His Son, Whom He hath appointed Heir of all things; through Whom also He made the worlds; Who, being the effulgence of His glory, and the very Image of His substance, and upholding all things by the word of His power, when He had made purification for sins, sat down on the right hand of the Majesty on high. Having, then, a great High Priest, Who hath passed into the Heavens—Jesus, the Son of God—let us hold fast our confession. For we have not a High Priest that cannot be touched

*with the feeling of our infirmities; but One that hath been in all
points tempted like as we are, yet without sin. For, though He was
a Son, yet learned He obedience by the things that He suffered. And
having been made perfect, He became unto all them that obey Him
the Author of everlasting salvation. So we have then a High Priest
Who sat down at the right hand of the Majesty in the Heavens; even
Christ; Who, having come as a High Priest of the good things to
come, through the greater and more perfect Tabernacle, not made
with hands (that is, not of man's building) nor yet through the blood
of goats and calves—but through His own blood, entered in, once, for
all, into the Holy Place, having obtained eternal redemption—even
by the blood of Christ; Who through the Eternal Spirit offered Himself without blemish unto God.*

(V) THE WITNESS OF THE APOCALYPSE

*Grace be to you, and peace, from Him which is, and which was,
and which is to come, and from Jesus Christ, the Faithful Witness,
the Firstborn from the dead, the Prince of Glory over the kings of
the earth. To Him Who loves us, and hath loosed us from our sins
by His blood—to Him be glory and dominion forever and ever.
Amen.*

(a) The Vision in the dawn over the sea, seen from the cliffs of
Patmos' Isle.

*On the Lord's Day, I found myself rapt in the Spirit ... and I heard
a great voice, as of a trumpet calling. And I saw seven golden candle-
sticks, and One like unto the Son of Man, clothed with a long robe,
belted with a girdle of gold. And His head and His hair were white as
snow, and His eyes flashed like fire. His feet glowed like burnished
bronze, and His voice was as the sound of many waves. He had in
His right hand seven stars, and out of His mouth issued a two-edged
sword; and His face shone like the sun in full strength. And when
I saw Him, I fell down at His feet like a dead man. But He laid
His right hand upon me, saying, "Fear not. I am the First, and the*

Last. I was dead . . . and, behold, I am alive for evermore, Amen; and have the keys of Hell and of death."

(b) The Vision of the Throne and of the Lamb.

I found myself once more rapt in the Spirit . . . and, behold, there was a Throne set up in Heaven; and One sat on the Throne; and there was a rainbow round about the Throne; and out of the Throne issued flashes of lightning, and loud blasts and peals of thunder; and before the Throne there was a sea of glass—clear as crystal; and I saw in the right hand of Him that sat upon the Throne a scroll, with writing on both sides, sealed with seven seals. And I saw a strong Angel proclaiming with a loud voice:

"Who is worthy to open the scroll—even to break the seals of it?"

And no one in Heaven, or on the earth, or under the earth, was found worthy to open the scroll or look into it.

So I began to weep bitterly, because no one had been found worthy to open the scroll, or look into it.

But one of the Elders said to me: "Weep not. For lo! the Lion of the tribe of Judah, the Heir of David, has won the power of opening the scroll and breaking its seven seals."

Then I saw in the midst of the Throne a Lamb standing—as though It had been slain. And He came and took the scroll out of the right hand of Him that sat on the Throne. And they sang a new song, saying:

"Worthy art Thou to take the scroll and to break the seals thereof! For Thou wast slain, and hast purchased for God by Thy blood men of every tribe and tongue and people and nation, and madest them to be Kings and Priests for our God; and they shall reign upon the earth."

And I looked—and heard the voice of myriads of Angels round about the Throne—even thousands of Angels—saying with a loud voice, "Worthy is the Lamb that hath been slain, to receive power and wealth and wisdom and might and honour and glory and blessing."

And every creature in Heaven and on earth and under the earth heard I crying, "Blessing and honour and glory and power be unto

Him that sits upon the Throne, and unto the Lamb, forever and ever."

And after this, I beheld, and lo! a great multitude which no man could number, of all nations and kindreds and people and tongues stood before the Throne and before the Lamb, clothed with white robes and with palms in their hands, crying with a great voice, "Salvation comes from our God, Which sits upon the Throne, and from the Lamb."

And all the Angels stood gathered round the Throne, and fell before the Throne upon their faces, and worshipped God, saying, "Amen. Blessing and glory and wisdom and thanksgiving and honour and power and might, be unto our God forever and ever. Amen."

And one of the Elders spoke unto me, saying, "Who are these which are arrayed in white robes, and whence came they?"

And I said unto him: "Sir, thou knowest. . . ."

And he said unto me, "These are they which came out of great tribulation, and have washed their robes, and made them white in the blood of the Lamb. There are they before the Throne, and serve Him day and night, in His Temple. And He that sits on the Throne shall dwell among them. They shall hunger no more; neither thirst any more; nor shall the sun strike them down, nor any scorching heat; for the Lamb which is in the midst of the Throne shall be their Shepherd, guiding them to fountains of living water; and God shall wipe away all tears from their eyes. . . ."

(c) The Vision of the Word of God.

And I saw Heaven wide open, and behold! a white horse: and his Rider was called faithful and true. Yea, His judgment and His warfare are just. His eyes were as a flame of fire, and on His head were many diadems; and He bore a written name which none knew but Himself. He was clad in a vesture dipped in blood. . . . His name was called "The Word of God." And the Hosts of Heaven followed Him—also upon white horses—arrayed in pure white linen. A sharp sword issued from His lips; and on His vesture, covering His thigh as He rode, was His name written: KING OF KINGS—AND LORD OF LORDS.

(d) The Vision of the New Jerusalem.

And I saw the Holy City, New Jerusalem, coming down from God out of Heaven, prepared as a bride adorned for Her husband. And I heard a great voice out of Heaven, crying:

"Behold, the dwelling place of God shall be with men—yea, with men shall He dwell. They shall be His people, and God Himself shall be with them, and be their God. And He shall wipe away all tears from their eyes; and there shall be no more death, neither sorrow, nor crying; neither shall there be any more pain. For the former things are passed away."

Then He that sat upon the Throne said, "Behold, I make all things new! All is accomplished. I am the First and the Last; the Beginning and the End. I will give unto him that is athirst of the fountain of the water of Life, freely. He that overcometh shall inherit all things, and I will be his God, and he shall be My Son."

And I was carried away—rapt in the Spirit—to a vast mountain, where He showed me the city, New Jerusalem, descending from God out of Heaven, having the glory of God. The sheen of it shone like clear glass. I saw no Temple in the city; for its Temple was the Lord God Almighty and the Lamb. And the city needed no sun or moon to lighten it; for the glory of God illumined it, and the Lamb gave light to it. By its light shall the nations walk, and into it will the kings of the earth bring their glories. And the gates of it shall never be shut by day—and night there shall be none. Nothing profane or abominable or false shall enter therein—only those whose names are written in the Lamb's scroll of Life. And He showed me the River of the Water of Life, clear as crystal, flowing from the Throne of God and of the Lamb, through the streets of the city; and on both sides of the River grew the Tree of Life, whose leaves are for the healing of the nations. And the Throne of God and of the Lamb shall be in it; and His servants shall serve Him—yea, they shall see His face . . . and His name shall be on their foreheads. Blessed are they that do His commandments, that theirs may be the right to the Tree of Life, and to enter in through the gates of the city.

"I, Jesus, have sent Mine Angel to give you this Testimony. I am

the Root—and the Offspring—of David: the Bright and Morning Star. I am the First and the Last, the Beginning and the End. Lo! I am coming very soon, with My reward!"

"Come!" say the Spirit and the Bride.

"Even so . . . I am coming very soon!"

"Amen. Lord Jesus—come!"

THE END

INDEX

INDEX

Abraham, 235-238, 299

Adultery, woman taken in, 356-358

Aenon, 67*f.*

Andrew, 59-62, 131, 181, 182, 360

Angels, 17*f.*, 30, 33, 40*f.*, 47, 159, 192, 264, 299, 352, 363*f.*, 385, 387, 394, 432, 436

Anna, 18

Annas, 27, 76, 159, 330, 335, 343, 389-392

Apostles, 129-131, 171*f.*, 190*f.*, 204, 209, 211, 214*f.*, 242*f.*, 291, 369-373, 445-449

Appearances, Resurrection, 433-439, 442-449

Aretas, 174, 281, 283

Ascension, 434, 437, 448

Assize, the Great, 363-365

Authority of Jesus, 76-79, 81-83, 110, 115, 120*f.*, 156, 183

Banquet, parable of the, 297*f.*

Banquet in Bethany, 336-339, 366

Banquet in Jericho, 295-300

Baptism, John's, 39, 43*f.*, 67*f.*, 77*f.*, 166

Baptism of Jesus, 45-48, 53, 55, 59, 82, 282, 292

Barabbas, 404-408, 410*f.*

Bartimaeus, 294*f.*

Beelzebub, 198, 269

Belief in Jesus, 229, 231

Benefactors, 293

Bethany, 168, 171, 267, 311*f.*, 324, 447

Bethsaida, 62, 99, 179, 221, 270*f.*

Bethzatha, 159

Betrayal, 371*f.*, 386

Blind, the youth born, 316-319

Blind man, the, 221

Boy, epileptic, 260

Bread, 189, 208, 437

Butaiha, Plain of, 181, 183, 187, 193, 203, 224

Caesarea Palestina, 37*f.*

Caesarea Philippi, 210, 239-250

Caiaphas, 76, 159, 195, 330*f.*, 335, 341, 343, 347-349, 365, 367, 381-383, 389*f.*, 393-395, 397, 405*f.*, 408-412, 419, 425

Cana, 61, 64-66, 79, 94*f.*, 98*f.*

Capernaum, 66*f.*, 99, 107*f.*, 114*f.*, 138, 174, 177*f.*, 204, 267, 270*f.*, 364

Carmel, 20*f.*

Centurion of Capernaum, 107, 138-140

Childhood of Jesus, 17-33

Children, 263*f.*, 269, 343

Chorazin, 99

Church of Christ, 62, 120*f.*, 186, 245*f.*, 248*f.*, 347, 375, 438, 443

Chuza, 94-98, 102, 108, 167, 171, 178

Cleopas, 121, 435-438

Cloth, new, 126

Coin, the lost, 305

Commission of Jesus, 46-48, 53, 55

Compassion of Jesus, 112*f.*, 180, 213, 215, 218, 222, 295, 356, 359

Courage of Jesus, 73*f.*, 76, 186*f.*, 284, 321, 421

Covetousness, 287

465